The 1982 Yearbook of Agriculture

Food
From Farm to Table

United States Department of Agriculture

It takes big investments to stay in farming, more to get in—

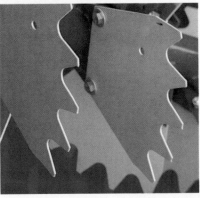

William E. Carnahan

Gordon Baer

but some still do it.

A young Maryland farmer checks out (top) new equipment on display at a county fair. Equipment is a big and necessary expense for farmers. A tractor can cost as much as a small home; bigger things—like combines—well over $100,000. Yet there are still some young families, like Wilmer and Ramona Minisee (left), of Niles, Michigan, who are doggedly determined to get started in farming, bucking a national trend of generally declining farm populations.

Farming 80's style

Today's farmer relies a lot on electronics. Norman Martella (above) of Salinas, CA installs a device on his tractor to monitor his lettuce seed planter. Above right, "Buster" Finneman of Beach, ND uses 2-way radios to coordinate his fleet of six combines, while a computer in a feed mill in Mabee, MS controls the blending of a complex recipe of feed for young chickens (top right). Right, laser-guided earthmovers level fields to provide uniform distribution of irrigation water.

"Double Cropping", plant and animal versions

Soybeans growing in grain stubble (right) were planted just behind the harvester (below). Such "no-till" farming permits two crops on the same plot, reduces energy consumption, and protects the soil from erosion.

Tim McCabe

Tim McCabe

Bruce Fritz

These calves (above), posing with their biological mother, all were produced by transplanting embryos from that cow (left) into surrogate mothers. Because the offspring carry the characteristics of the biological parents, breeders can increase many fold the calving potential of genetically superior cows.

Bruce Fritz

Mechanization and specialization—

Mechanically harvested green peas (far left) on this Wisconsin farm will be canned and ready for supermarket shelves within hours. The same is true for these California tomatoes (below) which could end up as canned whole tomatoes, stewed tomatoes puree, sauce, juice, or a main ingredient in catsup or spaghetti sauce. Special tomatoes are bred for special purposes. These "peeler pears" (left), named for their shape, were developed especially for ease of peeling. They are canned whole or in big chunks and draw premium prices.

—but room for hand work

But it's not all machines down on the farm, as these workers can attest. Above and right, lettuce and oranges— particularly oranges destined to be sold as fresh fruit—are still largely gathered by hand. Far right, Jenny Riffel of Stockton, Kansas, shovels smooth a truckload of wheat before tarping it and hauling it to a grain elevator.

David F. Warren

After the field, a diverse journey begins.

After harvest, farm products journey many ways and in many forms, across the nation and the world. For most grains, the first trip is a truck ride from the field to a local elevator.

William E. Carnahan

William E. Carnahan

Buyers and sellers, far from the farm . . .

These people at the Kansas City Commodity Market are buying and selling grain. They, and others like them all over the world, are setting the price for grain—higher or lower. Thus, many basic farm decisions, like whether a Kansas farmer will plant more or less wheat next year, or whether an Illinois farmer will sell corn or feed it to hogs, are made in other states and even in other nations.

. . . work in a world-wide arena.

Grain prices depend on world markets.
This barge (far left), being loaded
on the Columbia River between
Washington and Oregon, will go to a
Pacific port for shipment to Japan.
There it will feed Japanese livestock.
These animals in turn will provide the
meat for school lunches (left) and the
Japanese equivalent of the popular
American burger dispensary (top).

David F. Warren

David F. Warren

Farm groups woo foreign buyers.

Farmers don't set their prices, but they have learned to promote their products. Here a group of Oregon wheat growers are hosting a group of potential buyers from Japan—part of an annual attempt to increase the Pacific northwest's share of the world wheat market.

Warren Uzzle

Fresh vegetable marketing: a race against the clock.

"Sell it or smell it!"—that's always on the mind of the fresh fruit and vegetable grower. This wholesale market in Faison, NC (top left) serves about 400 area farmers who truck in their fresh produce—squash, beans, bell peppers, and egg plant—to be auctioned off to the highest bidder. Buyers bid on truckload lots (below left) for shipment around the country. The next stop for these perishable items is usually a food distribution center, like this one in Jessup, Maryland (above). Here, buyers convene daily to select fresh produce and truck it to supermarkets and restaurants in cities and suburbs (left).

Robert Llewellyn

Direct and Indirect avenues to the consumer.

Truckloads of ripe oranges go into this Florida plant (top); cans of frozen concentrated orange juice leave it. The whole process is orchestrated from this control panel. Right, fast-food hamburger chains are among the largest beef buyers in the country.

But sometimes there is no processing and no middleman. Far right, farmers unload their watermelons for sale directly to consumers at this Washington, DC, Farmers Market.

Fred Witte

William E. Carnahan

William E. Carnahan

Bob Greiser

Farmers' markets: The ultimate buyer meets the initial seller.

Many produce growers sell directly to the public, eliminating intermediate steps in the marketing chain. Some farmers' markets are elaborate affairs like this one that sets up several times a week in a Washington, DC, stadium parking lot; others are no more than stands by the side of the road operated by a single farm family.

Everything under one roof—

Modern supermarkets are the largest retail outlets for food. All food items—fresh meat and produce, dairy products, canned goods, dry food items, beverages—can be found under one roof. Many times they are accompanied by such non-food materials as drugs, cosmetics, housewares, and clothes—all for one-stop shopping convenience. Many such markets have butchers on duty so shoppers may order custom-carved USDA inspected and graded meats.

Fred Witte

Thanks for shopping Gia

William E. Carnahan

David F. Warren

Supermarket shoppers have more than just different brands to choose from.

Here, Janice Johnson (far left) compares a cake mix with a ready-made cake at a Maryland supermarket.
Many modern markets offer unit pricing (top) and automated checkout, using an electronic sensor to read the universal product code on each item (left).

William E. Carnahan

**"No Frills" Marketing gains
appeal.**

*In an effort to trim costs and attract
bargain-conscious shoppers, many supermarket chains are offering no-frills
stores. Here, food items are shelved in
their shipping container and customers
are expected to bag their own groceri-
ies. For the cost-conscious it's an
alternative to the traditional supermarket.*

Foreword

*F*armers power today's world! Without skilled farmers and the food they raise, we would be a sorry lot indeed—half-starved or worse, grubbing for anything we could find to eat and devoting nearly all our time to this dismayingly difficult effort.

Such a prospect isn't pleasing. Fortunately, of course, we in the United States will continue eating well, for less than a fifth of our average family incomes. Thanks to modern farmers. And thanks as well to the work of millions of the Americans who help farmers do their job, and see that food gets to our tables in the form we want and when we want it.

Farmers and supporting activities and industries make up an agricultural system intertwined with the general economy. This system generates about 20 percent of the Nation's gross national product, and employs 23 percent of the U.S. labor force. Yet only 3 percent of the labor force is engaged *directly* in farming. Where just 10 years ago one farmworker (farmer, family labor, and hired help) supplied enough food and fiber for 47 people, an American farmworker now supplies enough for 78.

Total agricultural output has more than doubled in the past 50 years, though the agricultural land base has not changed substantially. Since 1940, output per hour per farmworker has increased tenfold. While reflecting more farmer knowhow and continued hard work, this surge in productivity is aided strongly by production goods and services. These include improved seed varieties, use of commercial fertilizers, synthetic pesticides, and more efficient tillage and harvesting equipment.

The United States is the world's largest exporter of farm products, with two in five acres of our farmland harvested for export. Agricultural exports are crucial in limiting the amount of red ink in the Nation's trade balance. While the 1981 agricultural trade surplus topped $26 billion, the nonagricultural trade deficit exceeded $56 billion. With agriculture's contribution, the total trade deficit was limited to a little over $30 billion.

Agriculture employs more workers than any manufacturing industry. Nearly one in five nonagricultural workers in this country is providing farm inputs or processing and distributing farm products. Food wholesaling and retailing, including food service, alone employed 8.2 million workers. I might note that U.S. farmers received $85 billion for the food which went to American consumers in 1981. The overall job of marketing that food cost $200 billion.

We in the U.S. Department of Agriculture assist in providing efficiency throughout the food chain—from the production of food to its use in nutritious, satisfying meals. Research we conduct moves us toward more efficient practices. People around the country benefit from authoritative information about agriculture and food, developed by experts from inside and outside the Department.

Informed shoppers searching out bargains in food of high quality can be the major force that guides producers and marketers toward greater efficiency. Proper selection and handling of food can result in money savings, increased eating pleasure, and improved nutritional well-being.

One way to reach that goal is to share knowledge through the Yearbook of Agriculture. The audience includes thousands of farm families, community leaders and groups, as well as thousands of other individuals. General information in the economics of food production, in food marketing, and in consumer food buying is included in this Yearbook, along with a good deal of how-to-do-it material for farmers and consumers. I hope you will take time to become aware of the contents, and keep this Yearbook close at hand.

John R. Block
Secretary of Agriculture

Preface

Jack Hayes
Yearbook Editor

*F*rom my office overlooking the Mall in Washington I can see the Capitol and other monumental buildings that testify to our Nation's greatness. Agriculture, of course, has always been and is today a major contributor to that greatness. In this Yearbook of Agriculture you will find what's going on amid the earthshaking energies that feed us three times a day, day in and day out, year in and year out.

Three major sections make up this book: Sect. I, *Changing Economics of Agriculture*; Sect. II, *Farm Marketing in a New Environment*; and Sect. III, *Food Buying— Making Decisions*. The third section, as you might guess, is primarily for consumers—and we are all consumers. The general reader, along with farmers and other agriculturists, should find things of interest in all three sections. I might add that the book contains a variety of viewpoints.

William T. Manley of the Agricultural Marketing Service was Chairman of the Committee that planned this book. Subcommittee chairmen for each of the sections were: Sect. I, George H. Hoffman. Sect. 2, Charles Beer. Sect. 3, Sara Beck. Members of the Committee, by agency, were:

Agricultural Cooperative Service—Jack H. Armstrong
Agricultural Marketing Service—Elizabeth Crosby, Georgia Stevens Neruda, J.C. Williamson
Cooperative State Research Service—Elizabeth Y. Davis
Economic Research Service—Clark R. Burbee, Reed Friend, David H. Harrington, Richard G. Heifner, Ronald L. Meekhof, James A. Zellner
Extension Service—Evelyn H. Johnson, Roger H. Wilkowske
Food Safety and Inspection Service—Elizabeth W. Murphy
Foreign Agricultural Service—Dewain Rahe
Human Nutrition Information Service—Betty B. Peterkin
Soil Conservation Service—Peter F. Smith
World Agriculture Outlook Board—James R. Donald

Photography—William E. Carnahan, Extension Service

Contents

Foreword xxxiv
John R. Block, Secretary of Agriculture

Preface xxxvi
Jack Hayes, Yearbook Editor

I. Changing Economics of Agriculture

Agriculture's Vital Role for Us All 2
James A. Zellner and R. McFall Lamm

Profile of Farming and Rural America 10
Harold F. Breimyer and Lyle P. Schertz

Farmers, Society Share a Policy Interest 20
Kenneth C. Clayton

How a Dime Can Help Us Save Our Resource Base 28
James N. Benson and Chris Risbrudt

What Farmers Buy Makes Production Fly 41
Paul Andrilenas and Ted Eichers

Productivity and the Real Cost of Our Food 52
Lloyd D. Teigen

Whys and Hows of Credit, Finance 59
Stephen C. Gabriel and John R. Brake

Financial Planning and Management 72
Thomas L. Frey and Neal Sox Johnson

Getting Started in Farming Is Tough 82
Michael Boehlje and Ron Durst

Farm Exports—A Key to Our Economy 92
Dewain Rahe and Reed Friend

World Economic Shifts Affect Agriculture, All of Us 105
Jim Longmire, Arthur Morey, and John Nuttall

Tariffs, Embargoes, Other Trade Barriers 112
G. Edward Schuh and Philip L. Paarlberg

Tracing Your Food Dollar Back to the Farm 119
Harry H. Harp and John M. Connor

II. Farm Marketing in a New Environment

The $200 Billion Job of Marketing Our Food.................................. 128
Alden C. Manchester

Links That Make Up the Marketing Chain..................................... 137
Edward V. Jesse

Who Does What in the Marketing Field.. 145
Joseph N. Uhl

How Markets Coordinate Decisions... 151
Wayne D. Purcell

Grades and Promotions in the Food System 159
Mary C. Kenney

Timing Sales for High Returns 170
Gene A. Futrell and Robert N. Wisner

Selecting the Best Market Alternative... 179
V. James Rhodes

How to Minimize Marketing Risks 187
T. Everett Nichols, Jr.

Fair Treatment in the Marketplace... 191
Thomas M. Walsh and Everett O. Stoddard

Exploiting New Marketing Opportunities....................................... 198
James L. Pearson and Harold S. Ricker

Rules of the Game—for Market Stability 209
Bruce Gardner

Transportation Handles the Surge in Production 216
William W. Gallimore

The Challenge of Foreign Marketing... 223
Robert J. Wicks

III. Food Buying—Making Decisions

Food Patterns—Where Are We Headed? 230
Betty B. Peterkin and Richard L. Kerr

Where to Eat—At Home or Away 237
Robert B. Reese and Sharon J. Mickle

Where Consumers Buy Their Food... 242
Edgar P. Watkins

Motivating Factors in the Marketplace 250
Effie Hacklander

Family Economics and Food Purchases 253
Carolyn G. Carter and Frances Cogle Lawrence

Personal Beliefs, Preferences and Food.. 257
Merry Jo Davis and Joyce R. Garrick

Nutritional Needs: Eat for Good Health All Your Life........................ 263
Chung Ja Lee

Appliances and Their Effect on Food Buying.................................. 270
Fern E. Hunt

How to be a First-Rate Food Manager... 276
Mary E. Mennes

Buying Food for the Nutrients it Provides.................................... 285
Linda E. Cleveland

Food Safety From Farm to Market 290
Patricia F. Stolfa

Consumer Guidelines for Food Safety 295
Carole A. Davis

Let the Grade Be Your Guide in Buying Food.................................. 302
Sara Beck, Elizabeth Crosby, and Martha Parris

Better Buymanship—Know Your Labels and Standards...................... 318
Elizabeth W. Murphy and Cheryl Garrett

Cost Comparison Tools to Stretch Your Food Dollar......................... 326
Cynthia Cromwell Junker

Convenience Foods—What They Cost You 343
Dianne Odland and Julein Axelson

How We Waste $31 Billion in Food a Year.................................... 352
William Rathje and EE Fung

How Consumers Can Affect the Marketplace................................. 358
Georgia Stevens Neruda, Mildred Brooks, and Karen Brown

For Additional Information 363
Credits... 367
Index... 369

Section I.
Changing Economics of Agriculture

Agriculture's Vital Role for Us All

By James A. Zellner and R. McFall Lamm

At the time of the American Revolution the United States was almost totally agrarian. Ninety percent of our population was engaged in farming and 60 percent of income went for food. Almost all our exports were agricultural products, and the basic structure of society depended on the agrarian economy. Through time the U.S. agricultural system has produced an increasing abundance of food and fiber, using relatively fewer resources. The unparalleled productivity gains in American agriculture have resulted in a broader choice of nutritious foods available for a declining portion of income.

Societies the world over face periodic crop failure, economic mismanagement, and a chronic inability of their food and agricultural systems to perform adequately. The inevitable results of a failure to provide adequate diets are political and economic instability, a compromised national security, and ultimately, chaos. American agriculture has an envious record of providing a safe, secure, affordable, and wholesome domestic food supply while increasingly contributing to the easing of food security problems in the rest of the world.

Today Americans spend less than 17 percent of family income on food. Only 3 percent of our labor force is engaged directly in farming. And agricultural products now account for only about 20 percent of total exports. The importance of farming seems to have diminished. But it would be erroneous to conclude that agriculture is no longer vitally important to our economy. As the following sections explain, the food and agricultural sector — as a source of productivity gains, a user of resources, and a source of employment — remains large and important by any standard.

Increased agricultural productivity, the rise in output per unit of input, has been a major contributor to improved living standards for Americans. Where just 10 years ago one farm worker supplied enough food and fiber for 47 people, he now supplies enough for 78, up from a mere seven persons at the beginning of this century. Total agricultural output has more than doubled in the past 50 years, though the agricultural land base has not substantially changed.

These increases in agricultural productivity have contributed to the domestic economy by enabling consumers to upgrade their diets at lower cost while simultaneously expanding their consumption of nonfood items. At the same time increased productivity has facilitated the

James A. Zellner is an Agricultural Economist in the National Economics Division, Economic Research Service.

R. McFall Lamm is Director of Forecasting and Economic Analysis with Pillsbury, Minneapolis, MN.

transfer of production workers from agriculture into industrial and service industries, expanding the supply of nonfood goods and services, and enabling our economy to meet the new demands of consumers.

The great strides in productivity have been accompanied by major changes in the input mix. From the earliest periods of American history hand power gave way to horsepower then to mechanical power, and ultimately to "science power." New technologies introduced over the past 50 years have resulted in a nearly fifteenfold increase in fertilizer use, a fivefold increase in tractor numbers, and a tenfold increase in tractor horsepower used in farming. Purchased inputs are now 2.6 times their 1930 levels and farm labor input only 30 percent of 1930 levels. Farms are larger and

significantly more dependent on capital and purchases from the nonfarm economy.

As farming has come to rely more on purchased inputs and less on inputs supplied on the farm, the sector has become more fully integrated with the general economy. Consequently, farming is influenced by and has an influence on the same factors that determine conditions in the general economy. Where once, for instance, credit market conditions had little influence on farm well-being or farmers' decisions, modern production agriculture depends heavily on credit to finance capital and other purchases from the nonfarm economy. Specialized industries have evolved in the nonfarm sector to service the input needs of agriculture and to process and market farm products. As agriculture has become more important

Agricultural Productivity Grows Throughout U.S. History

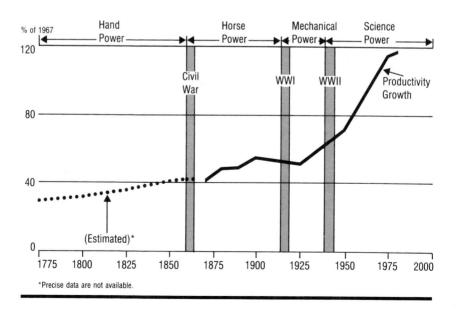

*Precise data are not available.

Employment in selected industries, 1979

Industry	Employment	
	Number	Percent of total
Agriculture	3,297	3.1
Mining	957	0.9
Construction	4,644	4.4
Manufacturing	20,972	19.9
Food and kindred products (O)	1,176	1.1
Textile mill products (O)	777	0.7
Apparel and other textiles (O)	1,899	1.8
Chemicals and allied products (I)	637	0.6
Petroleum & coal products	140	0.1
Leather and leather products (O)	244	0.2
Primary metal industries	1,244	1.2
Machinery, except electrical (I)	2,463	2.3
Motor vehicles and equipment	983	0.9
All other manufacturing	11,357	10.8
Transportation	3,037	2.9
Communications	1,308	1.2
Electric, gas & sanitary services	809	0.8
Wholesale trade (I, O)	5,170	4.9
Retail trade (I, O)	14,966	14.2
Finance, insurance & real estate (I)	4,963	4.7
Services (I, O)	17,043	16.2
Government	15,612	14.8

(I) Closely related to agriculture as input suppliers.
(O) Closely related to agriculture as output processors and distributors.

Source: U.S. Bureau of Labor Statistics, *Employment and Earnings,* monthly.

in world trade, particularly during the past 20 years, this interdependence has taken on important international dimensions.

One of Biggest Employers
Agriculture employs more workers than any manufacturing industry. Only government and the construction, trade, finance, and service industries employ more people than agriculture, and agriculture's role as a purchaser of inputs or supplier of its output looms large in several of those. Food processing, of course, is highly related to agriculture, as are textiles, transportation, and trade — all users or marketers of agriculture's output. Also, agriculture is an important customer of the chemical, machinery, finance, real estate, and service industries.

Production of grains and oilseeds by U.S. farmers has expanded 2½ times over levels of just 30 years ago. At the same time there has been a tenfold increase in exports of these commodities. About a third of U.S. cropland is used to produce commodities for export. The United States now accounts for 55 percent of total world grain exports, over half of

world soybean exports, and almost a third of cotton exports. Exports of grains, oilseeds, and other unprocessed items reached nearly $28 billion in 1981. Another $13.5 billion of export earnings was generated in the nonfarm food and fiber sector through the sale of processed products. These exports provided jobs for 1.2 million workers, two-thirds of them in the nonfarm sector.

Rising agricultural exports have been a major factor holding down the U.S. trade deficit in recent years. The agricultural trade surplus in 1981 stood at $26.5 billion as exports of $43.3 billion offset $16.8 billion of imports. The nonagricultural trade account was in deficit by $56.6 billion. Agricultural exports are important to our economy for reasons beyond the income and jobs they create in agriculture and the food and fiber system. The narrowed trade gap that results from our agricultural trade surplus helps strengthen the American dollar, which reduces the prices of imported goods and contributes to a lower inflation rate.

The internationalization of agriculture has had significant impacts beyond the in-

Value of US. Agricultural Exports, Calendar Years

$ billion

	Animals and products		Other agricultural exports	$43.3
Food grains and products			$41.2	10%
Feed grains and products			$34.8	9%	23%
Oilseeds and products		$29.4	11%	19%	

	$21.9	8%	$23.0	10%	$23.6	11%	10%	19%	19%	24%	24%
28%		21%		15%	19%	22%			
24%		26%		21%	20%	26%	23%	22%
20%		22%		28%	28%		25%	21%
20%		21%		25%	23%	22%		
1975	76	77	78	79	80	81

The United States accounts for 55 percent of total world grain exports. Right: empty barges near Pendleton, Oreg., return for more grain that will be exported. Below: soft white wheat is loaded onto barges for export. Exports of grains, oilseeds, and other unprocessed items reached nearly $28 billion in 1981.

USDA

USDA

come and jobs it has supported. Conditions in U.S. agriculture depend greatly on world production and economic conditions. Large year-to-year changes can occur, and often do. This causes considerable instability in the U.S. agricultural sector as evidenced by wide price and income fluctuations. Even world financial conditions can strongly influence the price of U.S. farm commodities.

Several factors directly influence prices that U.S. farmers receive and prices that foreign customers pay for U.S. farm commodities. Changes in world food supplies and production are affected by the vagaries of weather, demand factors such as world income, and levels of economic activity. And the changing strength of the U.S. dollar relative to foreign currencies can cause major swings in U.S. farm prices and add to the uncertainties facing farmers.

Products of the food and fiber system are seen everywhere. The food we eat at home and in restaurants, the clothing we wear, our shelter and home furnishings, the beverages we consume, and other products such as tobacco all originate in the farm sector. Some form of agricultural output is used as input into production by every major industry. The agricultural industry itself uses output from more than 80 percent of the other basic industries in the United States. Some of the more important interdependencies are discussed next.

Farms were largely self-sufficient during much of American history. It wasn't until the early 20th century that farmers purchased more inputs from the nonfarm sector than were produced on the farm or by other farmers. Today nearly two-thirds of farm inputs, by value, are purchased from nonfarm suppliers. Feed, seed and livestock which originate in the farm sector are still among the major purchases made by farmers, though 80 percent of feed and nearly all the seed are purchased from commercial sources.

In 1981 farmers used 367 million acres of cropland, purchased $32 billion of inputs originating in the farm sector, and bought $84 billion worth of goods from nonfarm sectors of the economy. These inputs were used to produce livestock valued at $69 billion and crops worth $75 billion. Interest expenses accounted for nearly 23 percent of the value of nonfarm purchased inputs in 1981. Following in importance were chemicals — mainly fertilizer and pesticides, energy, and hired labor. Rent and taxes also were large items in the farmer's budget, accounting for nearly 14 percent of production expenses.

Farmers are, of course, particularly important customers for industries providing specialized goods and services to farmers. For example, 80 percent of the output of the farm machinery industry is purchased by farmers (the remainder being exports). Farmers are the third largest buyers of chemicals and chemical products. In addition they purchase virtually all of the nitrogenous fertilizers, two thirds of the phosphate fertilizers, and 95 percent of the pesticides produced in this country. Besides, farmers are prime customers for several other important industries. They are the largest users of wooden containers, the sixth largest users of petroleum, the fourth largest customer of the finance and insurance industry, and the fourth largest user of real estate and rental services. Only five industries use more transportation and warehouse services than agriculture.

Processors Employ 1.1 Million

The food processing and manufacturing industry accounted for about 13 percent of all manufacturing in 1981. Over 23,000 processing plants employed 1.1 million workers to produce food and beverages valued at $276 billion. Meat packing and meat products with shipments of $66 billion accounted for nearly 25 percent of processed food and beverage shipments. Other leading food and beverage industries are processed fruits and vegetables with shipments of $29 billion; beverages (including alcoholic beverages), with ship-

ments of $34.7 billion; bakery foods, with shipments of $18 billion; and dairy products with shipments of $37 billion. Together these five industries account for more than two-thirds of the output of the food and beverage processing industry.

Processors of nonfood agricultural products include the leather tanning and finishing industries, related footwear and leather apparel industries, tobacco manufacturers, cotton and wool weaving, textile finishing mills, and related apparel

manufacturers. These processors added about $36 billion in value to the fiber produced on American farms during 1981. Together these industries employ more than 400,000 workers at more than 17,000 plants in all 50 States.

The food and fiber marketing system includes all the transportation services required to move agricultural products from farms to storage facilities, from storage to processors, from processors to distributors, and from distributors to consumers in the United States and abroad.

Transportation services provided by food manufacturers, wholesalers, and retailers, and distributors of apparel, home furnishings, tobacco and other agriculturally related products are a major part of this system. But important as well are related expenditures on storage, energy, advertising, and fixed costs such as buildings and equipment.

Food wholesaling and retailing, including food service, added $155 billion in value to processed and semi-processed farm products in 1981, and employed 8.2 million workers to market food products. In addition, $15 billion of transportation services were used. Nonfood marketing is also a huge part of the economy. About $17 billion is spent and around 20,000 workers employed in wholesale marketing of apparel and piece goods derived from agricultural fiber. And another $20 billion of apparel sales and some 100,000 employees are accounted for by retailing of apparel and piece goods.

This discussion serves to highlight the immense complexity and importance of America's most crucial industry. Clearly, agriculture and the food and fiber system are an integral part of the domestic and world economies. Success of the U.S. economy as a whole depends in large part on how well our agricultural system performs, but agriculture also depends on nonagricultural industries for inputs. Millions of workers and consumers depend on continued effectiveness of the agricultural system for security, for their sustenance and their livelihoods.

Tim McCabe

In 1981 farmers produced crops on 367 million acres of farmland, such as this corn and soybean farm in Carroll County, Md.

Profile of Farming and Rural America

By Harold F. Breimyer and Lyle P. Schertz

*T*he business of farming, farm families' way of living, and the welfare of rural communities are interlinked in a mutually supportive manner that is not found elsewhere in the Nation. The unique connection among farms, farmers, and their community arises primarily from the geography of an agriculture of small units scattered over space. A farm on which crops are produced or animals grazed is space-using. It is also a managerial unit that, paradoxically, is independent yet increasingly depends on others in both economic and cultural activities.

Both the farm and the farm family must reach out for supporting help — for fuel, feed, and fertilizer for use in farming, for markets to which products can be delivered and sold, for nonfarm work opportunities, and for items of living as well as educational and cultural activities for the family. Hence the close tie between farms and farmers on the one hand, and the rural community on the other.

Such a symbiotic relationship between farms, farmers, and the farming community is not new. On the contrary, it is as old as the Nation. It has changed in form and intensity but it dates from the Nation's first years. The idea that pioneer farms existed in total self-sufficiency is lore of song and story, but invalid. With rare exceptions, U.S. farmers have always produced at least some product for a market, and have depended on a business firm or artisan for some service or supply. Farmers have likewise contributed to and depended upon schools, churches, and other community institutions.

Trends of recent years have been almost contradictory. The economic interdependency between farms and their communities has become even greater than before, and crucial to both, even as cultural distinctions between farmers and other members of the community have just about faded away.

Pioneer farms had to buy nails for barns and medication for horses, but the technology of today's farming calls for a big and constant flow of materials and services received from off the farm. Early in this century a fourth to a third of all the inputs of farming were bought from outside the farm, and the rest were internally supplied (feed for horses, for example). Now two-thirds to three-fourths of inputs are obtained from off-farm suppliers.

A few of the largest farms may go directly to big cities for machines, fertilizers,

Harold F. Breimyer is Professor, Department of Agricultural Economics, University of Missouri, Columbia.

Lyle P. Schertz is Economist, Economic Research Service, USDA, Washington, D.C.

and other supplies, but the majority of farms buy within the local community. In doing so, they incidentally make the local farm-supply businesses as dependent on farmers' buying from them as farmers depend on the businesses. During the decline in farmers' income in the early 1980's, for example, farm machinery dealers in county seat towns suffered an even sharper drop in income than farmers did, because farmers were not financially able to continue their previous level of machinery purchases.

American Gothic No More

The farmer and the farm family may at one time have been culturally distinctive, even to the point of justifying the somber caricature of Grant Wood's American Gothic. Not so now. By any test of living style in homes, furnishings, and dress, of preferences in recreation, of literacy and religion — by any of these tests farmers and nonfarm members of the rural community are indistinguishable.

Marvelous improvements in transportation and communication in our century are usually credited with breaking down cultural barriers. They doubtless are important. But the amalgam has other origins too. Common efforts by all citizens in two world wars, nationwide merchandising of items of everyday living, and of course the gradual erosion over time of islands of ethnic identity have all been involved.

Still another trend has been barrier-breaking. If highways and automobiles took farmers to town for both shopping and cultural activities, they also took many industrial (manufacturing and commercial) enterprises out of the big cities and put them in the country. These rural businesses have provided employment

for hundreds of thousands or even millions of farmers (husbands and wives), and their sons and daughters.

The ultimate outcome has been to blur age-old distinctions between farms, farmer, and the nonfarm part of the rural community. In 1978, 18 percent of all farmers did not live on their farms. Currently nearly half of all persons who are "farmers" by the Census criterion of selling more than $1,000 worth of farm products in a year do not call themselves farmers by occupation. They produce and sell farm products, but they identify themselves as schoolteachers, salespeople, steamfitters, or corporate vice presidents. And, as will be noted later, part-time farms have become about as numerous as farms on which the farm operators work full time, without other employment.

Farms and farming may be described in so many ways! Perhaps the starting point is the nature of the farm itself. An irony arises immediately. Everyone has a mental picture of a "farm." Yet, each person's picture is different. And well it should be. For the first feature of agriculture is its internal heterogeneity. Its farm units vary extremely widely.

Nonetheless, U.S. agriculture and its farms have one distinguishing feature: the farms are numerous. Even though they range in size from tiny to immense they appear relatively small when compared with giant industrial firms in steel, automobiles, and oil. And their 2.4 million number in 1981 compares with the dozens or at most hundreds of firms in those three industries.

Among all the characteristics of U.S. farms, the nature of the proprietary unit attracts most interest. It is even more important than size of farm. Farmers are especially concerned for their status and role in farming. They are sensitive to whether they are owners, tenants, or wage workers, for example. All operating farmers are touchy about whether they are independent proprietors or are bound to suppliers or outlets under production contracts. Related issues arise as to whether they may join together in cooperative marketing, collective bargaining, or other group action that circumscribes the farmer's latitude in exchange for a stronger position in the market.

Almost everywhere in the United States except parts of the Southwest and Pacific Coast, the traditional mainstay of farming has been the family farm. It comes closest to being a "typical" farm. It is usually defined as a farm on which the farmer and members of the family own at least part of the land, do at least half the work, are the managers and have limited if any nonfarm work activities. The family farm buys and sells in the market, rather than being contractually integrated. However, it may be linked with other farms in cooperatives. Its size and productivity are sufficient to provide an acceptable living for the family.

Family Farm Fading

The family farm remains foremost in images about farms and farming, and it continues to rank high in announced goals for agriculture in the future. Yet it is gradually disappearing. Data are inexact but at most only half of all farm marketings now come from family farms. The predominance of family farms in U.S. farming is giving way before a trend toward a dual agriculture. It is being displaced in number by smaller farms, the majority of which are part-time, and in

volume of marketings by larger-than-family farms and by large corporate or agribusiness farms.

Family farms are losing out also in their market relationships. Family farms and indeed most farms traditionally have bought supplies from a nearby dealer and sold products in an open market. In recent years integrative arrangements have replaced open markets in many instances, most notably in poultry and eggs. The kinds of proprietary farms now found in the United States may be classified as follows:

    I. Linked to local market
       A. Smaller-than-family size
       B. Family size
          1. Primarily owner-operated
          2. Primarily tenant-operated
    II. Not linked to local market
       A. Larger-than-family size
       B. Contractually integrated
       C. Large corporate

Smaller-than-family-sized farms number more than one million, yet their total volume of marketings does not exceed 5 percent of all farm marketings. The majority of these farms are part-time operations in which the farmer holds a job off the farm. Some are retirement farms where the farmer receives a retirement income. A significant number, however, are unproductive and unrewarding full-time farms. These are the instances of the "poor small farmer" that are publicized and in fact may be bypassed in educational and other public services to agriculture.

The family farm remains foremost in images about farms and farming and continues to rank high in expressed goals for agriculture in the future. This young Wisconsin farm family is an example.

13

Family farms already have been defined. Some family farmers, as noted, may be tenants rather than owner operators. Ideally, though, farmers are tenants only temporarily as they hope to climb the ladder to ownership, or they may rent some land in addition to that which they own. This latter arrangement is known as part-ownership. It has become common, as will be noted later. Other groups of farms are not linked closely to local markets for outlets for their products or for their farm inputs other than labor.

Many family-owned farms of larger-than-family size depend heavily on hired labor yet are not big enough to be classified as corporate bureaucracies, although some have incorporated for tax or other advantages. Some of these have multifarm units. They now form a sizable part of U.S. agriculture. They especially increased in number and size during the inflationary 1970's, when it was attractive for larger farms to keep adding to their holdings by borrowing all the money they could ("leveraging") at the relatively low interest rates of the time. Allegedly, the goal was to "buy one farm a year." However, the trend toward continuous expansion slowed in the early 1980's as interest costs increased, inflation eased, and land values adjusted downward.

Two other kinds of farms are not linked closely to local markets. They are usually less closely identified with the local community than are the first three categories of farms. One of these consists of the various arrangements in contractual integration. Broilers provide the best example. The broiler industry includes a great many small farmers known as "growers," but financing, management, and marketing are all in the hands of the integrators.

Contracts normally are used instead of open marketing for production of fruits and vegetables for processing. But the terms of contracts are not as restrictive as those in broilers. About 20 percent of all farm products move from farmers to processors or handlers under some kind of production contract. If all delivery contracts with cooperatives are included, the figure exceeds 30 percent.

Corporate-Type Farming

Large corporate approaches to farming are most common in the feeding of cattle in feedlots that may hold as many as 100,000 head, and in "egg cities" where a million or more hens try to lay an egg a day in order to avoid being removed for slaughter. Some confined hog opera-

The broiler industry includes farmers known as "growers" but financing, management, and marketing are all in the hands of integrators.

tions are large. Corporate management is less common in field operations, yet Tenneco in the west and First Colony farms in North Carolina are examples of huge holdings that operate with hired workers and specialization in labor and management tasks. Estimates are inexact but possibly as much as a tenth of all farm products arise in this kind of large corporate-type production.

Farms vary widely in size. Size may be measured by acreage, value of assets held, man-years of labor employed, or value of marketings. Number of acres may be the poorest measure. A cattle feedlot or a greenhouse may use only a few acres yet be highly productive.

Value of annual marketings is used often. This measure reveals many but decreasing numbers of small farms and few but an increasing number of large farms. The large ones, of course, account for a large

part of U.S. farm production. For example, the number of farms with sales of more than $200,000, though only 5 percent of all farms, account for about one-fifth of U.S. net farm income. In contrast, the number of farms with sales of less than $20,000 account for more than half of all farms but for only about 15 percent of net farm income.

U.S. agriculture of the last couple of decades has been marked by an uptrend in the price of land based heavily on expected increases in farm earnings but inconsistent with "current" earning power. Only in 1982 did the long inflationary surge abate. As land prices kept going up, younger farmers found it difficult to enter farming as owners. Some did so as full tenants; they rented all their land from a landlord. Others bought a small home base and rented numerous individual tracts. The latter arrangement is called partownership.

Murray Lemmon

The proportion of full tenancy is not high nationwide. In some regions, though, it now accounts for a substantial part of all farming. Nationwide, one-third of all farmers are classified as part owners. They own some land and rent some land from others, and their farms account for 57 percent of all land. The proportion of farmland operated by its owner varies somewhat across the country. However, it approximates two-thirds of the total farmland in all regions except the Northeast, where it is 78 percent.

Dual Agriculture Forces

U.S. agriculture is moving toward a dual makeup of many small and few large units because of a number of pressures that are felt. They, in turn, are interrelated. Those pressures may be divided into 1) Technological, 2) Expanded demand, and 3) Institutional.

The technology of machines and electric power and chemical herbicides and other trappings of modern farming have had a major effect in reducing the number of farms, increasing the size of some and making it easier for others to combine farm and nonfarm activities. Tractors and other farm machines are available in all sizes and shapes. The newer four-wheel tractors and associated machinery are capable of being combined with large amounts of resources such as land.

Commercial cattle feedlots and egg cities are instances where power equipment and industrial processes are so well suited that they lead to large size. In these operations, modern technologies facilitate control over large-scale production units. Some techniques can also be

Farms vary widely in size. Size may be measured by acreage, value of assets held, man-years of labor employed, value of marketings, or product value added on the farm. This corn-hog farm is in the heart of America's farmland—Iowa.

adapted to facilitate small farming as well. Thus, some people holding off-farm jobs find it possible to keep up with the farmwork with evening and weekend work. Mechanical power, chemical fertilizers, pesticides, and drugs for control of livestock diseases are all involved.

In contrast, the middle size farm is under increasing pressure to get smaller or larger. With modern technology the operators of middle-sized farms are only partially employed. Getting smaller would permit doing off-farm work since the farming work might be done in the even-

ings and/or weekends. In contrast, getting larger permits using managerial talents and machinery on a larger scale, thus increasing the returns to labor and management. This pressure need not extend, however, to conversion into multiunit farms that rely extensively on hired labor.

Part-time farmers buy land by drawing on their income from nonfarm sources and being able to accept a low return for their farm labor. Among large farms, landholding may be financed by landlords or by large corporations using capital funds from nonfarm financial sources outside agriculture. The family farmer may be left with the fewest means to finance ownership of land. One outcome of this is the persistence of tenancy, mentioned earlier, either as full tenancy or as part ownership.

Agriculture has felt the effect of an expanded demand for its products. Our own growing population and its increased incomes have expanded the demand for farm products. Increased exports have also. We are feeling the effect of a worldwide need for food. These in-

Commercial cattle feedlots are instances where technology, power equipment, and financial and legal arrangements are so well suited that they lead to large size.

Fred Witte

18

creased demands underlay land price increases in the 1970's. It therefore became more difficult for operating farmers to acquire land of their own to farm.

Economic Slowdown Effect

Demand conditions shifted sharply in 1981 and 1982 as economic activity slowed in the United States and around the world. These conditions combined with high crop production levels to bring about lower farm crop prices, lower farm income, and in turn lower farmland prices. The supply-demand balance can shift quickly, as obviously happened in the early 1970's and again in recent years. Thus while many projections point to continued long-term expansion of demands, the balance between demands and supplies in any year is very unpredictable.

The third pressure brought to bear is institutional. It relates to access to credit, the differential effects of tax laws, the provisions of national programs to support farmers' prices and incomes, and conditions in the general economy. This is the most complex of all the influences on current trends in farming. Some critics say that institutional forces work, in total, very much in favor of large units in agriculture and against the family farm. Certain it is that any farming enterprise that can get credit on favorable terms, or that can use income tax shelters advantageously, or can take fuller advantage of commodity price supports gets "one leg up" in the contest to survive in agriculture.

The entire cooperative credit system, for example, was designed as a way to make sure that the rank and file of farmers would be able to get credit at rates that are not usurious. And, the Farmers

Home Administration is charged with making credit available to farmers of average size, as well as to some smaller farmers. Price support programs were designed to support farm product prices and reduce farming risks.

None of these institutions was designed specifically to favor large units in agriculture. However, for many years these institutions operated in an environment experiencing inflation of the general price level, attractive nonfarm employment, and technological changes permitting effective control of large as well as small amounts of farm resources and expanding markets. The net effect has been to encourage some farmers to leave farming, others to expand their farming operations, and still others to combine farm and nonfarm pursuits.

This quick sketch reminds us that U.S. agriculture of the 1980's is far from homogeneous. Everyone may have a mental image of the "typical" farm, but it is certain to be wrong if only because there scarcely is such a farm. The only accurate picture is of an agriculture of extreme diversity. Furthermore, the trends are toward even wider diversity. The traditional family farm may have, at one time, come closest to typifying all agriculture. It is fading slowly from the scene, however, as many part-time farms and a relatively few large units replace it.

This sketch also reminds us that the makeup of U.S. agriculture is not entirely happenstance. It is affected by human institutions — those for education, research, credit, taxes, and farm programs — as well as developments in the general economy and markets for U.S. farm products.

Farmers, Society Share a Policy Interest

By Kenneth C. Clayton

Although specific objectives of our farm policy vary over time, several widely held purposes provide a common thread. Among these are increased stability of market supplies and prices, enhanced farm income, abundant quantities of food at reasonable prices to consumers, food aid for the domestic poor and foreign countries in need of assistance, and expansion of commercial export markets. Farm programs adopted over the years have been the principal vehicles for achieving these policy goals.

Agricultural policy really began with the land settlement programs that were promoted throughout the Nation's first hundred years. Effort devoted to getting people onto the land culminated in the Homestead Act of 1862. Railroads were established to move commodities to eastern markets. In the mid-1840's, mechanization was introduced to agriculture. By the time of the Civil War, manpower had largely been replaced by animal power. The Morrill Land Grant College Act and the law setting up the U.S. Department of Agriculture in the 1860's established the base for a more scientific approach to farming. Agriculture moved from self-sufficiency to a greater market orientation.

By the 1870's, the United States had a growing commercial agricultural industry. Farm numbers were increasing and the acreage devoted to agricultural production was rising. Exports grew significantly over the last half of the century with Western Europe becoming a major consumer of U.S. agricultural commodities. Because of the tremendous productivity gains realized through mechanization and scientific advances, the proportion of the population needed in agriculture began to decline. Employment in agriculture was still increasing, but not as fast as the overall population. With the advent of commercial agriculture, the importance of national policies — monetary, trade, and others — in the daily life of farmers became increasingly evident. The Populist movement and the growth of farm organizations reflected the concern of farmers that their interests be considered in the conduct of national affairs.

Seeds of Modern Policy

While agriculture experienced its ups and downs during early years of the 20th century, it was by and large a prosperous period. Most of America's good farmland was under private ownership. Technological advances continued; mechanical power gradually replaced animal power. Farm prices rose markedly with both production and exports continuing to increase. Deficiencies in the banking and credit system were addressed and debate was focused on an appropriate tariff policy. Food safety became an issue with the Food and Drug Act and the Meat In-

Kenneth C. Clayton is Chief, Food and Agricultural Policy Branch, National Economics Division, Economic Research Service.

spection Act of 1906. Public regulation of the railroads and the conservation of natural resources emerged as policy issues.

As World War I drew to a close, there was a brief downturn in prices but an overall aura of optimism prevailed. Domestic purchases previously restricted by the war put upward pressure on prices. European nations were permitted to use war credits for acquiring U.S. foodstuffs. A relaxed credit policy was followed by the Treasury Department and the Federal Reserve, giving rise to general price inflation. Much of the increased return to farmers was capitalized into land values. Between 1918 and 1920 land prices rose by a third; mortgage debt in 1920 was more than double what it had been in 1914. But the bubble soon burst.

The postwar boom turned to bust in late 1920. Farm prices fell while nonagricultural prices and wages did not. The purchasing power of farm products in terms of the nonfarm goods that they would buy declined by a third. An economic disparity was emerging between farmers and others in society.

Relief Sought — the farm community and policymakers alike sought some type of relief. One set of policies that was adopted allowed farmers greater strength in the marketplace. The Capper-Volstead Cooperating Marketing Act of 1922 as well as subsequent legislation encouraged farmers to form cooperatives to market their commodities.

A second policy thrust would have meant greater direct government involvement in agriculture. The so-called McNary-Haugen bills were twice passed by Congress and each time vetoed by the President. These bills would have established a Federal export marketing corporation to handle foreign sales of "surplus production" (beyond domestic needs). Farmers would have received for domestically consumed commodities a price equivalent in purchasing power to that received in the prewar years. The world market price would have been received on "surplus production."

Among policy actions taken was creation of a Federal Farm Board in 1929. Mandated to work with and through cooperatives to enhance farmers' marketing power, it included in its authorities the ability to make loans to cooperatives for their use in purchasing commodities to stabilize markets. Some success was realized in the support of wheat and cotton. The Board ultimately exhausted its funding, however, and gave way to the current Farm Credit Administration.

The situation confronting farmers during the years of the Great Depression was fundamentally one of excess capacity. Farmers simply produced more than was needed to meet domestic demands. With the world in economic depression, foreign demand was down and prices had fallen precipitously.

A domestic allotment plan, first proposed in the late 1920's, was enacted into law with the Agricultural Adjustment Act of 1933. This was the first instance of production controls being used to constrain excess capacity within the farm sector. The Secretary of Agriculture was authorized to enter into voluntary agreements with producers to reduce acreage or production, to enter into marketing agreements with processors to affect prices, and to spend money for the expansion of markets and the removal of surpluses.

The 1933 Act eventually was invalidated by the Supreme Court, although it was quickly replaced by similar acceptable legislation. The concept of an "ever-normal granary" featuring balanced supplies of commodities emerged in the 1938 Agricultural Adjustment Act with a program of loans, acreage allotments, and marketing quotas for the so-called basic crops. This foundation of programs continues to the present day.

During World War II and the period that followed, first our allies and then those countries that had been defeated clamored for the foodstuffs that our farm sector could provide. The excess capacity that had and would continue to plague agriculture in more normal times was not of immediate concern. Land previously retired was brought back into production. Adoption of various technological advances was swift and effective. As the war drew to a close, continued high demand for foods for foreign relief and continued government price supports stimulated an even greater adoption of mechanical advances, increased use of fertilizers, and the expanded use of improved seed and feed.

Crisis of the Fifties

The full dimensions of overproduction came more clearly into focus in the 1950's. Total farm output during this period increased at a rate nearly one-third greater than population. Since per capita consumption remained largely unchanged, domestic demand for food could

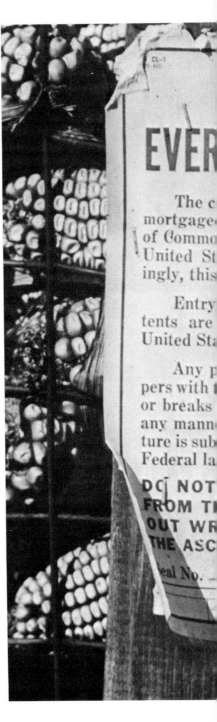

The "Ever-Normal Granary," forerunner of today's agricultural programs, came into being with the 1938 Agricultural Adjustment Act. The corn "sealed" here, "has been mortgaged to secure a loan made under a program of the Commodity Credit Corporation. . . ."

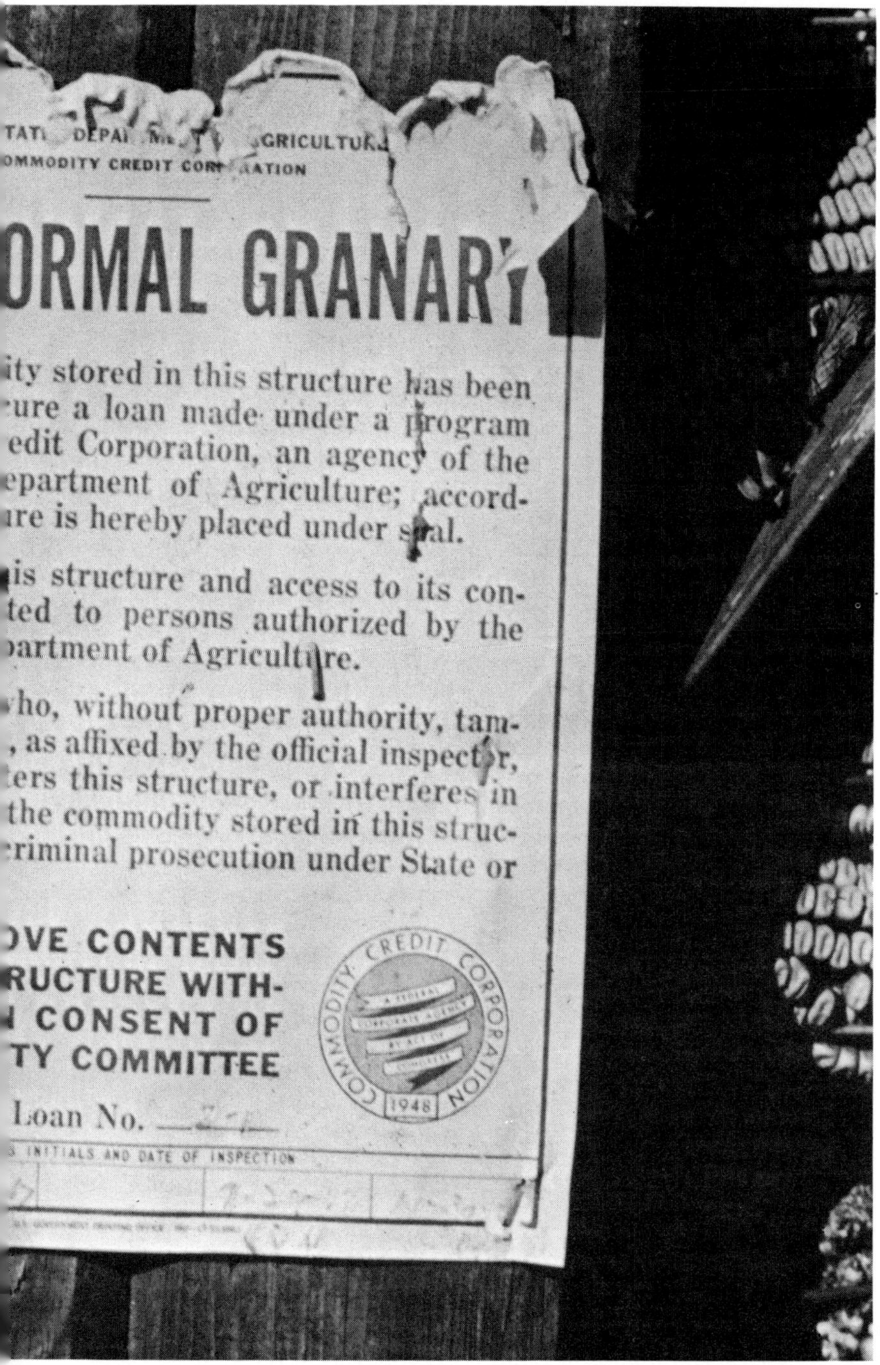

TAT. DEPAT ..T .GRICULTUR.
OMMODITY CREDIT COR ATION

ORMAL GRANAR

ity stored in this structure has been
ure a loan made under a program
edit Corporation, an agency of the
epartment of Agriculture; accord-
re is hereby placed under seal.

is structure and access to its con-
ted to persons authorized by the
artment of Agriculture.

ho, without proper authority, tam-
, as affixed by the official inspector,
ers this structure, or interferes in
the commodity stored in this struc-
riminal prosecution under State or

VE CONTENTS
RUCTURE WITH-
CONSENT OF
TY COMMITTEE

Loan No. _____

INITIALS AND DATE OF INSPECTION

COMMODITY CREDIT CORPORATION
1948

Roy Clark

23

not absorb the increases in production that occurred. Commercial foreign demand did increase somewhat and the PL 480 or Food for Peace distribution program was initiated in 1954. The result under the prevailing policy and programs, however, was massive government assumption of commodity stocks, increasing from $1.3 billion in 1952 to $7.7 billion in 1959. Price supports were clearly at levels that precluded the sale by farmers of all they produced.

A variety of reasons account for the chronic excess capacity that plagued agriculture through the 1950's and into the 1960's. Great emphasis was placed on scientific research, including that related to agriculture. Breakthroughs in hybrid seed varieties and the further development of equipment and farming techniques added to already serious overproduction. The markets in which farmers sold their commodities, moreover, were somewhat unique. Because there were so many producing units it was not possible for any one farmer to influence price. The result was an attempt to adopt technologies that would increase efficiency and decrease costs. This, of course, promoted adoption of productivity-enhancing technology.

In addition, the nature of the demand for agricultural commodities was rather insensitive to changes in price (and continues to be). Thus, improvements in price generally required a large or significant reduction in the quantity of agricultural commodities made available for sale. Even then, the difficulty of the surplus condition would not have been so severe if the resources used in agriculture — land, labor, equipment, and the like — were able to move easily into and out of production. Such was not the case.

As supply outpaced demand throughout the decade of the fifties, farmers and others sought policies for the farm sector that would deal with the chronic surplus situation. The response during the fifties had been to keep price supports at relatively high levels, with the government assuming responsibility for excess production. In effect the price support, which operated through the nonrecourse loan program, set the market price. If the market price were to fall below the loan rate, farmers could forfeit their commodity to the government without penalty or recourse. These relatively high levels of support did much to encourage farmers to adopt the new technology. A system of allotments and quotas was also employed. Productivity increases, however, often rendered acreage allotments ineffective in limiting production.

Shift in Policy — The programs of the sixties reflected dissatisfaction with events of the fifties and an emerging shift in policy. Frustration over large government stocks along with a concern that farmers were producing for government programs and not for the market prompted a change in strategy. For wheat and the feedgrains it was decided in the early sixties that a greater market orientation was necessary. Two major changes were initiated: 1) more producer flexibility in supply control decisions and 2) a separation of price and income supports.

The first change involved a movement away from rigid acreage allotments, with greater reliance on program incentives to induce producer participation in acreage reductions. The second change was fundamental to the regaining of a competitive position in world markets. Loan rates, or price supports, were reduced from their relatively high levels of the 1950's to world market price levels. The difference in support was made up through direct government payments for land diversion and other actions on the part of farmers. Through this shift, an opportunity for market clearing prices was created while maintaining income support to farmers.

Policy continued its shift toward greater producer response to conditions of the marketplace under the 1970 and 1973 Farm Acts. The individual commodity approach to production control was increasingly discarded in favor of restraint on the total farm unit. Direct payments were continued for wheat, cotton, and feed-grains. In the search for a workable criterion to set equitable support levels, the use of production costs was initiated in place of parity for several commodities, including the food and feed grains and upland cotton.

Agricultural policy, in attempting to deal with the problem of excess capacity, had shifted noticeably toward working in concert with the market as we moved into the decade of the seventies. But significant change was occurring both within the farm sector and in farm product markets that foretold yet further evolution in U.S. agricultural policy. A number of events are especially noteworthy. In 1971, foreign exchange rates were realined, leaving U.S. farm exports in a much stronger competitive position. Exports did in fact increase significantly, due initially to poor harvests worldwide and more basically to a shift in the food import policies of several major countries.

The result was a buoyant agricultural sector during early years of the decade.

Export sales were at historical highs. Prices were up, costs were rising rather slowly, profits were at near record levels, and the surplus stocks of earlier years finally disappeared. Reaction within the farm sector was perhaps quite predictable. New entrants and expansion by many existing farmers caused land prices to be bid up and generally raised the level of debt, much of this debt being incurred at inflated asset values. Cash flow needs to service this debt were to become a serious problem later in the decade.

Volatile Markets — While crop farmers tended to benefit from this newly found prosperity, livestock producers became extremely susceptible to volatile grain markets and high feed prices. A serious liquidation of livestock herds resulted. Consumers were buffered initially by price controls but soon experienced a significant increase in food costs; an export embargo was imposed in response to the food price concerns. Thus, while policy goals for one group in agriculture were met, others for whom a policy interest also existed tended to fare somewhat less well.

Beyond these current circumstances, more fundamental changes appear to have occurred in the organization and operation of the farming industry by the end of the seventies. A number of observers suggest that the chronic farm problem of excess capacity, or too many resources devoted to producing agricultural commodities, may well have passed. Available evidence seems to suggest that the exodus of labor and land from agriculture that had been occurring since the 1930's had ended. Certainly the net labor outmigration from farming had slowed, and it appeared that labor use was actually on the increase. Readily available cropland was essentially back into production.

Economic returns in the farm sector were, in most years, on a par with those earned elsewhere in the economy. But commodity prices and farm income had become noticeably more erratic. This was due in part to increasing dependence on an inherently volatile export market, and in part to the fact that prices had been set free to respond more to market signals than to artificial support programs.

Future Farm Policy

If this assessment of agriculture as it emerged from the seventies is correct, it suggests the likely motivation for further evolution in our farm policy. Quite clearly the notion that the chronic excess capacity problem has passed is in a major way contingent upon continued strong foreign demand for U.S. commodities. With two-thirds of our wheat and two-fifths of our feedgrains moving to world markets, this factor is critical.

As we have learned, the world market can be rather fickle in its treatment of U.S. farmers. The success of harvests in both importing countries and major exporting nations is an annual unknown. Movement of exchange rates in response to changes in world economic conditions can cause the price of a commodity to vary substantially from one month to the next. And the purchase behavior of many nations, especially the centrally planned

countries, may not respond to prices but to other more general policy considerations.

U.S. agriculture's efforts to respond to the challenges of world markets seem likely therefore to provide much of the basis for further evolution in public policy for the farm sector. Implied policy issues will include assisting farmers to secure a

Foreign demand for U.S. wheat and feedgrains is strong. Two-thirds of our wheat crop, perhaps some of it from this Oklahoma wheat farm, is sold in world markets.

fair and competitive access to world markets, dealing with the negative aspects of market instability, maintaining competitive technology, and enhancing the productive capacity of our land and water resources.

Clearly, farmers will manage their businesses in a more market-oriented environment characterized by both new opportunities and risks. How they deal with this environment will be their individual decision. But the public will not be disinterested because the way the farming industry performs is enormously important to the Nation's well-being. Thus, how society and farmers will choose to share the risks of producing under these new circumstances remains to be seen.

USDA

How a Dime Can Help Us Save Our Resource Base

By James N. Benson and Chris Risbrudt

G ot a dime? Look at the edge. It's so thin you can hardly see it. But the thickness of a dime represents the difference between maintaining our soils in good condition and allowing them to deteriorate. The dime reminds us what a thin line there is between sound and unsound resource management. Keep that dime in mind. It can help us remember how fragile our resources are.

Through the action of water, air, and soil micro-organisms, topsoils form very slowly. On the average, topsoils form at the rate of about 1/30th of an inch a year — about the thickness of a dime. The average topsoil also loses a certain amount through erosion. But if the top-soil erodes no faster than it forms, the erosion is considered tolerable. There is no net loss in topsoil thickness, and the soil's inherent productivity is maintained. Excessive soil loss, however, eventually reduces inherent productivity.

Our soils sustain the crops, livestock, and trees upon which a healthy agricultural economy depends. Careless or exploitive management can lead to excessive soil erosion, water pollution, and other problems that generations of work may not be able to correct. Civilizations have perished as the fertile soil they were founded upon washed away. If we treat our soils, water, and forests right, they will serve future generations as well as they have served us.

The United States is blessed with vast areas of fertile soils that support the most productive agriculture the world has known. The total area of the United States is about 2.36 billion acres, including more than 100 million acres of inland and coastal waters. About one-third is owned by the Federal Government. The other two-thirds — about 1.5 billion acres — is owned by individuals, organizations, and State and local governments. Most of the Nation's crops, livestock, and forest resources are on nonfederal lands.

Nearly 90 percent of the nonfederal land is crop, forest, range, and pasture land. The rest is urbanized or otherwise developed, mined, or barren. The Nation's agricultural lands and related water resources produce enough food and fiber not only to meet domestic needs but also to supply about one-tenth of total overseas consumption. But will America's cornucopia always overflow? Resource problems in some areas threaten our farmers' ability to continue to increase productivity. Much agricultural land — especially sloping cropland — is eroding faster than the soil can rebuild itself

James N. Benson is Writer-Editor, Appraisal and Program Development, Soil Conservation Service.

Chris Risbrudt is Staff Economist, Cooperative Forestry Program, Forest Service.

through natural processes. Each year about 3 million acres of agricultural land are converted to nonagricultural uses. Once converted, these acres are permanently lost to food and fiber production. Depletion of ground water threatens continuation of irrigated agriculture in extensive areas of the West. Floods threaten life, property, livestock, and crops in many upstream watersheds. Because of continued development on flood plains, the likelihood is for greater damage in the future. Deterioration of water quality limits potential use of water for irrigation, municipal and industrial supply, fish and wildlife habitat, and other purposes.

In 1977, the most recent year for which accurate data are available, there were about 413 million acres of cropland in the United States. Cropland acreage has increased slightly since about 1970 but is still some 10 percent lower than in 1958. The decline in the sixties reflects the abundance of farm products during the period. The increase in the seventies reflects the recent strong growth in foreign demand. Nearly half of all cropland is in row crops — corn, soybeans, cotton, and the like. About one-fourth is in close-grown crops such as small grains. The rest is in orchards, hay, or truck crops.

The acreage of irrigated cropland has doubled in the last 30 years. Most of the Nation's irrigated land is in the 17 Western States, but the irrigated acreage in the Midwest, Southeast, and Middle Atlantic States is increasing. Most of the recent growth in irrigation has been concentrated in Nebraska and Kansas, where irrigation water is pumped from deep aquifers. From 1971 to 1973, the 12 percent of the Nation's cropland that was irrigated produced more than 25

percent of the total value of U.S. crops.

Use of the land is governed largely by inherent soil productivity and by conditions at a given site. Productivity is influenced by many factors, including natural fertility, moisture-holding capacity, and soil temperature. Other site conditions such as salinity, soil density, and slope can also determine what crops a farmer can grow.

Many problems can stem from land uses that ignore natural soil conditions. Too much irrigation can cause leaching of salt into ground water and re-emergence of that salt somewhere else. Where the salt seeps back to the surface, it damages or destroys crops or grasses. Or, sloping land that might be perfectly suited to pasture could be severely eroded if cropped.

Remember that dime? It represents a tolerable amount of soil erosion. Across the Nation, the average rate of soil erosion is just about at that tolerable level. On cropland, however, the average erosion rate is higher.

Rates of soil loss vary but are generally low on undisturbed soil under native vegetation. On about one-fourth of the Nation's cropland, however, sheet and rill erosion — the removal of soil in thin layers or small channels by moving water — exceeds the tolerable rate. The most severely eroding 10 percent of the Nation's cropland accounts for more than half of all sheet and rill erosion. Add soil loss through wind erosion, and one cropland acre in three is eroding faster than the tolerable rate.

Conservation tillage, a form of tillage in which a crop is planted in residue of the

On about one-fourth of the Nation's cropland, sheet and rill erosion exceeds the tolerable rate. This west Tennessee cornfield is eroding severely following one brief storm.

previous crop, is gaining favor in many areas. It not only reduces erosion as much as 90 percent but also saves time and fuel. And it provides more food and cover for the wildlife that normally lives on cropland. The major factor limiting conservation tillage is cost of the specialized equipment required. Conservation tillage also relies heavily on chemicals to control insects and weeds, and therefore increases the risk of subsequent water pollution. Despite these potential drawbacks, acreage under conservation tillage probably will increase steadily during coming years.

Forests Cover Third of Our Land

The picture is considerably brighter for the forests in the United States. Despite a declining trend, the Nation has a huge and productive forest land base that can meet our needs as far into the future as we can see. The problem is to intensify our forestry and wood-using practices to make full use of the potential productivity available.

Forests cover about one-third of the Nation's land area — 737 million acres. Nearly two-thirds of this is suited to and available for commercial timber production. Most of this commercial forest land is in nonindustrial, private ownership. One-fifth is administered by the U.S. Department of Agriculture's Forest Service, and the forest industries own a productive 14 percent. Nonindustrial, private ownership is concentrated in the Eastern United States. Nearly half of these forests are in the South, and a substantial portion are in the North. Relatively few nonindustrial private acres exist in the West; most are publicly or industrially owned.

Harvest of timber in the United States totaled more than 14 billion cubic feet in 1976. About 48 percent of this volume came from nonindustrial private forests such as farm woodlots, while almost 30 percent came from forest industry lands. Seven-tenths of timber harvested in the U.S. is softwood. Annual growth of American forests presently exceeds the amount of timber harvested by about 50 percent. In 1976, growth on commercial forest lands amounted to 21.7 billion cubic feet. About 57 percent of this growth was in softwood trees. Most of the total growth occurred on nonindustrial private forests. Since 1952, annual growth on all ownerships has increased, although the greatest increase has been on nonindustrial private ownerships.

Despite the fact the forests are presently growing more wood than we are using, Forest Service projections indicate even more is needed to meet future demands. Should present trends continue, prices for softwood and desirable hardwood logs will rise 2 to 2.5 percent faster than inflation as demand overtakes supply. However, economically feasible investments in forest lands exist on 168 million acres. Nearly three-fourths of these economic opportunities are on nonindustrial, private lands.

Products from the forest play an important role in the U.S. economy. In 1972, timber-based economic activity accounted for 4.1 percent of the Gross National Product. Employment in timber-related

U.S. Commercial Forest Land (millions of acres)

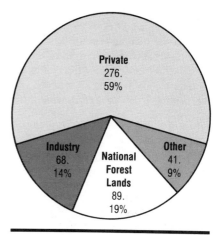

Private
276.
59%

Industry
68.
14%

National
Forest
Lands
89.
19%

Other
41.
9%

Current and Potential Net Annual Growth per Acre of U.S. Forests by Region

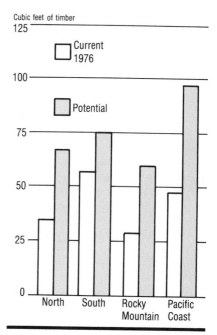

Cubic feet of timber

Current 1976

Potential

North   South   Rocky Mountain   Pacific Coast

activities — from timber management to retail trade — totaled 3.3 million. With forests, the problems do not usually involve soil degradation. Rather, they are ones of motivating forest owners to tap full productive potential. While growth in U.S. forests is substantial, it falls short of the potential. Current growth on commercial timber lands is only three-fifths of the potential which would be achieved with reasonably intensive management, such as reforestation, thinning, and pruning.

Increased management of our forests is necessary if we are to produce the wood needed in the future. Most of the increase must come from nonindustrial private lands. However, for many reasons these owners are not making the needed investments in their forests. Surveys of commercial forests in the South, where most of the potential exists, show that less than one-third of the pine forest lands harvested are regenerating in pine trees. Instead, in many instances, low-quality hardwoods take over. Should this process continue, the Nation will be unable to supply the softwood we are likely to need in the future.

Some of the constraints which discourage landowners from more intensively managing their forests are lack of investment money, scarce technical knowledge and advice, limited market information, long time periods before investments pay off, low prices, and risks from fire, insects, and disease. Many forest land-

owners probably consider forestry a poor investment relative to other possibilities. Also, many people own forests for reasons other than growing timber, such as recreation, second home sites, speculation, and simply the satisfactions of ownership.

Land Management Needs

In general, grazing lands are divided by a climatic line at about the 96th meridian. Most rangeland is to the west and most pastureland to the east. The condition of rangeland is measured by comparing existing plant cover with the potential natural cover for the site. Experts claim overall condition of the nonfederal rangeland has improved continuously since the 1930s, and improvement since 1963 can

Only about 40 percent of the Nation's rangeland is in good to excellent condition. On this Kansas range, cattle are feeding on reseeded native grasses.

be documented. Nevertheless, only about 40 percent is in good or excellent condition. Almost one-third of the Nation's nonfederal rangeland is eroding at excessive rates. And because rangeland generally recovers from erosion more slowly than other agricultural lands, the effects of erosion on rangeland are magnified.

There are three times as many acres of nonfederal rangeland as of pastureland, but the pastureland provides more total forage. Even so, better management could improve pastureland production by about one-third. Excessive erosion is not as widespread on pastureland as on cropland or rangeland. Only about 10 percent of the pastureland is eroding at rates that

eventually would reduce inherent productivity of the land. The average rate of erosion on pastureland is less than half that on cropland.

In some areas, grazing lands are being converted to cropland or to nonagricultural uses. Because demands for red meat currently are low, the losses of grazing lands have not yet led to production shortfalls. Should these demands rise again, however, shortages in available grazing lands could lead to meat shortages and higher prices.

From 1958 to 1977, almost 40 million acres of rural land were developed for housing, industry, roads, and similar uses. Most of the conversions were

made during the second half of the period. Almost one acre in three of the conversions during this period was forest land, less than one in four was cropland, and about one in five was pasture or range.

Conversion of agricultural lands to nonagricultural uses is considered irreversible because reclamation generally is costly. For each acre developed, an average of one additional acre is isolated and lost from potential or actual production. Of the nonfederal rural land not now being cropped, only about 12 percent (127 million acres) has potential for conversion to cropland. This potential cropland now is mainly grazing and forest lands, however, so there would be fewer acres available to grow forage and wood products.

Wildlife Habitat — Wild animals and birds need food, cover, and water to survive. Many people view the condition of wildlife habitat in an area as a barometer of resource conditions. Irrigation, conservation tillage, and other management practices can change the character of the land and thus its suitability for various kinds of wildlife. Habitat quality on cropland has declined in many areas because of larger fields, removal of windbreaks, continuous cropping, and other factors.

Since the condition of nonfederal rangeland has been improving, wildlife habitat on rangeland also has been improving. Habitat quality on privately owned woodland is low in some places where wooded areas are either being overgrazed or unmanaged. In 1977 more than 70 million acres of nonfederal land were classified as wetlands. Wetlands provide habitat for a variety of wildlife. They also serve as sediment and nutrient traps for the

streams that flow into and through them, and in this way enhance downstream water quality. Since 1958, however, wetlands have been drained for agricultural and other purposes at the rate of 500,000 acres a year. In recent years, the conversion rate slowed to about 300,000 acres a year.

Water Management Needs

Without water, the most fertile soil could not support a single blade of grass. Water requirements of different plants vary, and natural precipitation can be supplemented by various water management techniques, including irrigation. Recent dry periods have underscored the need for improved management so that all water users — farmers and nonfarmers alike — have enough. Precipitation in the 48 contiguous States ranges from less than 4 inches to more than 200 inches annually. The annual average is about 30 inches. In the western half of the United States, most areas receive less than the average, and seasonal and year-to-year variations tend to be greater than in other regions. In general the 17 Western States are considered "water short."

To ensure an adequate, steady water supply for all users, dams and reservoirs have been constructed, water has been transferred between regions, and ground water sources have been tapped. Withdrawals from surface waters exceed 250 billion gallons a day. Withdrawals from ground waters exceed 80 billion gallons a day, including 21 billion gallons a day that are not replaced through natural recharge.

Four times more water is used for producing food and fiber than for all other purposes combined. In semiarid parts of the country, agricultural production depends heavily on water storage systems. In arid regions, production of many crops depends almost totally on irrigation. Even in humid areas, farmers are irrigating cropland to compensate for periodic dry spells during the growing season.

Of the water diverted from surface sources or withdrawn from the ground for irrigation, about 78 percent reaches the farm. Of the water that reaches the farm, about 53 percent is taken up by the crop. Inefficient irrigation can degrade water quality (by leaching minerals into ground water or carrying agricultural chemicals into surface water), waste water and energy, reduce instream flows, and increase production costs.

In arid and semiarid areas, increasing demands for water for nonagricultural uses could limit the amount of water available for agriculture. Much water could be conserved through better management of soil moisture, control of unwanted vegetation, and improved water handling techniques. It is unlikely that water supplies can be increased significantly by constructing more reservoirs. Many of the best sites have been developed

In California's Imperial Valley, a technician takes soil moisture readings with a neutron probe. The information will help the farmowner conserve irrigation water through better management of soil moisture.

Tim McCabe

When it rains, animal wastes and other runoff from this feedlot pollute a nearby stream, degrading its water quality.

Areas Where Potential for Degradation of Water Quality Is High Because of Agricultural Nonpoint Source Pollutants.

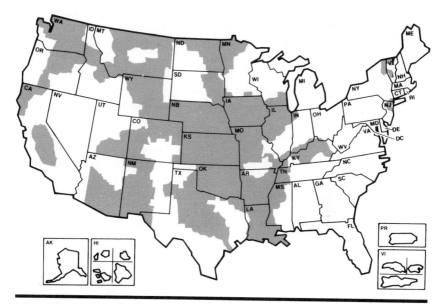

Use of Nonfederal Land in the United States and Caribbean Area, 1977.

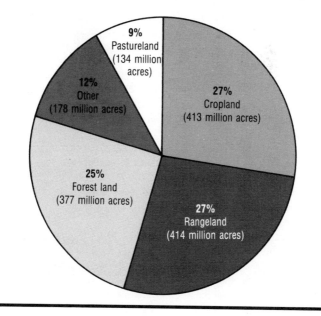

9%
Pastureland
(134 million acres)

27%
Cropland
(413 million acres)

12%
Other
(178 million acres)

25%
Forest land
(377 million acres)

27%
Rangeland
(414 million acres)

already and development costs at most remaining sites are becoming prohibitive.

Pollution — As food and fiber production is increased to meet domestic and foreign demands, likelihood of water pollution will increase. As more farmland is converted to other uses, marginal land will be brought into production. Because marginal land is generally more erodible than good farmland, more sediment and associated pollutants will enter lakes and streams.

To some degree, 95 percent of the Nation's drainage basins are polluted. Bacteria, nutrients, salts, sediment, and chemicals are the most common and most serious water pollutants associated with agriculture. These pollutants are carried mainly in runoff from fields and feedlots and in irrigation return flow. "Acid rain" is degrading water and lowering the pH of the soil in parts of the Nation, especially the Middle Atlantic and Northeastern States. Heavy concentrations of acid rain can kill fish and plants and require farmers to apply more lime than normal.

Upstream flooding — Nearly 12 percent (175 million acres) of the Nation's nonfederal rural land is subject to flooding. Almost half of these flood-prone lands are in the Southeast. Some 21,000 communities have flooding problems, including 6,000 with populations exceeding 2,500. Annual flood damage to cropland, pastureland, built-up areas, and other property in upstream watersheds of 400 square miles or less totals about $2 billion per year. Damage to cropland and pastureland represents two-thirds of the total. By the year 2000, annual flood damage to all lands is projected to increase by nearly half. Almost all the in-

creased damage will occur on real estate improvements and community developments.

The Outlook — American agriculture has doubled production in the past 30 years in response to increasing domestic and foreign demands. Forest wood production has remained somewhat above demand. We can expect demands for both agricultural and forest products to continue to increase, and we can expect concurrent pressures on our natural resources to meet the rising demands. The Nation can increase and protect its agricultural production by

- Developing new technology
- Protecting agricultural lands from erosion, and
- Limiting conversion of agricultural lands to nonagricultural uses

Because of technological improvements — better crop varieties, fertilizers, equipment, and farming techniques — crop yields have increased nearly 2 percent per year since the 1930's. In the short term, such increases can offset losses of inherent soil productivity caused by erosion. Some experts predict, however, that annual increases in yields due to technological improvements will be smaller in the years to come. Controlling erosion will become more important because continued excessive erosion over a long period will reduce productive capability of the Nation's soils.

To meet future demands for farm com-

Because of technological improvements, crop yields have increased steadily since the 1930's. This Iowa farmer is harvesting a record soybean crop that was planted using conservation tillage on land contoured and terraced to reduce erosion.

Woodlands can often be used for dual purposes. A Louisiana dairy farmer is using this woodland to graze his dairy cows.

Tim Shiflet

Tim McCabe

modities, we can continue to depend on improved technology alone, or couple it with conservation. The increasing use of conservation tillage shows that saving the soil can be compatible with production technology. The best soils for agriculture are also among the most attractive for urban development, so we can expect competition for agricultural lands to remain strong. Loss of farmland could severely reduce the choices available to coming generations of farmers.

Forestry — In forestry, greater and more efficient productivity is also possible, and practical, by 1) applying technology for intensifying timber-growing practices on forest land, but particularly on nonindustrial private woodlands, and 2) continuing research and application of findings to make better use of the wood supplies we have. Intensified management of the Nation's forest lands can reduce the rate of increase projected for forest product prices by expanding wood supplies. At the same time, it can enhance other benefits of the forests, such as recreation, range, wildlife, and fish.

Recent studies highlighting economic opportunities for private investment in forest lands have shown that such investments can yield good returns. In addition, new tax provisions encourage reforestation. Crop insurance for timber is in the pilot testing stage, and as it becomes feasible will be expanded. Market information consisting of prices landowners can receive for their trees is now widely available in the South, and is extending to other regions. Technical assistance for forest management is available from State Foresters, forestry consultants, and Extension and industry foresters, who also disseminate new research information. These factors will

help increase forest productivity in the future. Present work on genetic improvement of trees will result in seedlings that will grow 19 to 25 percent faster by the year 2030.

Improving utilization of our timber resources can also greatly help meet future demands and hold prices down. Better harvesting and processing practices can reduce waste and increase the amount of valuable products obtained from each log. Research into manufacturing processes can encourage substitution of our abundant hardwood resources for the more scarce softwood. Today about 70 percent of our harvests are softwood. In the future, new knowledge and expertise will allow more use of our hardwoods.

The other choice is to continue forest and wood utilization as we are currently, and wait for the inevitable wood shortages and the spiraling prices that accompany them.

We must look beyond today's agricultural surpluses if we want to avoid shortages tomorrow. Remember that dime? It reminds us how fragile our resources are. Protecting those resources is a job that never ends.

Further Reading

Soil, Water, and Related Resources in the United States: RCA Appraisal Parts I and II. Soil Conservation Service, P.O. Box 2890, Washington, D.C. 20013. Free.

An Assessment of the Forest and Range Land Situation in the United States. Forest Service. For sale from the Superintendent of Documents, U.S. Government Printing Office, Washington, D.C. 20402. $9.00.

What Farmers Buy Makes Production Fly

By Paul Andrilenas and Ted Eichers

Farmers have relied increasingly on the use of purchased items or inputs to produce the Nation's food and fiber. Gains in agricultural productivity in the last 40 years were largely associated with farmers' use of purchased items which increased nearly seven times in terms of dollars spent. Since 1940, use of purchased inputs enabled farmers to double crop output per acre. The combination of improved seed varieties, use of commercial fertilizers, synthetic pesticides and improved tillage and harvesting equipment has resulted in increasing output per man hour tenfold while the amount of land used remained almost unchanged.

Once largely self-sufficient, U.S. farmers now spend nearly two-thirds of their cash receipts to purchase and finance things used in the production process. Between 1940 and 1980 purchased inputs (including credit) increased from 44 percent to 61 percent of cash farm receipts. Anticipated increased demands on the limited land and water resources of U.S. agriculture assure that purchased inputs will become even more critical in the future. Major purchased farm input items include fertilizer, pesticides, farm machinery, feed, fuels and energy, and seed.

The growing use of fertilizer has been a major factor in doubling crop output per acre in the last 40 years. However, after increasing steadily for several decades, the growth in U.S. fertilizer use is beginning to slow. Little expected growth in crop acres and reduced yield gains — along with the potential to increase the efficiency of fertilizer use — will further trim the fertilizer growth rate. Major plant nutrients used by farmers are nitrogen, phosphate, and potash. In 1980/81 farmers used 23.5 million tons of these materials, a 478 percent increase over 1950. They spent over $9 billion in 1981 on fertilizer, of which about half was for nitrogen.

Use of chemical fertilizer enabled farmers to take advantage of the production potential of improved seed varieties. However, agronomic considerations were not the primary purpose for developing new fertilizer products. Since fertilizer production is usually located away from the areas of use, fertilizer product development has concentrated on developing products with a high nutrient content that are more economical to transport, store, and apply. Bulk handling has become very popular in recent years, greatly reducing the cost of transporting, storing and applying fertilizer. Special services such as soil analysis to determine crop nutrient requirements are also generally available from fertilizer dealers.

Paul Andrilenas and Ted Eichers are Agricultural Economists, National Economics Division, Economic Research Service.

Trends in acres harvested, crop output, and labor 1940-80

Year	Acres harvested	Crop output	Labor in crop production
	Million acres	Index	Million hours
1940	341	67	652
1950	345	76	428
1960	324	93	268
1970	293	100	179
1980	353	131	141
Percent change 1940-80	+4	+96	−78

Trends in cash farm receipts and expenditures for purchased inputs, 1940-80

Year	Cash farm receipts	Expenditures for farm inputs[1]	Inputs' share of cash receipts
	Billion dollars		Percent
1940	9	4	44
1950	29	13	35
1960	35	17	47
1970	55	27	50
1980	140	85	61

[1]Includes interest. Does not include livestock, labor, services, taxes, or land.

Trends in expenditures for selected farm input items, 1950-1980.

Year	Expenditures 1/				Percent change 1950-1980
	1950	1960	1970	1980	
	Billion dollars				Percent
Feed	3.3	4.6	8.0	18.6	463
Fertilizer	1.0	1.3	2.4	9.5	850
Pesticides	0.2	0.3	0.9	3.1	1450
Farm machinery	2.2	2.0	4.0	9.1	314
Fuels and energy	1.3	1.7	3.0	10.2	685
Seed	0.5	0.5	0.9	3.9	680
Machinery repair and operation	1.1	1.7	1.9	6.3	473
All production inputs 1/	13.4	20.7	34.2	105.2	683

1/ Not including rents, labor, or taxes.

Pesticides — In 1981 U.S. farmers bought over 700 million pounds of pesticides (chemicals used to control crop or livestock pests). Farmers' annual expenditures for pesticides rose from about $300 million in 1960 to $3.6 billion in 1981, a 10-fold increase. While much of this jump was a result of price rises, purchases more than quadrupled during the 21-year period after accounting for inflation.

The dramatic rise in pesticide use during the 1960's and 1970's resulted largely from development of new types of weed control chemicals (herbicides) that could control specific weeds and were designed for use on specific crops such as corn, soybeans, wheat, or cotton. Herbicides essentially eliminated the need for mechanical and hand weed control for many major crops. Use of insecticide chemicals enabled cost-efficient farming systems which permitted farmers to plant large acreages of a single crop on a continuous basis without serious pest problems.

Total Tractor HP Doubles

Modern machinery has been one of the major factors in reducing labor requirements in agriculture. Although the total number of farm tractors remained almost unchanged between 1960 and 1981 at about 4.7 million units, total tractor horsepower available on farms nearly doubled. This trend represents an increase in average horsepower per tractor from 33 to 58. Half the new tractors purchased in 1981 had a power rating greater than 100 horsepower. This compares with only 3 percent of the new tractors produced with over 100 horsepower in 1965. Large-scale tractors and equipment have enabled one person to perform nearly all the tillage, planting, harvesting, and other mechanical operations on several hundred acres of land.

Over time the capacity of machines has increased, as has the variety of tasks and the precision with which tasks are performed. Manufacturers have introduced many features to add comfort, convenience, durability, and flexibility. Tractors produced today have many automatic functions. Traction boosters can auto-

matically transfer weight from front to rear axle. Automatic speed controls provide precision timing needed for planting and chemical application, while hydraulic controls and improved transmissions allow for greater ease in handling farm implements.

Combines can harvest more grain with less grain loss. Some self-leveling models are designed for use on hilly terrain. Large cotton pickers with improved handling of picked cotton have reduced the

need for onfarm cotton storage. Planting, tillage, and forage and hay harvesting equipment have all been improved to provide greater operating precision, maneuverability, capacity, and flexibility.

Availability of commercial feeds has made possible large-scale specialized livestock operations. In 1981 livestock feed purchases amounted to $19.0 billion, about 15 percent of all U.S. farm production expenses. Besides the feeds farmers purchase, a large portion of feed concentrates are consumed on the farms where they are produced.

Activities from feed manufacturing to marketing and processing the final farm-fed commodity are often carried out by the same management. Almost all broilers are produced by growers who have contracts with the feed producer. Over 80 percent of the farmers producing eggs have some form of contractual arrangement with their feed supplier and/or the egg marketer. Contractual production agreements between hog producers and feed suppliers are also becoming quite common.

Fuel Use — Agriculture accounts for a very small share of U.S. fuel and energy consumption. For example, farmers accounted for only 4 percent of total U.S. motor gasoline use in 1981. That year farmers spent nearly $11 billion for fuels and energy, a 7-fold increase over 1950, with most of the increase occurring in the 1970's. Direct natural gas and liquefied petroleum gas (LP) use, for agricultural production purposes, represents only 1 or 2 percent of the domestic market for these fuels. However, agriculture accounts for about 20 percent of all diesel fuel used in the United States.

Modest gains in agricultural energy demand during the period 1960-1974 can be explained to a large extent by the switch from gasoline to diesel fuel powered engines. Diesel tractors are more energy efficient than gasoline powered units despite their higher horsepower. Most of

In 1981, U.S. farmers spent an estimated $3.6 billion on about 700 million pounds of pesticides to control livestock pests, or crop pests as in this Michigan cherry orchard.

45

the indirect energy (energy used to produce other products) consumed in agriculture is provided by natural gas and is put to work primarily to produce nitrogen fertilizer. Nearly 40 percent of the energy consumed in crop production in 1980 was used indirectly to make fertilizer and pesticides.

$4 Billion to Buy Seed

In 1981 farmers spent about $4 billion to buy seed. Although this amount is dwarfed by several other production items, seeds have accounted for an increasing share of agricultural input expenditures in recent years. This rise reflects both an increase in the amount of seeds farmers purchased and a significant jump in seed prices. Genetic improvements in seed varieties resistant to insect and disease pests and capable of responding to higher fertilization rates have been a major factor in increased crop productivity. Hybrid seeds have been developed to provide higher yielding plant varieties to grow under various climatic and farming conditions.

Farmers long have relied on custom services for seasonal or infrequent farming operations. Custom application of pesticides and fertilizers, and custom harvesting of crops, are common throughout U.S. agriculture. Farmers are also increasingly using such services as soil testing, animal health care, artificial breeding, and seed treating. Repair and

A soil test tells the farmer how much fertilizer, especially nitrogen, to put on his cropland. Too much nitrogen wastes money and not enough can result in lower crop yields. The lab technician here is preparing soil samples for analysis.

Changes in price indexes for farm commodities and production items, 1972-82.

	Percent change
All farm commodities	102
Crops	110
Livestock	95
All production items	150
Machinery	209
Fuels and energy	292
Pesticides	85
Fertilizer	181

maintenance of trucks, tractors, combines, and other farm equipment is an important adjunct to agricultural production.

The Squeeze — Increased expenditures for purchased production inputs are the result of higher prices, as well as greater input use. Prices of purchased production items increased as costs to produce, transport, and retail these products climbed. In the last 10 years prices farmers paid for purchased items increased at a rate about 50 percent greater than prices they received for products they sell, resulting in a "cost-price squeeze."

Economic conditions have had some dramatic effects on the use of purchased farm inputs and prices paid for them in the 1960's and 1970's. Expenditures for fuel, fertilizer, pesticides, and farm machinery went up much more between 1970 and 1980 than from 1960 to 1970. During the 1970's fuel expenditures soared nearly 400 percent compared to a 15-percent rise in the 1960's. Fertilizer expenditures increased more than 3 times as fast in the 1970's as in the 1960's. On the other hand, in the 1970's (except for chemicals) quantities used rose little or not at all. Because of low farm incomes, unit sales of nearly all farm machinery items dropped in the early 1980's. For example, 2-wheel drive tractor unit sales fell 15 percent in 1980, 13 percent in 1981, and in the first 5 months of 1982 sales were 20 percent below the same period for 1981.

Financing requirements increased dramatically as farmers substituted capital items for labor and expanded the size of their farms. While interest rates began to rise in the early and mid-1970's, it was not until the 1978 to 1982 period that interest costs had an appreciable dampening affect on the purchase and use of farm production items. The high interest rates caused farmers to delay purchases of many major items in order to minimize the interest costs on debt. Machinery purchases may be put off several years, while purchases of such items as fertilizers, pesticides, and seed can be delayed until planting time. Farmers have thus forced farm supply dealers and producers of these items to maintain the necessary inventories. As a result, there is greater uncertainty about the availability of supplies of input items and the prices farmers pay for them.

Farm Supply Industries

The farm machinery and fertilizer industries specialize in producing farm supplies and are largely devoted to producing them. However, production of some farm input items is only incidental to the manufacturers' overall operations. For example, farm energy and pesticides account for less than 5 percent of the petroleum and farm chemical producers' total sales.

The three major fertilizer nutrients

(nitrogen, phosphate, and potash) each have unique production characteristics. While producers tend to specialize in one of these products, some firms turn out two or all three nutrient items. Nitrogen fertilizer is produced as anhydrous ammonia by combining nitrogen from the air with hydrogen from natural gas. About 53 firms operating about 80 plants produce nitrogen fertilizer. In periods of rapid expansion in the nitrogen fertilizer market, there is usually an influx of new firms, increasing competition in the industry. In periods when sales are slow, smaller firms often discontinue operating and their market is absorbed by stronger dominant firms.

Phosphate fertilizers are produced by treating phosphate rock with sulfuric acid. The United States has major phosphate rock deposits, particularly in Florida and North Carolina. Our country exports large amounts of phosphate either as rock or as processed fertilizer. Many of the phosphate fertilizer manufacturing facilities are located in phosphate mining areas. Frequently, phosphate fertilizer manufacturers also produce nitrogen.

Potash is a mineral extracted from the earth. Little additional processing is required once the mineral has been extracted. While most potash was provided by U.S. mines in New Mexico in the past, U.S. farmers currently obtain more than 75 percent of their potash fertilizer from Canada. The Province of Saskatchewan controls a substantial share of Canada's potash industry.

Pesticides are complex organic chemicals produced by major chemical companies. However, pesticide chemicals account for a very small share of the manufacturer's total business, generally less than 5 percent. About 70 firms produce agricultural pesticides, but four firms accounted for well over half of all the farm pesticides turned out in 1976. Pesticide markets for specific crops are often dominated by a few firms. In 1976, the leading firm accounted for 28 percent of the total weed control market. The two leading firms accounted for 42 percent of the weed control market for corn and 37 percent of this market for soybeans that year.

Research capability to develop new products is probably the most important factor preventing new firms from entering the pesticide market. Increasing complexity of the pesticide chemicals designed to control specific pest problems on specific crops, and the increasing regulatory requirements, are likely to continue exerting upward pressure on research and development costs. As a result, fewer firms are likely to devote large expenditures on new pesticide research.

Machinery, Fuel

While four or five firms produce most of the tractors and self-propelled equipment, about 2,000 establishments manufacture some specialized farm machinery items. These specialized farm implement markets have provided opportunities for new firms in the industry and made possible the continued existence of some small machinery manufacturers. Efficiencies obtained through use of large-scale production facilities, the seasonal nature of farm equipment demand, and the high capital costs involved in establishing a dealer network prevent new firms from producing tractors and self-propelled farm machinery.

Since agriculture accounts for a very

small share of the total U.S. fuel consumption (less than 5 percent), the petroleum industry is not primarily concerned with farm fuel markets. The supply system for producing and distributing refined petroleum products is most complicated. About 25,000 fields produce oil and/or gas in the United States, with over 500,000 wells owned by some 10,000 producers. These fields and wells provide crude oil and natural gas for around 300 refineries, 30,000 bulk terminals, and 200,000 retail service stations.

The domestic petroleum industry consists of large multinational corporations which may operate various combinations of wells, pipelines, terminals, refineries, and service stations. The Organization of Petroleum Exporting Countries (OPEC) is also a major determinant of U.S. oil supplies and prices. In addition, more than 16 major national legislative and executive actions initiated since the 1973 OPEC embargo complicate the petroleum supply system.

Development of the commercial feed industry has made possible large-scale specialized livestock operations, and provided livestock producers who grow their own grains with feed supplements to help meet their animals' complete dietary needs for maximum production. Competition in the commercial feed industry has changed in recent years through mergers, consolidation, and other forms of concentration, particularly on a local and regional basis. However, on a national basis feed manufacturing competition has increased. While the four largest companies accounted for about one-fourth of all feed industry shipments in the mid-1930's, their market share has declined steadily to about half that level today. Currently, it would require about 20 companies to account for one-fourth the tonnage manufactured.

R and D — Research and development within the farm input industries varies with the industry. The pesticide industry funds most of the research and development programs needed to develop new pesticide products, which are protected by patents. While the farm machinery and feed industries also fund research and development, they draw heavily on research conducted by publicly funded universities and experiment stations. The fertilizer industry probably relies most heavily on research and development in the public sector.

The environment in which seed research and development takes place underwent a significant change in the 1970's. Passage of the Plant Variety Protection Act in 1970 made it possible for seed companies to obtain patents on new plant varieties they developed. This sparked the interest of many multinational companies to acquire seed companies and boosted the capability for undertaking extensive research.

Foreign trade has had a growing impact on the fertilizer, pesticide, and farm machinery industries. The United States is the world's major producer and user of pesticides. Nearly half the pesticides produced in this country are exported, either directly or through farm products that are exported. Imports account for a small share of domestic pesticide use, less than 10 percent. Exports of farm machinery and equipment in 1981 reached an estimated $3.1 billion, an increase of 20 percent over 1980, and accounted for about one-fourth of all U.S. farm machinery production. Imports of farm machinery and equipment were estimated at $2.37 billion for 1981, up 15 percent from 1980.

In the last decade the United States has developed into the world's largest exporter of phosphate fertilizer. Nitrogen exports and imports have been about equal, with the trade balance varying from year to year. However, with rising natural gas costs it is expected that the United States will become a net importer of nitrogen in the future. Most of the potash U.S. farmers use is imported from Canada.

Effects of Public Action
Government regulations play an important role in activities of some of the input industries. For example, public action concerning pesticides has resulted in rules and regulations to safeguard people and the environment. Restrictive actions may be reflected in the marketplace, with higher farm production costs and higher consumer food prices. Environmental and health concerns also impact on other input industries. The feed industry is affected by community concern over noise, odor, and dust pollution. Also, regulations concerning feed additives will continue to be an important factor in commercial feed production. In the fertilizer industry, phosphate rock producers must take into consideration the effect that phosphate rock mines have on air and water pollution in contiguous areas.

Government agricultural programs also have an effect on input industries. Programs that reduce crop acres tend to cut the need for fertilizers, pesticides, and other inputs. Conversely, programs that increase farm income or reduce the uncertainty of income tend to spur use of inputs.

Future Directions — In the future the United States will be called upon to provide additional food to feed a growing world population. Since land and water available to grow crops is limited, increased U.S. food production must come primarily from greater or more efficient use of fertilizers, pesticides, farm machinery, and other inputs.

The growth rate of U.S. farm pesticide use for the eighties is expected to remain stable or even decline slightly. This assumes greater use of more highly concentrated formulations, improved pest management, better pesticide application techniques, and more government restrictions. Because of higher energy costs and potential labor and moisture savings, more farmers will adopt reduced tillage practices. This will increase demand for pest control chemicals. However, such rises are not likely to offset pressures toward overall reduced pesticide use. Larger exports of farm commodities should result in increasing demand for equipment with greater capacity, and could affect the future of farm machinery design.

The U.S. fertilizer industry can expect increasing production, transportation, and retailing costs. Specifically, rising prices of natural gas feedstocks will add to the cost of producing nitrogen fertilizers and increase the proportion of nitrogen fertilizer imported. Higher energy costs will also increase the cost of sulfur, and consequently the cost of phosphate fertilizers. In addition, increasing mining costs associated with protecting the environment and with utilizing lower grade phosphate rock deposits will add to the cost of producing phosphate fertilizers.

Rising fertilizer prices will encourage farmers to adopt practices that will improve the efficiency of fertilizer use. Some of the fertilization practices that farmers will employ are better timing of application and placement of materials, use of nitrification inhibitors and slow release materials, and more accurate assessment of the availability of plant nutrients in soils.

New Feed Era — The feed industry, in many respects, is entering a new era. Many trends and changes that evolved during the past 10 to 15 years have run their course and the feed manufacturing industry will become more complex and specialized during the next decade. Because of the growing predominance of local mills and the rising volume of feed concentrate and premix sales, the industry probably has more than adequate capacity in most areas of the country. Future physical additions to existing feed facilities probably will involve installation of more sophisticated controls, including use of computers to perform mixing and pelleting functions. Greater attention will be paid to automatic recordkeeping and quality control. Fewer new drug products for use in medicated feeds will be introduced in future years, primarily because of high research and clearance costs.

Energy prices will continue to go up. But price increases in the 1980's are not likely to match those of the 1970's. Rises in natural gas costs are likely to result in higher nitrogen fertilizer prices, more efficient fertilizer use, and larger nitrogen imports. In summary, farming in the future will be ever more dependent on the use of nonfarm inputs to assure efficient food and fiber production.

Productivity and the Real Cost of Our Food

By Lloyd D. Teigen

D ime-a-loaf bread and 50¢-a-pound beefsteak bring to mind the "Good Old Days." But were those prices such a bargain? Not really. The last time bread and beefsteak were priced at those levels was in 1946 when an hour's work would bring the factory worker a little over a dollar ($1.075) before taxes or other deductions. The price of food expressed in hours of effort is a much better bargain today than then. Productivity gains have reduced the amount of labor required to produce and market food and have increased the number of dollars the worker reaps for his time.

Over long periods of time, prices and wages both tend to change so that the dollar value of an item often loses meaning. The real cost of something can be better visualized using barter terms, where workers trade time directly for goods they consume instead of using money in exchange. An hour of time today means the same as it did in history, while a dollar today and one in 1930 do not. The working consumer is obviously better off when the proceeds of his or her work will purchase more goods and services or when the same consumption is possible from fewer hours of work. The choice between consuming more and working less becomes a matter of individual preference.

An hour's work today will buy twice as much food as an hour's work did in 1930. This can be illustrated by individual food commodities or by the market basket represented by the Consumer Price Index. Points of time are chosen to illustrate some of the changes of both the absolute and relative prices of food over time. While round steak and bacon were nearly equal in price in 1930, changing supplies and consumer preferences have raised the price of steak to twice that of bacon. Changing production technology and vertical market coordination have dramatically reduced the real price of eggs. The real prices of coffee and sugar have risen nearly 50 percent between 1970 and 1980. The vagaries of the international market and U.S. import policies are major considerations here.

The trend toward decreasing food prices has not been without interruption. The 1940s through the end of the Korean War was a period of considerable price instability in which food prices were higher at the end of the period than the beginning. The last decade, particularly since 1973, has seen considerable fluctuation in the real price of food in a time of overall price inflation. In retrospect, it appears that, for food, 1972 was a pretty good year for the consumer.

Lloyd D. Teigen is an Economist, National Economics Division, Economic Research Service.

Individual farmers have gained in real terms, since each farmer and farmworker is receiving more consumer time for their efforts than before. The farmer's return is his or her portion of the consumer's cost of food. The farm price per unit of food product is found by multiplying the consumer's cost in worktime by the farmer's share of the consumer food dollar. The farm price per unit of food expressed in consumer's time has decreased since 1930, although the change from 1970 to 1980 is much less than earlier changes. Consumer time per unit of food output in recent years has been shared among a much smaller number of farmers than in 1930, so that the consumer time received per unit by each farmer and farmworker in 1970 and 1980 is more than 10 percent greater than earlier years. This represents a real gain in the well-being of the farmer.

The increased labor productivity on the farm has lowered the time requirements for each unit of output and reduced the total employment necessary for food production. Higher levels of total output further increased the real returns of the individual farmer and farmworker. In fact, livestock production in 1980 is 2.1 times its 1930 level, crop output is 2.2 times the 1930 level, and the volume of output available to the consuming public and export market is 2.3 times its level in 1930.

How Was Real Cost Brought Down?

The interaction of supply and demand explain part of the change. U.S. population growth has averaged 1.2 percent per year, contributing to the demand for food and farm products. Annual increases of hourly earnings averaged 4.5 percent before 1970 and more than 7.3 percent since 1970, although these were offset some by increasing marginal tax and social security rates and shorter work-

Minutes of work equal to the price of selected food items 1/

Item	Amount	1930	1950	1970	1980
			Minutes		
Round steak	1 lb.	48.4	43.8	28.8	29.4
Potatoes	10 lb.	40.9	21.6	19.9	20.2
Bacon	1 lb.	48.3	29.8	21.0	15.5
Eggs	1 doz.	50.6	28.3	13.6	8.9
Bread (2 loaves)	3 lb.	29.3	20.1	16.1	16.2
Butter	1 lb.	52.7	34.1	19.2	20.0
Milk	1 gal.	64.1	38.6	29.2	22.3
Coffee	1 lb.	44.9	37.2	20.2	33.3
Sugar	5 lb.	34.7	22.7	14.4	22.8
Rice	5 lb.	54.0	39.3	21.2	27.2
All the above	1 ea.	467.9	315.5	203.6	215.8
Total food CPI	2/	60.0	40.9	28.8	31.9

1/ Price of food item relative to manufacturing wage rate after taxes and employee social security contributions.

2/ Quantity of each item in Consumer Price Index market basket such that the entire market basket required one hour in 1930.

Minutes of Nonfarm Labor Equal to the Farmer's Share of Retail Food Prices 1/

Item	Amount	2/1930	1950	1970	1980
			Minutes		
Round Steak	1 lb.	35.8	32.8	17.9	18.5
Potatoes	10 lb.	16.4	8.6	5.8	5.7
Bacon	1 lb.	30.9	19.1	10.7	7.9
Eggs	1 doz.	35.4	3/19.8	8.6	5.7
Bread (2 loaves)	3 lb.	6.2	4.2	2.3	2.4
Butter	1 lb.	40.6	26.3	13.6	14.0
Milk	1 gal.	35.3	21.2	14.6	11.6
Coffee	1 lb.	—	—	—	—
Sugar	5 lb.	12.8	8.4	5.9	9.1
Rice	5 lb.	18.4	4/13.4	6.6	8.1
All of the Above	1 each	231.8	153.8	86.0	83.0
Total Farm Employment (BLS)	Million	10.450	7.160	3.463	3.364
Minutes per Farmworker	5/	22.2	21.5	24.8	24.7
Total Farm Output	Percent of 1967	52.0	74.0	101.0	122.0

1/ Price of food item relative to manufacturing wage rate after taxes and employee social security contributions, multiplied by farmer's share of the food dollar.
2/ Farmer's share for 1950, or nearest year, was used to compute 1930.
3/ 1953 share used for eggs.
4/ 1960 share used for rice.
5/ Total minutes for all of the above divided by farm employees.

weeks. Increasing labor force participation by women added to the demand for prepared foods. On the supply side, since 1930 livestock output has averaged 1.5 percent growth per year, crop output 1.6 percent per year and the total output of final products has averaged 1.7 percent annual increases.

The increase in per capita food supplies is a major source of the lower real food prices. But for the working consumer, the higher wages and income made possible by productivity gains on the job are even more important. Output per man-hour in the nonfarm business economy increased more than 2 percent per year during 1950-72, and money wages increased almost 4.4 percent per year, or 2 percent faster than the general price level. Since 1973, the increase in output per hour has averaged only a fraction of a percent a year, and output per hour has not yet exceeded the level in 1977. The 1981 dollar purchases what only 91 cents purchased in 1973, even though money wages increased more than 7.6 percent per year.

The increased supply of farm products and food derives from the increasing productivity of agricultural resources and the increase in the amount of resources used. Virtually the entire change in crop production is due to higher yields per acre of land, with increased fertilizer and pest control playing a substantial role in the changes. The increased use of feed concentrates has increased the livestock output per breeding animal, and improved animal health practices have permitted the concentration of large animal populations in efficient feeding and grow-out operations.

Output per man-hour for factory workers, such as these and others in the nonfarm business economy, increased more than 2 percent per year during 1950-72 and money wages increased almost 4.4 percent per year, or 2 percent faster than the general price level.

USDA

Employment and Productivity Change in the Food and Agriculture System

Industry	Employment		Change in output per hour	
	1970	1980	1958-72	1973-79
	Thousands		Percent per year	
Total Civilian Employment	78,678	99,303	—	—
Nonagricultural Sector:	75,215	95,938	2.49	1/0.77
Agricultural Sector:	3,463	3,364	6.07	1/2.81
Inputs Sector:				
Farm and Garden Machinery	129	172	2.3	2/2.3
Agricultural Chemicals	55	73	5.9	2/0.2
Agricultural Services	170	3/166	—	—
Processing Sector:				
Food and Kindred Products	1,783	1,711	4/2.26	1.86
Tobacco Manufacture	83	69	5/1.8	2.9
Textile Mills	976	853	—	—
Apparel and Other Textile Products	1,365	1,266	—	—
Leather and Leather Products	320	233	—	—
Transportation Sector:				
Class I Railroads	559	482	6/3.8	0.8
Trucking and Warehousing	1,083	1,276	7/2.1	1.4
Water Transportation	215	212	—	—
Distribution Sector:				
Retail Food Stores	1,731	2,386	3.0	-1.0
Wholesale Groceries	550	674	—	—
Eating and Drinking Places	2,488	4,666	1.2	-2.4

1/ 1973-1981 data used.
2/ 1973-78 data only.
3/ 1977 employment; data since 1977 is not available.
4/ 1967-1972 data only.
5/ Excludes cigar manufacture; data for 1954-72 and 1973-79.
6/ 1954-72 data.
7/ Output per employee. Intercity trucking of general freight; data for 1954-72 and 1973-78.

But the supply of food to the consumer is more than just the supply of farm products. The transportation, processing, wholesaling, and retailing sectors must be considered. And labor productivity is an important factor in the final cost of food, since salary and employee benefits in the food marketing system nearly equal the farm value of domestically produced foods. The significant gains in output per manhour in these sectors prior to 1972 contributed to lower real food prices. As output per manhour increased, labor costs per unit declined, lowering the price markup in the food industry.

Agriculture-related industries account for more than one-seventh of civilian employment in the United States and are significant users of fuels and energy. The constellation of forces set in motion by the realinement of energy prices in 1973 has reduced the annual increase of output per manhour from an average increase of more than 2 percent per year to a decrease of 0.7 percent per year, when weighted by employment levels. The productivity decrease is passed to the consumer, as retail prices rise in response to higher labor costs per unit. Indeed, the real cost of food since 1973 has risen to levels that prevailed in the early sixties.

U.S. consumers spend a smaller fraction of personal income on food (16 percent

U.S. consumers spend a smaller fraction of personal income on food than any other people. This homemaker also has the widest choice of foods from which to select.

William E. Carnahan

before taxes, or 19 percent after taxes last year) than any other people. The proportion varies considerably worldwide: 27.5 percent in Britain, 62.5 percent in India, 59.3 percent in Sierra Leone (West Africa), and 45 percent in the Soviet Union.

This fraction has continued to decrease despite the leveling off of real food prices. The ratio of food consumption expenditures to disposable (after tax) income which was 19 percent in 1980 was 20 percent in 1970, 23 percent in 1960, 26 percent in 1950, and nearly 27 percent in 1940. The share of the consumer's budget spent on food reflects both 1) the price and quantity of food and 2) the wage rate and hours worked. Our measure of real food price — the minutes of work per item of food — is one side of the budget share. The other side, quantity of food consumed divided by hours actually worked, has continued to fall as labor force participation has increased faster than the workweek has been reduced. Although the budget share for food has historically shrunk as real prices of food declined, it is now diminishing because households trade leisure time to increase the income with which to purchase goods and services. Current trends in the labor market indicate that the budget share for food will continue to decline.

Can We Keep Costs From Rising?

With some qualifications, yes. The agricultural production sector has the capacity to respond to higher levels of demand for farm products. This productive capacity depends on the natural, human, and physical resources in agriculture and the productivity of those resources. The capacity of the food and agriculture system responds to the economic signals of price and cost and to the changing technologies brought about by scientific breakthroughs and commercial development. The capacity, then, will change over time.

The other side of the coin is the productivity of the working consumer. That productivity determines the wage and income commanded for his or her time and, consequently, the amount of time which must be given up to fill the shopping cart. Many factors have been suggested as causing the post-1973 productivity slowdown — energy prices, regulatory burdens, inadequate or unproductive capital investment, tax-related disincentives, changing character of the workforce, the increasing size of the service economy, uncertain expectations of inflation, and more. Changing Federal policies governing taxation, expenditures, regulation and monetary growth address some of the factors, but other factors are part of a different environment to which the economy must adjust. Certainly, not all the adjustments have been completed.

Of particular interest is the effect these adjustments will have on the industries which affect food and agriculture. Restoring the pre-1972 productivity growth rates will substantially reduce the price markups in the food industry and lower the real price of food — the hours you work to fill your shopping cart. In all likelihood the number of dollars which change hands in the grocery store and eating place will continue to increase. The 50$^\textit{¢}$-a-pound steak and dime-a-loaf bread are history. But the number of working hours required to earn the money which changes hands can decrease nonetheless if we overcome the problems which have plagued the productivity growth of the economy.

Whys and Hows of Credit, Finance

By Stephen C. Gabriel and John R. Brake

*I*n the last two decades, both investment per farm and the cost of operating a farm have risen dramatically. In 1960, investment per farm was $53,036. By 1980 that figure had soared to $413,685, almost an eightfold increase. This represents a compound annual rate of increase of 10.8 percent. The rate of increase was much more rapid from 1970-80 than from 1960-70. Investment per farm doubled from $53,036 in 1960 to $106,780 in 1970. However, it nearly quadrupled from 1970 to 1980.

In like manner, production expenses per farm increased from $6,909 in 1960 to $53,812 in 1980, a compound annual rate of increase of about 10.5 percent. But cash receipts per farm grew at a rate of only 9.8 percent during the same period. Hence, farm profit margins in 1980 were lower than in 1960. In 1960 production expenses absorbed about 78 percent of farm cash receipts. Today roughly 93 percent of cash receipts go to pay production expenses. In addition, farming has become more mechanized, requiring in many cases that farmers obtain a large amount of funds to purchase necessary equipment. Both the increased investment per farm and the increased production expenses as a proportion of gross income have resulted in greater credit use by farmers. Credit has become an important tool of the farm business for larger farm enterprises.

Over the last two decades, new and improved machinery, equipment, and facilities have made it possible for one person to accomplish more than ever before. These improvements, however, required substantially greater capital investments, not just for the larger scale machinery and equipment but also for the additional acreage or animals that could be handled per person. Financing the acquisition of more and/or larger capacity durable inputs required a substantial amount of credit. Credit is also used to bridge the cash flow gap from declining profit margins as well as to finance the application of inputs until the output is sold later in the year. And debt capital has been instrumental in financing farm enlargement.

Growth in farm debt directly resulted from the increase in investment in the agricultural sector. Non-real-estate farm debt grew at a rate of about 6.5 percent during the sixties. This growth rate almost doubled in the seventies, reaching a rate of about 12 percent annually. Real estate debt also grew faster in the seventies than in the previous decade.

Stephen C. Gabriel is an Agricultural Economist with the Economic Research Service.

John R. Brake is W.I. Myers Professor of Agricultural Finance, Cornell University, Ithaca, N.Y.

However, the 11 percent growth rate of the seventies was only slightly greater than the 9.8 percent growth rate of the sixties.

Credit is used in farming for several different purposes. Operating credit tends to be used at times of heavy expenses — typically in the spring — to pay for inputs until sale of the farm product later in the year. Another important component of credit use is related to the continuing process of purchasing new machinery to replace old, and of incoming farmers purchasing farmland from those who are retiring. During periods of improved farm income, credit use tends to rise from increased purchases of new machinery. Also requiring additional credit are farmers expanding their acreage by purchases from neighbors or retiring farmers at the higher land prices. Still another type of credit need arises from disasters, as when farmers lose their crops due to weather problems or other natural disasters. Typically, disaster type credit needs are met in substantial part through emergency credit programs from the Farmers Home Administration or the Small Business Administration.

How Sound is Agriculture?

The financial condition of agriculture can be described in terms of liquidity, solvency, and profitability. We will attempt to analyze each of these measures of financial well-being and to provide some insight into how this "well-being" is distributed among agricultural producers.

Improved machinery makes it possible for one person to accomplish more than ever before. This Iowa corn and hog farmer is shown with equipment needed on his farm. It represents a substantial capital investment.

An asset is liquid to the extent it can be sold quickly at a market price which does not require a substantial discount to facilitate the sale. Cash, obviously, is the most liquid asset. Other liquid assets include financial assets (stocks, bonds, etc.), accounts receivable, and certain inventories such as grain and livestock. Relatively illiquid assets include land, farm machinery, and other durables. Since farmland tends to be a "big ticket" item and only a very small percentage (2 to 3 percent) of total farmland changes hands each year, it is considered the least liquid asset held by farmers.

Two trends point to a less liquid farm sector. In 1960 real estate assets represented about 65 percent of total assets in the farm sector. By 1982 the ratio had risen to over 75 percent. Since 1960 current assets (financial assets plus inventories) fell from 20 to 13 percent of total assets. Hence the farmer's present balance sheet contains more illiquid land and real estate than 20 years earlier. However, with rising land values, farmers have been able to borrow against farmland to generate cash or liquidity. If farmland values continue to fall, then the illiquidity associated with the farmland could be much more critical because credit secured by farmland values might be more difficult to obtain.

Solvency — Solvency refers to wealth. A frequently used measure of wealth is equity, total assets minus total liabilities. There are problems of looking at the total agricultural sector as though it were one giant balance sheet. The fact of the matter is, a sizable part of total real estate and some other capital items in the agricultural balance sheet are owned by nonfarmers rather than farm operators. Even so, it may be useful to consider some figures from the aggregate agricultural sector. Sector equity, currently about $900 billion, has increased considerably since 1960 when it was but $185 billion. Much of the increase in value was due to inflation in land values, and in fact most of the growth in real farm wealth occurred during the 1970's. From 1960 to 1970, real (inflation corrected) farm equity grew about 8 percent in total. From 1970 to 1980, however, it grew over 70 percent.

The growth in real farm equity during the seventies is the major bright spot in the financial condition of farmers over the last two decades. Real farm equity rose in response to improved farm income prospects in the early to mid-1970's. However, this improved income appears to have been transitory, with real farm income returning to a relatively flat trend. The farmland market, which accounts for most of farm equity, is only recently adjusting to revised expectations for farm income.

Equity growth of the seventies generated the credit used to finance considerable capital formation. This credit was also used to finance periodic shortfalls in farm income. Ironically, as will be explained later, the greater use of credit facilitated by these increases in farm wealth during the seventies also contributed to the increased volatility of net farm income which occurred during that era.

Profitability — One must be careful in discussing profitability in agriculture since the appropriate measure of profitability depends on the purpose of the analysis. If one is interested in the well-being of farmers, it is useful to look at per farm net income. Also, one should consider both farm and off-farm income. However, since off-farm income is not distributed evenly among farmers (smaller farmers receive the bulk of off-farm income), it would be more informative to consider total family income per farm by sales class.

On the other hand, if one is interested in examining ability of the farm sector as a whole to generate income, then total net farm income is appropriate. Agricultural input suppliers, for example, are less

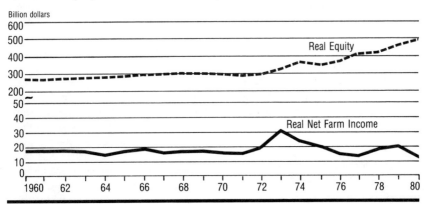

Real Farm Equity and Net Farm Income, 1960-80

Billion dollars

interested in whether $28 billion in farm income is divided among 3 million farmers or 2.4 million farmers than in whether $28 billion is high or low relative to the total resources devoted to agricultural production.

Profitability in agriculture can be viewed in an investment sense, in which case the rate of return on equity is a relevant measure of profitability. As one can imagine, there are a variety of indices which could be used for each concept of profitability. Discussion will cover several of these to provide insight into what has been happening in the farm sector.

Real net farm income per farm (in constant 1972 dollars and before inventory adjustment) rose from $4,084 in 1960 to $10,036 in 1973, an all-time high, and then started downward to $7,083 in 1978 and to $5,076 in 1980.

No Progress Since Mid-70's
When we consider real total family income (farm and off-farm) per farm, the level of income increases substantially. Real total family income was $7,199 in

1960, rising to as much as $17,999 in 1973, but finished the two decades at a figure of $13,431 in 1980. As a whole, farmers were much better off in 1980 than 20 years earlier, but they have not made progress since the mid-70s.

Note, however, that the largest farmers receive a relatively small share of total off-farm income. They depend largely on income generated from their farming operations. Specifically, U.S. Department of Agriculture data show that farmers in the $100,000 and over sales class generate about 70 percent of total cash receipts. However, they earn only about 9 percent of the total off-farm income. From a production standpoint, these large farmers are very important, although they represent only about 12 percent of all farmers.

The agricultural sector as a whole has been generating a lower real net farm income thus far in the 1980's than in the 1960's. The 1970's introduced an era of extreme farm income volatility, due primarily to the increased importance of international markets for agricultural commodities. While real net farm income

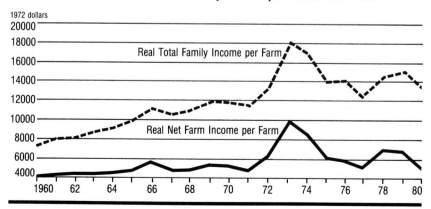

Real Net Farm Income and Total Family Income per Farm. 1960-1980

hit a peak in 1973, it has since been on a downward trend.

Off-farm income has grown to be a larger source of family income for farm families than net farm income. In 1960 off-farm income was about 42 percent of total income for farm operator families. By 1980 it had grown to over 64 percent of total family income. The growth in off-farm income has helped stabilize the total income of many farm families. However, as mentioned earlier, large commercial farmers have not benefited greatly by the growing importance of off-farm income since their share is proportionately smaller than the share for smaller farmers. Large commercial farmers rely primarily on farm product sales for their income.

Agriculture's income rate of return on equity averaged 3.7 percent in the sixties. During the seventies the average income rate of return on equity was about 4.7 percent. Many farmers realized substantial growth in real wealth as farmland values rose at an average annual rate of about 13 percent in the seventies. This wealth expanded farmers' borrowing capacity and allowed a substantially greater flow of credit into the farm sector.

Some analysts have attempted to add the return that results from the real capital gains associated with rising farm asset values to the current income return on equity. This is clearly inappropriate due to the tremendous liquidity differences in the two sources of "income." Indeed, these real capital gains, which exist only on paper, are not income at all. The market for farm assets, for example, is not the same as those for common stocks or bonds where an extremely active secondary market renders these financial instruments very liquid. Investors in

common stocks can and do sell their shares frequently to realize the capital gains which previously only existed on paper. And they derive an income upon doing so. They may then reinvest their funds in other securities.

Farmers, however, do not behave in a similar manner. It would be a closer analogy to compare farmers with manufacturers. While an increase in the value of their physical assets increases their wealth, manufacturers generally do not sell their entire physical plant each year to realize their gains.

Financial Leverage

As mentioned earlier, there are problems in examining balance sheet figures for the entire agricultural sector. About one-third of the real estate is owned by nonfarm landlords. Hence, the balance sheet does not represent a combined balance sheet of all farm operators. Still, some of the changes that have occurred in agriculture are perhaps best shown by use of these balance sheet figures. The farm debt to asset ratio was 11.8 percent in 1960. That ratio increased to 16.8 percent in 1970 and then trended slightly downward to 1980. The reason for the downtrend throughout the 1970's was that farm real estate values and the values of other assets increased more rapidly than did farm debt, even though farm debt went up at a very rapid rate. By 1979 the farm sector debt to asset ratio was 15.6 percent. The ratio now appears to be headed higher due primarily to stable or decreasing real estate values.

Although the debt to asset ratio declined during the 1970's, the debt burden increased dramatically. The ratio of interest expenses to net earnings before deducting interest and taxes rose from 17 percent in 1970 to 26 percent in 1979 to 42 percent in 1980. This rising debt service burden was due not only to the growth in farm debt, but also to the surge in interest rates which occurred in the late 1970's and early 1980's. The growth in interest expenses relative to farm earnings has made residual farm earnings (net income after paying interest) more volatile. Since interest is a fixed expense that must be paid regardless of the level of earnings, it acts as the fulcrum of a lever, magnifying both increases and decreases in farm earnings that have resulted from, among other things, our greater dependence on international markets.

Comparison of the farm with the nonfarm sector may be questionable since the nonfarm sector is so much less homogeneous. Nevertheless, perhaps limited comparisons can be made using the Federal Reserve Board's flow of funds accounts. Net income for nonfarm noncorporate businesses shows considerably more stability than that of farm businesses. Also, real net income for nonfarm noncorporate business has trended upward since 1960. Purchasing power of the income of nonfarm businesses was about $10.4 billion greater in 1980 than in 1960 when it stood at $60.5 billion (1972 dollars). Based on the Federal Reserve's data, real net farm income dropped from $16.6 billion in 1960 to $13.2 billion in 1980. While there was some upward trend to 1973, the trend has been downward since that time to the 1980 figure.

One must keep these characteristics of net income in mind when comparing the debt to asset ratios of farm and nonfarm businesses. Although the levels of the debt ratios have been comparable for farm and nonfarm noncorporate businesses, 16.1 percent for farm businesses and 15 percent for nonfarm noncorporate businesses in 1980, the differences in income variability indicate that farmers are exposed to far more risk than their nonfarm counterparts. One can only conclude that relative to the business risk associated with farming, the 16.1 percent debt ratio is high and would need to be reduced to bring total farm risk in line with that of comparable nonfarm businesses.

In summary, the farm sector balance sheet contained a higher proportion of value in land and real estate in 1980 than in 1960. Farm debt was relatively larger in relation to total assets in 1980 than in 1960, and real net farm income was lower in 1980 than in 1960. One must include off-farm income in order to come up with a measure which shows significant improvement over 1960. However, even then the improvement tends to be associated with specific sizes of farms. Large commercial farms, for example, earn little off-farm income, making them dependent upon the rather stagnant purchasing power of farm income. From 1960 to 1980 the debt burden of the Nation's farmers has increased substantially.

Suppliers of Farm Credit

Farm credit is provided by seven categories of lenders: 1) The Cooperative Farm Credit System (FCS), 2) All Operating Banks (AOB's) — commercial banks, savings and loans, mutual savings banks, etc., 3) Individuals and Others (I&O's) — merchants and dealers, individuals and other lenders, 4) Life Insurance Companies (LIC's), 5) The Farmers Home Administration (FmHA), 6) The

Commodity Credit Corporation (CCC), and 7) The Small Business Administration (SBA).

The FCS accounted for 32 percent of all farm credit on Jan. 1, 1981. AOB's held 23 percent of farm credit on that date. Loans outstanding to I&O's represented 23 percent. And, LIC's market share of total farm credit was about 7 percent. Government lenders — the FmHA, CCC, and SBA — accounted for about 11, 3, and 1 percent of farm sector credit, respectively. From 1976 to 1980 FmHA was the most rapidly growing lender to agriculture in percentage terms.

Farm Credit System — This system (FCS) is the largest lender to farmers, with over $56 billion in loans outstanding on Jan. 1, 1981.

FCS consists of three different entities: the Federal Land Banks (FLB's), the Federal Intermediate Credit Banks (FICB's) with their local Production Credit Associations (PCA's), and the Banks for Cooperatives (BC's). All of the FCS banks are wholly owned farmer cooperatives.

FCS interest rates generally have been lower than those of other farm lenders due to their loan pricing practices and

Net Income for Farm and Nonfarm Business

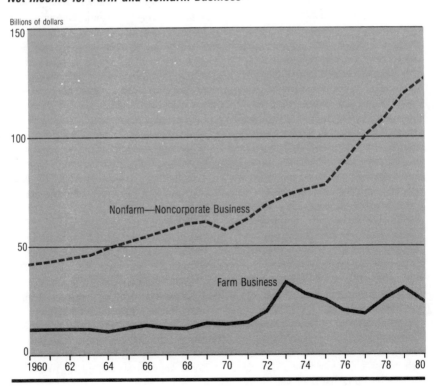

Billions of dollars

their means for obtaining funds. Instead of charging borrowers at rates based on current costs of funds (marginal cost pricing), the FCS banks charge for their loans based on the average interest rate costs on all of their bonds outstanding (average pricing). In periods of increasing interest rates, FCS loan rates tend to lag behind those of other lenders who typically practice marginal cost pricing. Since interest rates have been generally rising throughout the 1970s and early 1980s, loans from FCS have been the lowest cost source of credit in most years.

The Farm Credit Banks obtain the money they loan to farmers directly from the Nation's bond markets, where they are able to generate virtually unlimited funds at the market interest rate. Therefore, they have not been subject to the same periodic shortages of funds sometimes faced by commercial banks.

Commercial Banks — These banks have concentrated their lending in non-real-estate shorter maturity loans. Although their market share has declined in recent years, they remain the most important source of non-real-estate credit to agriculture.

Agricultural banks are typically small, rural businesses using local deposits to lend to local businesses. Because agricultural operators are often their largest borrowers and farmers are major depositors, certain seasonal problems have always been a part of rural banking. Since farmers' needs for funds tend to be highly seasonal, especially in the spring at planting time, those farmers with deposits at the banks tend to draw down their deposits at the same time when other farmers have the greatest need to borrow. Hence, the rural bank has sometimes had

problems in meeting seasonal credit needs of farmers. Also, farmers' credit needs have tended to grow more rapidly than deposits at rural banks. Sometimes rural banks simply are not able to make the size of loan required by their large farm customers.

Several approaches have been used to mitigate these problems. Correspondent relationships have been formed connecting rural banks with metropolitan banks that have other sources of funds. When seasonal needs are especially great or when certain farm customers need larger loans than can be provided by the local bank, the bank enters into a participation agreement with the correspondent or sells the farm loan to the correspondent to provide additional funds. Another special program has been provided by the Federal Reserve System, allowing member banks to borrow directly at the discount window to meet seasonal borrowing needs. In more recent years, there have been a limited number of participations between rural banks and the Farm Credit System at the local level. Also, some rural banks have organized agricultural credit corporations which then discount their loans directly to the Federal Intermediate Credit Banks in their district.

It is likely that the Depository Institution Deregulation and Monetary Control Act of 1980 will make banks more responsive to national monetary conditions. The most obvious implications of these changes in the banking environment are: 1) Rural banks will be less likely to lose funds to national money markets in periods of high interest rates, 2) Interest rates that rural banks pay for deposits and charge on loans will be more closely tied to national money markets and will therefore be higher and more volatile, and 3) Interest rates to farmers on their loans from commercial banks will also be more closely tied to money market rates.

In addition, because of the volatility and higher level of interest rates in the late 1970's and early 1980's, a number of commercial banks have changed from fixed-interest rate loans to variable-interest rate loans. Interest rates on loans outstanding are adjusted upward or downward from time to time in line with movement in market interest rates. The change to variable rates has added a new risk to farmers of cost increases over which they have no control.

Individuals and Others — These lenders consist of merchants, dealers, and other individuals including family members. They supply both real estate and non-real-estate farm credit. Although still a valuable source of credit to farmers, this group of lenders has been declining in importance in recent years. Merchants and dealers who are holders of most of the non-real-estate debt provide credit primarily as a sales tool. However, since credit activities are not their primary function, availability of credit from them is highly variable.

Individuals who finance the sale of farmland provide an important source of farm real estate credit. In 1981 outstanding farm real estate loans held by individuals amounted to $26.7 billion compared to $35.9 billion held by Federal Land Banks. Installment contracts can provide the seller with tax advantages in terms of spreading a gain over several years. Contracts also typically provide the buyer with a lower required downpayment than

would a conventional mortgage.

Life insurance companies have played an important though declining role in farm real estate debt markets. Reasons for the decline include an increase in demand for policyholder loans, increased returns on nonfarm investments of life insurance companies, restrictive State usury laws, and a relatively slow growth in investable funds at life insurance companies. If interest rates should stabilize in the future and return to more normal levels, life insurance companies may increase their role in farm real estate financing.

Public Agricultural Lenders

The Farmers Home Administration (FmHA) was created by Congress in 1946 to provide credit assistance to rural residents unable to obtain credit from private lenders. FmHA is the primary rural credit agency of the Federal Government. The agency is referred to as a lender of last resort since its policies require that prospective borrowers demonstrate inability to obtain credit from other lenders.

FmHA obtains its lending authority and programs from Congress. This means that when Congress or the administration sees a new need for credit in rural areas, there is a tendency to authorize FmHA to lend for that program. During 1976 to 1980, for example, FmHA non-real-estate loans grew faster than those of any other lender group. Some of the more important farmer programs of FmHA in terms of volume of lending are the Emergency Disaster, Economic Emergency, Farm Ownership, and Operating Loan Programs. Other authorities cover such purposes as soil and water, recreation, irrigation and drainage, grazing, and Indian land acquisition programs.

The Farm Ownership Program was basically designed to enable beginning and tenant farmers to become owner-operators. Loans under the program can also be used to refinance existing debt; purchase, improve, or enlarge farms; develop water resources, and finance selected nonfarm enterprises. This loan program has been of prime importance to beginning farmers who do not have the equity to obtain funding through more traditional lending sources. The Operating Loan Program of FmHA provides short and intermediate term loans to family farmers for a variety of purposes including purchase of livestock, farm supplies, food and clothing, as well as for purchase or construction of nonfarm enterprises such as campgrounds and riding stables.

Emergency disaster loans are limited to farmers in places declared disaster areas. Funds can be used to reconstruct buildings, purchase farm supplies, or refinance other debt. The Emergency Disaster Program has expanded considerably over the past 20 years, and in some years has been an important source of funding for selected farmers in disaster areas. However, the Emergency Disaster Program is expected to be replaced gradually by the Federal All-Risk Crop Insurance Program. The intent is that the government will shift this risk management function from the public sector to the private sector through Federal All-Risk Crop Insurance.

Economic emergency loans are made to farmers at times when credit is scarce due to local or widespread economic stress. Such stress might be induced by monetary policy or by low product prices coupled with high production costs. The loans enable farmers to continue normal operations.

Commodity Credit Corp. — The Commodity Credit Corporation (CCC) is an agency of the U.S. Department of Agriculture operating through personnel and facilities of the Agricultural Stabilization and Conservation Service and other Department agencies. A primary objective of the CCC is to minimize the effect of depressed commodity prices. This is done through orderly commodity purchases and nonrecourse loan provisions — including the farmer-owned grain reserve program — that assure eligible participants a specific minimum commodity price for their product. In addition, recourse type loans for storage facilities and drying and grain handling equipment are available.

The Small Business Administration (SBA) is an independent government agency designed to provide credit to small businesses unable to obtain credit in the private sector. Although SBA was created in 1953, farmers began receiving assistance only after a congressional mandate in June of 1976. At present, farms with gross annual receipts under $1 million may be eligible for SBA loans. The principal program under which farmers have participated is the Disaster Loan Program. Disaster loans provide funds to victims of natural disasters for repair or replacement of damaged realty, machinery, equipment, or personal property. Currently, farmers must attempt to obtain an FmHA emergency disaster loan before applying for an SBA disaster loan.

Leasing, Other Techniques
Limited cash flow has constrained many farmers' ability to acquire the use of "big

ticket" assets such as land, combines, and tractors. Since the initial outlay associated with leasing is generally less than that of debt financing, farmers with limited resources may find it more feasible to obtain the control of such resources through leasing. Typically, these financial leases allow the farmer to have control of the machinery, facility, or cattle for 3-, 5-, and 7-year periods for an annual charge. At the end of the financial lease period, the farmer may be able to purchase the item for a nominal charge or may simply give up control of the item. For nondepreciable assets such as land, rental on an annual basis or a renewable rental contract over a period of time has a tax advantage over debt financing. The entire rental payment is deductible, while under a purchase only the interest expenses are deductible.

Prior to recent tax legislation which introduced safe-harbor leasing, a major disadvantage of leasing was that the net cost was usually higher than under debt financing. That is to say, the implied interest rate under leasing was greater than the interest rate under debt financing. Also, the lessee typically did not have access to residual value of the asset when the lease expired unless there were specific provisions in the lease to provide the opportunity to purchase. Safe-harbor leasing, however, facilitates transfer of tax benefits to the lessor, allowing for a reduced rental charge. It also permits the lessee to capture the residual value at a price determined at the beginning of the lease. These tax provisions, however, are now being reconsidered and may be revised in the future. Still, despite the uncertainties regarding future advantages, use of financial leasing may well increase during the 1980's.

The high cost of entry into farming, as well as the rising debt burden carried by many farmers, has sparked increased interest in finding ways of attracting outside equity capital. Infusion of outside equity into the farm firm has the effects of 1) spreading the risk of the enterprise among more investors, 2) reducing financial risk by lowering the debt burden, and 3) in some cases reducing the control the operator has over his business. There are a variety of approaches to attracting outside equity capital into the farm business. This chapter will outline just a few.

Form a Corporation — One of the common ways of bringing outside capital into a business is to sell stock and form a corporation. This has been used in agriculture only on a limited basis. More often than not, its purpose has been more to facilitate intergenerational transfer of the business rather than as a means of bringing capital into the farm sector. Stock ownership makes it easier to divide up the farm ownership through shares of stock rather than specific acreages or animals being owned by each member of the partnership. One of the difficulties of using this means to bring nonfamily capital into a farm business is the difficulty of transferring the stock ownership when one wishes to sell. Usually there is no established market for the relatively small transfers of stock associated with the typical farm corporation.

Some farmers seek to reduce their debt load by selling land and then leasing it back from the investor who bought it. Strictly speaking, this does not constitute an infusion of equity capital, but the effects are similar. Farmers reduce their debt burden using funds generated by the sale of farmland. However, they retain use of the sold farmland. Depending on terms of the lease, their financial risk may be reduced. The *Sale-Leaseback Buyback* option is similar to the *Sale-Leaseback* except that the seller has the option to buy back the property after a specified period, say five years (to coincide with tax law provisions). The buyback can be specified either at market value at the time the property is bought back, or at a specified percentage increase in value over time. This option seems to be most attractive when the property in question has high depreciation potential for the buyer (hog confinement facilities, for example).

Under the *Grain Joint Venture* approach, an outside investor pays for post-harvest expenses in late fall, such as for tillage and fertilization. That gives the investor a tax writeoff at yearend. In return, the investor receives a share of the crop the following year. *Limited Partnerships* have long been used to draw outside equity capital into agriculture. However, the attraction of such arrangements varies over time. At present there appears to be renewed attention given such mechanisms as farmers become wary of expanding operations with high-cost borrowed funds.

Tax Provisions for Farmers

Farmers are subject to Federal income taxes just as other businesses are. There is a farm income tax form, 1040F, that must be filed by farmers. Tax laws allow farmers to charge as expenses all current outlays for operating a business. They also are entitled to take depreciation on durables used up in the business. Depreciation alternatives are specified, and farmers may choose from among them as other businesses do.

Farmers do have the choice of whether to report income for tax purposes on a cash basis or an accrual basis. Most farmers choose cash basis accounting, and this choice has important benefits for them. Being on a cash basis makes it possible to alter income and expenses between tax years, for example, by storing commodities for sale in a later year or prepurchasing expense items such as fertilizer prior to the year in which it is used.

Perhaps even more important is the benefit for livestock producers, who often raise their own replacements or expand breeding herds with the offspring of their best animals. These animals have a zero-cost basis. When sold from the breeding herd, an animal can typically be treated as sale of a capital asset taxed at a capital gains rate somewhat lower than that of ordinary income. Hence there is both the advantage of delaying taxes on livestock inventory increases until the animal is sold, and also the advantage of capital gains treatment of the income when the livestock is finally sold. If farmers were on an accrual basis, value of the increase in livestock inventory would be taxed as the inventory increased in value rather than upon its sale.

Federal estate and gift taxes also are of great importance to farmers since the going concern farm business is often valued in the hundreds of thousands of dollars. Hence the increase in the amount that can pass untaxed from one generation to another, as specified in the Economic Recovery Tax Act of 1981, is of vast significance to farmers. A high proportion of farm operations do pass through the inheritance process to the next generation of the family.

Financial Planning and Management

By Thomas L. Frey and Neal Sox Johnson

Historically, agriculture and farming have been considered a way of life. Many still view farms as small, self-sufficient, independent operations, and they believe that long hours and hard work are the only key ingredients for success. In reality, agriculture seems to be well into a major revolution, a financial and business management era that is sweeping the industry and threatening to leave behind those who cling to ways of the past.

Financial and business management considerations have jumped to the forefront as prerequisites for success. Cash budgeting, sophisticated accounting systems, regular monitoring of financial performance, much greater use of debt, leasing resources, utilization of sophisticated business organization structures, and never-ending developments in tax law are a few characteristics of this new era. It is a transition from a way of life to a highly capitalized industry. Many farmers need assistance and training in financial and business techniques. This chapter identifies some of the changing needs and offers guidance through some financial tools and techniques.

Understanding a farm business in financial terms can be approached in three ways: 1) What is the financial condition and financial position at a given moment in time? 2) How well did the business perform financially for a past period — for example, the past year — in terms of profitability? and 3) How will the farm be operated for the next year — acres of the various crops, number of livestock raised or fed — and what cash revenue and cash expenditures can reasonably be expected under this plan? Further, how profitable will the operation be if all plans become reality?

A business must be proven *profitable* and *feasible* in order to continue over a long period of time. There must be sufficient profit (excess revenue over expenses) for family living withdrawals. At the same time, cash must be available to meet obligations as they become due, a condition referred to as "feasibility." An operation might be profitable without being feasible. For example, there might be a $100,000 land purchase that requires the principal to be paid off in five years, at $20,000 per year plus interest. At the same time, the operation might be generating $15,000, with $12,000 being required for family living, resulting in a $3,000 profit. However, that profit would not be enough to meet a $20,000 principal payment — clearly not a feasible situation.

Thomas L. Frey is Professor of Agricultural Finance at the University of Illinois, Urbana-Champaign.

Neal Sox Johnson is Deputy Administrator, Program Operations, Farmers Home Administration, USDA, Washington, D.C.

In contrast, some families may be selling off breeding stock or inventory of crops from a previous year, in a period of current losses, in order to make payments. Thus, the operation is temporarily feasible, but the situation cannot continue unless profits are generated. Likewise, some people find themselves borrowing more than they can repay, which is another way of keeping in operation without profits. However, the borrowing cannot last long, since it uses up the operator's net worth or equity. Fortunately, there are tools that can help one understand and exert control over what happens financially. These tools provide answers to the three questions raised earlier.

Balance Sheet — The financial condition and financial position of an operation at a given moment in time can be determined with the help of a balance sheet. This financial statement lists all the assets as well as liabilities, with the difference between the two being shown as net worth (often called owner equity). Assets represent anything owned and having value, and they must be valued as of the date of the statement. Liabilities are also expressed in dollar terms. Net worth could be considered as the amount an individual would pocket if all assets were sold and all liabilities paid. It is a measure of what the individual is worth.

Assets are divided into three categories: current, intermediate, and fixed. Current assets represent cash and near cash items — assets that could be converted to cash without disrupting the ongoing business, or ones that will be used in the business during the year. Cash crops on hand, crops held for feed, feeder livestock, and prepaid expenses are examples. Intermediate assets are primarily working assets that yield service to the business each year, such as machinery and breeding livestock. Balance sheets for businesses other than farms often omit the intermediate asset and liability category. For these businesses, machin-

Managing a successful dairy farm such as this one requires expertise in financial management as well as operating experience and capital.

Tim McCabe

ery and equipment, and the corresponding debt, are often included in the fixed category. Fixed assets consist mainly of real estate.

On the liability side, current liabilities are those obligations existing as of the date of the statement which must be repaid within the following 12 months. The intermediate section typically includes debts with a final maturity of one to 10 years beyond the date of the balance sheet. Long term liabilities are those that extend beyond 10 years. An example will clarify the structure of a balance sheet.

Two relationships are especially important. One is the current ratio, or current assets divided by current liabilities: $60,000 \div $30,000 = 2:1$ in the example. This is one measure of liquidity, the ability of the business to pay debts when due. Two to one is generally considered a good ratio. The same issue may also be evaluated by examining the *working capital*. That capital is the dollar difference between current assets and current liabilities: $60,000 - $30,000 = $30,000$ working capital in the example. As total assets grow, there should be a corresponding increase in working capital to assure that adequate liquidity is maintained.

Using the statement, farmers also are able to monitor financial performance. At the end of each month, budgeted amounts can be compared to actual performance, and a variance calculated on each revenue and expense item. The farmer evaluates every variance to understand its cause and to decide if any changes in the budget and the operation should be made. Increasingly, lenders are requiring farmers to prepare cash flow statements as a basis for loans.

Generally, all farm and nonfarm revenue and expenditures will be included in the cash flow statement. Any transaction generating or using cash should be entered. That includes family living, purchase of new machinery and equipment, and payment on loans. A cash flow statement is *not* a measure of profitability, but relates more to feasibility. It cannot be used to indicate net income, since some cash expenditures are not expense, and there is no indication of how the inventory changed to create the cash.

To determine if an operation will be *profitable* under the assumptions used, it is necessary to use a proforma (projected) income statement and proforma balance sheet. In contrast to the income statement described earlier that related to a past period of time, the *Proforma Statement* shows the estimates of revenue and estimates of expenses, with a resultant projected net income. Much of the data needed comes directly from the cash flow statement. Non-expense items, like family living withdrawals and principal payments on loans from the cash flow statement, are not included. Items such as estimated depreciation and inventory changes have to be added. Proforma statements used in conjunction with detailed cash flow statements provide a complete financial understanding.

Farm Operation Changes

What kinds of changes do farmers make on their farm operations? There are many, and most involve new investment. Expansion or change in the cropping and/or livestock program is a common change. New facilities are built, or old ones remodeled. Land may be purchased. Machinery may be replaced or

Joe Profitmaker: Balance Sheet 12-31-82

Assets		Liabilities and Net Worth	
Current	$ 60,000	Current	$ 30,000
Intermediate	$ 90,000	Intermediate	$ 40,000
Fixed	$300,000	Fixed	$130,000
		Total Liabilities	$200,000
		Net Worth	$250,000
Total Assets	$450,000	Total Liabilities & Net Worth	$450,000

Joe Profitmaker: Income Statement for 12-Month Period Ending 12-31-82

REVENUE

Crop Sales	$71,000	
Livestock & Sales	$ 7,300	
Other	$ 1,500	
Less Livestock & Feed Purchases	$(1,000)	
Value of Farm Production		(a)$78,800

EXPENSES

Cash Operating	$ 44,000	
Depreciation	$ 18,000	
Expense Adjustments	$+1,000	
Total Operating Expenses		(b)$63,000
Net Farm Income (a-b)		(c)$15,800
Plus Net Non-Farm Income		(d)$ 4,500
Less Income Taxes		(e)$(2,000)
Equals Net Income		(f)$18,300

new equipment purchased. How can or should such decisions be made, and how do these decisions relate to the financial statements?

Farmers need to clearly differentiate between investments made for production reasons and those made as personal or family living expenditures. Neither should be made on impulse, but should result from serious analysis. The guide for determining if production investments are feasible is when total expected dollar benefits should exceed the cost, and exceed it by enough to offset the interest outlay on the investment.

Income Statement — An income statement evaluates an operation's profitability for a past period of time by summarizing all revenues and expenses, and the resulting net income for that period — usually one year. The statement helps determine such factors as family living withdrawals, ability to repay capital debts, and the ability to buy new assets. The net income figure reflects the business' degree of financial success. Several complexities exist, however, in measuring net income. Most basic is performance on a "cash basis" versus performance on an "accrued basis."

Consider a beginning crop farmer who sells no crops within the first year, but holds the crop inventory into the next production year. On a cash basis, he will show a large loss since there is no cash revenue. The details would be reported as such on the IRS tax return. This large "cash" loss, however, should not suggest to the operator that he is necessarily doing a poor job.

A more accurate indication of the management performance can be determined

with an "accrual" basis income. In this case, the dollar increase or decrease in inventories would be added to cash sales to constitute total revenue. Expenses also need to be evaluated on an accrual basis, which includes items such as accrued interest and taxes.

Net income can be measured for both farm (net farm income) and nonfarm activities (net nonfarm income). By combining these two amounts and then deducting income taxes, an after-tax net income is identified. Family living expenses must come from that amount.

Capital Debt Repayment Capacity (CDRC) can be calculated once the net income figure is determined from the income statement. CDRC shows how much principal on capital debt the business can pay, and it reflects whether funds are available for new capital purchases. Capital Debt Repayment Capacity for past years provides some indication of what the business may do in the future. It is constituted by the farm's retained earnings. If a farm has $20,000 CDRC and, in analyzing the amount of existing commitment to pay off principal portions, finds $20,000 already committed, there is no money for new investments. Thus, the income statement can help many farmers make better decisions.

The Statement of Change in Financial Position, like the income statement, is a flow statement — it measures the sources and uses of funds in the business for the period being analyzed. It helps sort out and identify the relative importance of the various sources and uses. When all transactions are summarized into these categories, it becomes easier to understand a business. This statement

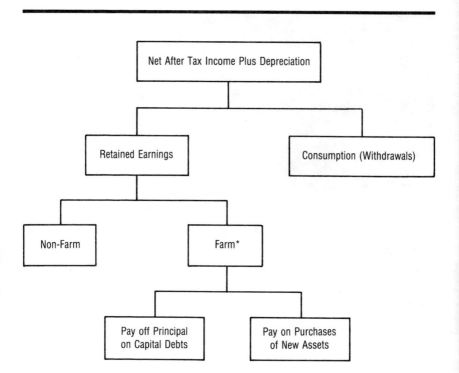

*It is the farm-retained earnings that we are calling Capital Debt Repayment Capacity. If a farm has $20,000 CDRC and in analyzing the amount of existing commitment to pay off principal portions finds $20,000 already committed, it becomes clear there is no money for new investments. The income statement is an extremely useful financial tool that could help many farmers make better decisions.

Using a cash flow statement, as this farmer is doing, has many benefits, including necessary planning for the upcoming operating year.

Statement of Change in Financial Position

Sources of Income	Uses of Income
Net income (before depreciation)	Withdrawals
Gifts received	Gifts given
Sale of assets	Purchase of assets
Borrowing	Repayment of debt
Equals Total Sources	Equal Total Uses

Total Sources Must Equal Total Uses

Joe Profitmaker: Projected Cash Flow Statement[1] for Calendar Year 1983

	Projected Total	Jan.	Feb.-Dec.[2]
1. Beginning Cash	$3,200	$3,200	← →
2. Operating Receipts	85,000	2,600	
3. Capital Receipts	4,600	—0—	
4. Non-Farm Income	5,400	500	
5. Total Cash Available	98,200	6,300	
6. Operating Expenses	48,500	4,200	
7. Livestock & Feed Purchases	2,200	700	
8. Capital Expenditures	30,000	—0—	
9. Other Expenditures	2,200	300	
10. Total Cash Required	82,900	5,200	
11. Cash Available Less Cash Required per month		+1,100	
12. Money to be Borrowed	23,000	2,000	
13. Payments on Operating Loans a. Principal	18,000	—0—	
14. b. Interest	1,600	—0—	← →
15. Ending Cash Balance per month		8,100	

[1]Categories at left would be further subdivided on a form used by a farmer, e.g. receipts would include crops, livestock, government payments, etc.

[2]Amounts in "Projected Total" column would be totally pro-rated in columns for January through December.

focuses attention on the changes taking place in the asset and liability accounts, enabling farmers to start analysis of changes in their working capital. They may see how the capital changed and determine the cause of the change. Farmers may then evaluate the increases or decreases in intermediate and fixed asset accounts, and determine whether growth is being financed with new borrowing or whether the financial position is being consolidated by paydown of debt. The Statement of Change in Financial Position is a relatively new statement in agriculture, but it embodies a process and approach that will become more important as it helps farmers better understand financial changes.

Budgeting Tools

Thus far the discussion has centered around financial tools best suited for use in analyzing past performance and existing financial position. A more important issue is future performance, since one can exert control over how the farm will be operated in the future. The following financial tools are useful in budgeting and planning future performance. First, let's take up the *Cash Flow Statement*. While a cash flow can be constructed for a past period, the most common and by far most useful approach to analysis is a Projected Cash Flow. This term will be used here to denote a statement where all anticipated cash revenues and expenditures for the 12-month period ahead are estimated on an item by item basis.

From a column of projections for the annual inflow and outflow, amounts are pro-rated either monthly or quarterly. Assuming monthly projections are used, it is possible to evaluate whether cash will be short or long for the month, and advance plans can be made. This evaluation is especially useful in working with lenders to design an annual financing plan. A cash flow statement can benefit farmers in various ways. Perhaps the greatest benefit comes from having to plan extensively for the upcoming year.

Farmers can plan, field by field, what crops will be grown, their estimated yields, and anticipated quantities and costs of all seed, fertilizer, chemicals and other input costs. Then a planned marketing program, including anticipated prices and dates of sales, is formulated. The analysis is carried through to show what ending inventory is expected for each item.

To determine net benefits, either net revenue must go up over the amount before the investment, or costs of producing the same revenue must drop. Even if benefits clearly exceed costs, the investment must be feasible, meaning cash flow must be sufficient to meet any principal and interest loan payments. For personal and family living investments (such as new car, television, home furnishings and remodeling) sufficient net income must exist to cover normal family living, plus the additional outlays associated with the purchase. This analysis relates back to use of the income statement.

A farmer should be cautioned on major investments that require transition of time before the full revenue is realized, such as a livestock facility that requires several months to several years before 100 percent production can be realized. Cash to meet principal and interest payments will likely be needed from some other source until the facility generates full revenue. This transition period can be very difficult.

Records — Historically, farmers have maintained records primarily to meet IRS tax filing requirements of cash revenue, cash expenses, and depreciation. There are many jokes about shoe box or barn door systems. But the fact is that for small, modest volume operations a very complex system is unnecessary, and the shoe box or simple system has worked reasonably well. However, as farming becomes an increasingly complicated business, many decisions must be based on good accounting data. Lenders are requiring a far more complete set of financial statements. Marketing decisions alone can make or break an operation. Therefore, one needs accurate records that show the cost of producing a unit of output, such as bushel of grain or pound of livestock. Marketing decisions can then be made by knowing exactly what price is needed to cover costs and generate a target profit.

What alternatives do farmers have for generating accounting information? The following are suggested: 1) Manually record cash receipts and cash expenditures in a record book using a *single* entry for each revenue and expenditure. 2) Manually record cash receipts and cash expenditures in a record book using a *double* entry system, which reconciles bank statements with the cash position shown by the records. 3) Manually record receipts and expenditures on input sheets, which are sent to an outside firm for computer processing. 4) Manually record details on your checks when they are written so that an outside firm can use this information to process the account. 5) Input receipts and expenditures directly into a computer. 6) Some combination of the above.

Where can one find a good accounting or record system? Good sources of information are local agricultural lenders, cooperative extension agents, other land grant university representatives, or accountants. Local libraries also are fine places to start. Service bureaus and Agricultural Finance consultants or accountants, though limited in their availability, are also good choices. And other farmers may be able to recommend an approach.

Caution — Some farmers are trying to move from a "shoe box" approach to use of a computer without first learning and having some experience with a manual system which works well. This is dangerous and should be avoided. Without a working knowledge of what the computer should be doing, it is very difficult to understand the output.

Several options also exist in determining who should do the bookkeeping. The farmer or a member of his family will usually be responsible. However, as operations grow, it may be necessary to employ someone part or full time as bookkeeper. Such individuals would then travel periodically to the farm. For tax assistance, accounting and tax specialists should be located. As computer usage continues to grow in agriculture, farmers will find themselves using the computer for many nonaccounting purposes, all related however to management decisions. Breakeven analyses, ration balancing, enterprise selection, and physical input/output data on both crop and livestock operations are examples of what can be done. The financial and business management revolution in agriculture will require farmers to get more outside advice and counselling than ever. Farmers also will be required to learn more and more about business management.

Getting Started in Farming Is Tough

By Michael Boehlje and Ron Durst

Many have expressed concern in recent years over how hard it is to get into farming. This issue not only affects those attempting to enter farming, it also has become a policy matter at both State and national levels with particular emphasis on its implications for the structure and control of the farming sector and the future of the family farm. There are no legal obstacles to becoming a farmer; no examinations, no minimum education requirement, no licenses. Anyone who wishes may try. Substantial barriers to an otherwise legally free entry into farming do exist however.

Historically, a substantial number of new entrants have moved into farming by the "agricultural ladder." Thus, a potential farmer began as a hired hand on the home farm or a neighbor's farm, and through hard work and wise spending accumulated enough money to buy a set of machinery. Subsequently the new entrant became a renter, then a part owner of real estate, and finally the pinnacle of success was reached with full ownership of land as well as machinery. Although the process required family sacrifices, the resource requirements were sufficiently modest that this procedure could be used successfully by a hard worker.

The "agricultural ladder" as a source of new farmers is now in question. With the substitution of capital for labor, the rapid price increase in durable resources (particularly land), and the expanding capital requirements of the economically viable farm firm, it is virtually impossible to acquire sufficient capital resources through this historically successful procedure. Besides, the procedure may not provide the entrepreneural training so important for a successful new entrant in today's agriculture.

Barriers to Entry

Farming in the United States has changed markedly in recent years and is still rapidly changing. As late as 1940, labor accounted for over half the resources used in farming. Today labor accounts for less than 20 percent of farm resources, being replaced by sharp increases in the use of capital. This adjustment has fostered much larger farms and capital investments. The average size of farm has increased from about 175 acres in 1940 to 429 acres today. Capital investment per farm has risen from about $7,000 in 1940 to about $380,000 today. In fact, farm records show investments per farm have more than doubled each decade in recent times.

Being short of capital, a prospective farmer faces an increasingly difficult task of gaining control of sufficient resources to make successful entry. This is particu-

Michael Boehlje is a Professor of Economics at Iowa State University, Ames.

Ron Durst is an Agricultural Economist with the National Economics Division, Economic Research Service, Washington, D.C.

Farm records show that investments per farm have more than doubled each decade in recent times. These include farm machinery and equipment like that shown here on a South Carolina farm.

David F. Warren

Successful use of modern farming methods, and of equipment like this soybean harvester in southwest Iowa, requires a high degree of technical knowledge and skill.

Tim McCabe

larly true of persons who must start with little family assistance. Of necessity, they must look for an opportunity that will make the most use of their labor when combined with their limited capital. Furthermore, because incomes and wage rates in off-farm employment are not rising as rapidly as the cost of farm inputs (particularly machinery and land), the strategy of working off the farm to obtain the necessary funds for entry does not always succeed.

Economies of size which result in lower costs as size increases also are an important consideration for the beginning farmer. Most studies indicate the cost curve declines rapidly with increases from very small to modest size farming units; after that point the cost curve becomes relatively flat with only modest reductions in cost with increased size. In essence, a "critical mass" of resources must be controlled to obtain reasonable levels of efficiency to be competitive.

As farms became larger and more complex, managerial requirements rose sharply. Successful use of modern farming methods requires a high degree of technical knowledge and skill. Handling large investments and cash flows in the face of high and rising costs, uncertain product prices, coupled with weather and other production risks, requires expert business and financial skills. It should be noted that some of these skills, particularly in the area of marketing and finance, are not acquired through the historical "hired man-agricultural ladder" approach to entry. Acquiring such skills may involve significant commitments of time and funds in formal training as well as practical experience.

One of the dominant characteristics of

beginning farmers is limited capability to withstand risk. The beginning farmer typically does not have the equity base nor the experience to cope financially and personally with wide fluctuations in income. Family demands require at least sufficient income to provide a reasonable standard of living from the farming operation. Yet the agricultural sector is characterized by increasing risk. Thus an individual who frequently does not have the mental and managerial capability to handle risk is attempting to enter a high risk industry, usually with a large amount of debt and high leverage which multiplies the risk even further. This conflict between the risk-bearing ability of the young farmer and the risk inherent in agriculture may be one of the key barriers to successful entry.

Another barrier for the beginning farmer is resource control, particularly control of the land. Since much of the land in the United States is either owned or rented by established farmers with relatively strong financial positions, it is increasingly difficult for a beginning farmer to bid competitively in the purchase or rental market to acquire control of the land base. Furthermore, the high risk associated with cash rental arrangements for land multiplies the beginning farmer's problems. Besides the risk associated with cash rental payments, many rental arrangements are short-term (one year) in nature, and thus the beginning farmer runs a risk of losing control of the land base after one or two years. With this tenure uncertainty, expansion in livestock which will typically generate the highest return to the beginning farmer's limited capital and relatively large labor supply is difficult, if not impossible.

Maybe most important in the decision of whether or not to begin farming are lifestyle considerations. The living style in rural communities may require significant family adjustments. Schools, health services, shopping facilities, and cultural opportunities are often less adequate than those available in cities. In many small towns, everybody knows everybody and their business and personal affairs. The work hours are frequently long and there often is little flexibility for family vacations or just having a relaxing weekend. And although farmers' incomes have improved considerably over the years, uncertainty and possible financial setbacks are always part of farming. An important decision for those considering a farming career is whether they want the lifestyle.

Alternatives — Numerous entry alternatives are possible; the choice among them depends to a large degree on the experience and know-how of the new entrant and the availability of capital. We

An important decision in considering a farming career is whether you want the lifestyle that is part of farming. That lifestyle includes living in a rural area, perhaps like this one in central Maryland.

William E. Carnahan

will discuss alternatives that do not involve family assistance first; then entering with family assistance will be reviewed.

The Resident Manager — One key strategy for entry that may be particularly appealing for those who have little farming experience or capital is to become a resident manager of a large established farm operation. As farm businesses grow bigger, additional managerial talent is frequently required. This may be in the form of a herdsman for a particular phase of the business such as the dairy enterprise, or overall manager of the entire farm business under the owner's supervision.

An advantage of the resident manager approach is that it can provide experience based on the latest technology in agriculture. It is important to choose an up-to-date operation that uses new technology if an entrant seeks experience by this route. Another major purpose of using this route for entry is to obtain knowledge of marketing and financial decisions. So the opportunity to exercise management authority and responsibility is important; avoid an operation that is simply looking for a "hired hand" to carry out the day-to-day farming activities.

In some cases, the resident manager's role will be so challenging and the rewards so high that some may decide to remain in this role throughout their farming career. But for others, the question will eventually arise as to when to resign from the manager position and establish their own operation. One approach is to accumulate sufficient funds to acquire a smaller established farming operation when the opportunity arises and sufficient experience has been obtained to operate

independently. An alternative is to use a phase-in approach. Accumulated savings can be used to purchase a piece of land which is then rented out. The advantage of this approach is that if the value of assets continues to rise, it may be possible to acquire control of some of these resources earlier at a lower price than if purchases are delayed.

Chance to Step In — On occasion, a prospective farmer has an opportunity to step in as a manager and part owner of a farming unit that is fully equipped and ready to go. The business is available because of illness, disability or death of the original farm operator, the lack of a farming heir, or for other reasons. Such a situation should prove particularly attractive to the experienced manager who has some capital. The basic resources needed are in place, and over time the manager can build equity to the point where eventual control is obtained over the operation.

In summary, a key advantage of the resident manager approach is the opportunity to obtain experience and knowledge without having to commit large amounts of one's own capital. Such an approach may be particularly appealing to an individual who has strong formal training and motivation but limited capital and practical experience. Resident managership may offer the satisfaction of working with a larger unit. However, spinning off from such an operation to your own smaller unit may be difficult since it may require a change in lifestyle as well as farming technique, scale of operation, and risk.

Putting It Together Yourself
"Starting from scratch" involves putting all (or much) of the resources together yourself, with assistance only from a cre-

ditor or supportive landowner. Under to-day's conditions, this option is generally feasible only for the exceptional manager with considerable equity of his own. Occasionally the exceptional manager (and family) can do it with limited equity following a period of part-time farming. Part-time farming may also serve as a hedge or a bridge — the nonfarm job can be used to augment income and reduce the risk of not having a reasonable standard of living from farming alone. Often, however, part-time farmers remain part-time rather than becoming full-time farmers; they get accustomed to a good family living and hesitate to give up the security they have acquired in their non-farm job.

Piggy-Back — For many, the most realistic way to start farming is to piggy-back on someone else's operation (joint venture approach). This may be an outgrowth of earlier employment where the employer is willing to help you get started. The joint venture might involve leasing of land and the exchange of labor for machinery. In some cases certain major machinery items such as a tractor or combine might be leased or the machine services obtained through custom hire. Alternatively, the beginning farmer might purchase some equipment and then do custom work for others to offset part of the costs and generate income to service debt that may have been used to finance the purchase.

In most cases land rental is preferred to purchase for the beginning farmer with limited financial resources. Land typically generates a low cash flow per dollar invested and also requires a large capital outlay to obtain a "critical mass." Cash rent or crop-share rental arrangements may be used. With crop-share rentals the landlord and the tenant share both production and price risk. Cash rentals require the tenant to bear most of the risks. Consequently, share rentals are preferred for most beginning farmers unless the cash rent terms are very favorable.

Finally, as noted earlier, capital is an important resource for the beginning farmer. The capital the owner can contribute includes savings and inheritances, and any family or other support or assistance. The latter may include a family member guaranteeing a loan, or directly lending funds to the beginning farmer. The assistance may also take the form of property sharing, such as exchanging labor for the use of machinery.

Most beginning farmers starting on their own must borrow a large proportion of the capital used in their farming operations. Numerous sources of credit are available including commercial banks, Production Credit Associations, Federal Land Banks, insurance companies, merchants and dealers, individuals, and government agencies such as the Farmers Home Administration. Most commercial lenders have only limited resources they can allocate to beginning farmers; the Farmers Home Administration has explicit farm ownership and operating loan programs that are tailored to the credit and financial needs of beginning farmers.

A farmer's credit worthiness depends on personal character as well as equity position and ability to service debt. Since most beginning farmers have limited equity, they must rely heavily on character and ability to repay debt from income when justifying a credit request. Consequently, a history of meeting financial obligations on time and an ability to develop realistic projections of income and expenses (cash flows) are key attributes for the beginning farmer. Ability to use scarce resources effectively in generating needed cash flows, and evidence of success in keeping family living demands in check, also affect the amount a lender is willing to loan and the debt that can be serviced. Income from off-farm employment may also be an important source of cash for debt servicing for the beginning farmer.

Starting on the Home Farm

The home farm typically provides favorable opportunities for getting started in farming. The first and possibly most important opportunity is access to land and other types of farm capital. In addition, a farming venture on the home farm offers a valuable opportunity for gaining managerial experience under guidance and encouragement of the more experienced parents. Note, however, that establishing a successful parent-child farming arrangement requires careful evaluation of the current farm and family situation as well as a clarification of personal, business, and family goals. Some of the more important questions that need to be answered include:

Most beginning farmers starting on their own must borrow a large proportion of the capital used in their farming operation. The farmer pictured here has a 340-acre grain farm in Howard County, Md., and works closely with his banker.

William E. Carnahan

What is the current farm business situation? What are current income needs of the parents? What are their expectations with regard to future income needs and financial goals? Is the farm business large enough to produce income sufficient to satisfy the current needs and future expectations of both parties involved? If not, can the farm business be expanded to a size sufficient to meet these needs? If expansion of the farm business is necessary or desirable, are the parents willing to incur more debt, and is the beginning farmer willing to reinvest a portion of farm earnings into the farm business? If expansion is necessary, how do both parties feel such expansion should be accomplished?

What are anticipated levels of involvement in the farm business at initiation of the arrangement? In 5 years? In 10 years? Is the ultimate goal of both parties to transfer the home farm to the beginning farmer (on-farm heir)? Are there brothers or sisters who want to enter farming in the future? If so, how will their interests affect the on-farm heir's eventual inheritance?

Answers to these questions will assist the parties in determining the type of arrangement under which the on-farm heir may enter the home farm business. Since family and farm circumstances differ, no one type of arrangement is suitable for every situation. In many cases, however, the on-farm heir will initially participate in the farm business under a wage agreement. As the heir assumes additional responsibilities, the agreement may be expanded into a wage-incentive or wage- and income-share plan. Such arrangements are particularly useful since they allow the on-farm heir to test his or her decision to enter farming with little

or no capital investment. These arrangements also provide the parties an opportunity to determine if they can work together in a joint farming arrangement. However, the testing period should not be prolonged.

Spin-Off — Once these issues have been resolved, the parties should move on to arrangements which afford the on-farm heir greater financial and management responsibilities. If a more formal joint farming arrangement does not suit the family circumstances, then a spin-off operation might be desirable. Although this type of arrangement can take on many different forms, a typical situation might involve sharing labor and machinery while the parents and heir own or rent separate tracts of land. A situation may also exist in which the parents may be ready to reduce involvement in the operation. Under these circumstances, the heir may prefer to rent or buy part of the home farm.

Finally, if both parties want to farm together in a formal multiperson operation, they should determine whether a partnership or a corporate type of business arrangement would best suit the situation. Both the partnership and the corporation have their advantages and disadvantages. Generally the partnership can provide many of the advantages associated with incorporating, yet partnerships may be far less complex. However, the corporation usually provides greater opportunities for income tax management.

The ultimate goal of the business arrangement should be the transfer of the home farm to the heir. If this goal is to be met without seriously disrupting the farm business, several objectives must be considered in the early stages of the arrangement. These include security for parents, equitable treatment of all heirs, and transfer of the farm with minimal estate tax liabilities and/or liquidity problems.

After operating the home farm for many years, some parents are reluctant to give up ownership and control of the farm business. This is especially true if farming is their primary means of financial support. However, tax and other farm business considerations may make it desirable to transfer at least part of the farm property to the heir who will be the future owner and operator of the farm business. Thus, the goal of providing income security for parents may conflict with farm management and tax planning goals. Retirement income security can be enhanced by income from business or nonfarm investments. Income may also be obtained through social security benefits or participation in self-employed or individual retirement plans. Regardless of the source, income security cannot be achieved overnight; rather, it must be established over a period of many years.

Off-Farm Heirs — Farm families with more than one child frequently face complications in transferring farm ownership to the on-farm heir. Most parents want to treat all children equitably. This goal can possibly be achieved by providing cash or other property not associated with the farm business to the off-farm heirs. In some cases it may be necessary to have the absentee heirs participate in the farm business either as landlords, debtors, or security holders. In such cases, the on-farm heir should be given the opportunity to purchase these interests at a fair price. Even with this option, however, without prior planning and continued communication among all in-

terested parties, the farming heir could eventually face severe financial problems associated with buying out these interests.

The trend toward larger farms combined with the increase in the value of farm property, particularly land, have resulted in greater concern regarding impact of the estate tax on transfer of the farm operation to the next generation. While the amount of estate tax varies with size of the estate, type of assets contained in the estate, how these assets are owned, and how the transfer is to be done, virtually every farm estate can benefit from estate planning. The increase in the unified credit and enactment of the unlimited marital deduction in the Economic Recovery Tax Act of 1981 should ensure that, with proper planning, there should be little or no tax on the death of the first parent. However, death of the second parent could create serious tax problems unless there is careful tax planning.

Although circumstances vary greatly, certain techniques are especially valuable in reducing the estate tax burden. These include maximizing the unified credit upon the death of the first parent, making lifetime gifts, developing balanced estates between husband and wife, using testamentary trusts or life estates, qualifying for "special use" valuation and the installment payment of tax, and selling farm property to on-farm heirs on an installment basis or in return for an annuity.

Two tax provisions of particular importance to the agricultural sector in reducing tax and liquidity problems are special use valuation and installment payment of tax. Qualifying family farm and ranch estates can value land at its "special use" (agricultural) value rather than fair market value. This can significantly reduce the value of the taxable estate and therefore estate taxes due. Since special use valuation is only intended for family farms which are to continue as family farms, numerous technical requirements must be satisfied to qualify for the provision. Qualifying could mean the difference between continued operation and forced liquidation of the farm business.

Even with proper tax management and estate planning, some farms will incur significant estate settlement costs and face the prospect of having to liquidate property to pay these costs. To reduce pressure to sell property to pay taxes, the Tax Reform Act of 1976 provided for paying estate taxes in installments. Under this provision, the Federal estate tax liability can be deferred for five years following death of the owner, and then paid in up to 10 equal annual installments thereafter. Interest is paid annually at a 4 percent rate (on the first $1 million of taxable estate) on the unpaid balance. This installment provision is generally available to estates in which the farm business comprises at least 35 percent of the adjusted gross estate.

Fundamentals — Following are some fundamentals the beginning farmer starting mostly on his or her own should be aware of:

1) Most successful businesspeople did not start at the top. So, therefore, don't try to be too big too soon. Develop your unit over time, keeping its size consistent with your management skills and financial position. Establish a good track record as to your ability to generate and manage income. Have longer term goals that you are shooting for with plans for attaining them.

2) Most beginning farmers in this country are long on labor and short on capital. Consequently, allocate scarce capital to items that bring high return to capital invested (for example, fertilizer rather than land). Piggy-back when possible to reduce pressure for capital, plus provide management help. Substitute labor for capital when possible. Use smaller equipment and existing buildings where feasible. When possible, select labor intensive enterprises to make fuller, year-round use of the labor supply (as examples, dairy, hogs). Gain control of resources in ways that will give good returns and make effective use of leverage, yet protect liquidity position of the business (for example, crop-share rental). Cash flow demands as well as risk of large losses should be minimized. Manage risks carefully; employ insurance, marketing strategies, and possibly diversify operations.

3) Over time, capital availability will depend upon management capability. Therefore, establish a good production and financial record. Spend time becoming a better manager; develop your production, marketing, and financial skills. Secure management help when possible from the adult vo-ag instructor, creditor, professional manager, or another good farmer.

4) Keep fully employed and keep family living costs in bounds. While the unit is being developed, full employment may require off-farm work. Usually the starting family must sacrifice their standard of living to a substantial degree or no financial progress will be made.

Farm Exports – A Key to Our Economy

By Dewain Rahe and Reed Friend

During the 1970's, American farmers became increasingly dependent upon exports as a market for their plentiful production. U.S. agricultural exports during the 1970's increased at an annual rate of about 20 percent, and exports of $43.3 billion in calendar 1981 were about six times the $7 billion in 1970. Over one-fourth of the cash receipts from marketings in the late 1970's came from exports, compared with about 15 percent in the early 1970's. While higher prices accounted for some of the value increase, volume also expanded rapidly, increasing from about 60 million tons in 1970 to 163 million in 1981.

The increase in U.S. agricultural export prices was much less than the gain in either consumer or wholesale prices. Thus, the real export price and farm price (deflated by the consumer price index) for export items were about 12 percent less in early 1980 than the 1969-71 average. The agricultural export price index showed a sharp increase in 1973, 1974, and 1981 as the result of sharply reduced crop output in the United States and in other major producing countries. Prices of primary items — grains, oilseeds and cotton — showed the widest fluctuation in export prices during the 1970's, while processed agricultural items showed price increases more in line with the general inflation rate.

However, the value of the dollar in relationship to other currencies has a very large impact on prices of U.S. farm products in foreign markets. For example during 1981 and 1982, when U.S. prices of corn and soybeans declined by 15 percent and 10 percent respectively, the prices of these commodities, in terms of Dutch guilders for instance, decreased only 9 percent and 6 percent.

The United States is the world's largest exporter of farm products. Our farm exports in 1980 exceeded the second ranked supplier, France, by over $25 billion. More importantly, our share of the world agricultural export market has risen to nearly one-fifth of total world agricultural exports, compared with around 15 percent at the beginning of the 1970's. The United States accounts for four-fifths of the world exports of soybeans, two-thirds of the feedgrains, two-fifths of the wheat and cotton, and one-fifth of the tobacco and rice.

The gain in U.S. agricultural exports during the 1970's has been in commercial sales for dollars. Exports under concessional programs, primarily Public Law

Dewain Rahe is Director, Trade and Economic Information Division, International Agricultural Statistics, Foreign Agricultural Service.

Reed Friend is Chief, Western Europe Branch, International Economics Division, Economic Research Service.

480 (PL 480) have been relatively constant — ranging between $1.2 to $1.5 billion annually. Food aid programs have helped many developing countries to meet their food needs in time of crises and are also an important instrument in developing markets for U.S. farm products. These programs can contribute to the economic well-being of recipient countries and allow them to achieve faster economic growth with accompanying higher incomes.

Countries once major recipients of U.S. food under PL 480 and now major commercial markets include Japan, Spain, Taiwan, Brazil, and South Korea. Short term credits also helped to assist exports during the 1970's, mostly to developing countries. Exports with direct credits or credit guarantees (considered commercial exports) increased from around $300 million in fiscal 1970 to over $1.7 billion in fiscal 1981.

Reasons for Export Growth

Many reasons lie behind the growth in U.S. agricultural exports. During the 1970's, there was generally a remarkable opening of many countries' economies to world trade. Total international trade (both agricultural and nonagricultural products) expanded at an annual rate of over 20 percent. Population outside the United States increased by about 1.8 percent annually to add 75 million more people each year. In addition, the rest of the world increased incomes in real terms by 3 to 4 percent each year. Thus the growth in both population and income was an important factor in growth in U.S. agricultural exports. While high in-

The United States is the world's largest exporter of farm products. This soft white wheat is being loaded onto barges in Oregon for overseas shipment.

USDA

comes lead to higher consumption of traditional foods, mainly grains in developing countries, the more dynamic effect is the shifts to meats, milk, eggs, and fruits and vegetables.

Once per capita incomes reach a certain level, further increases up to a relatively high per capita level result in rapid gains in meat consumption. Meat consumption outside the United States increased by nearly 4 percent yearly during the 1970's. Increased meat production, particularly pork and poultry, requires the feeding of considerably more grain. It takes about 7 pounds of corn to produce a pound of beef (under intensive feeding as opposed to grazing on pasture), about 4 or 5 pounds of corn for a pound of pork, and about 2 pounds of corn for a pound of poultry meat.

This "multiplier effect" of producing meat from grains has had a profound impact on the growth of U.S. agricultural exports during the past decade. Thus, the growth in U.S. exports of grain and soybeans for feed increased at a pace even faster than the per capita growth in world meat consumption. Since 1970, the volume of U.S. feedgrain exports increased 3.6 times, while soybean shipments were nearly two times larger by fiscal 1981.

Over the years, the American farmer has become the most productive and efficient producer of many agricultural products in the world. There are many reasons for achieving this high level of productivity, but most important is an agricultural area

Food aid programs, such as this one in Swaziland, have helped many developing countries to meet their food needs in time of crises.

which has highly fertile soil and a favorable climate for producing grains, oilseed, cotton, and livestock. The United States also has a widely diverse range of soils and climate which permits regional specialization in many different types of agricultural products. These circumstances provide American agriculture with a comparative advantage in the foreign market for many types of products.

During the last decade a dual dependency on U.S. agricultural trade has developed, affecting the consumers overseas and farmers in the United States. U.S. feedgrains and soybeans supply a substantial share of feeds used in commercial livestock production in foreign countries. The American farmer has become dependent upon foreign trade for more than one-fourth of his income. For some major commodities, the dependency is even greater. Some portion of nearly every crop grown in the United States is exported, but the share is very large for grain, oilseeds, cotton, tobacco, tree nuts, cattle hides, lemons, and numerous other commodities. Based on volume, the shares of U.S. production exported was 60 percent for rice and wheat; nearly 30 percent for coarse grains; over 50 percent for soybeans; and about 40 percent for cotton and tobacco.

Our Export Stake — Nearly 160 million acres of U.S. cropland, or the equivalent of two out of every five acres, were harvested for export. About 20 million acres were used to grow the agricultural prodcuts exported to Japan. To produce the record high 163 million tons of exports, over one-half million farmworkers are needed. This accounts for about 15 percent of the total agricultural employment devoted to commercial agricultural production.

In addition to the farm jobs created by agricultural exports, more than 630,000 individuals in the nonfarm sector were directly or indirectly related to assembling, processing, and distributing agricultural products for export. There were some 60,000 jobs in food processing, 300,000 in trade and transportation, 120,000 in other manufacturing sectors, and 150,000 in other services in the economy. U.S. agriculture has become a very capital intensive industry and depends on purchased inputs from the industrial sector to increase and maintain agricultural productivity. Thus the industrial nonagricultural sectors of the economy depend on expansion of U.S. agricultural exports to generate increased employment, utilization of capacity, and profits.

The net trade surplus of U.S. agricultural trade in calendar 1981 was nearly $27 billion: $43.3 billion of exports minus $16.8 billion in agricultural imports. But the benefits of agricultural exports are much greater and impact a wide range of business activities. An expansion in exports means more business for the trucker, more production of hopper cars and barges, more construction of port facilities, and more efficient use of the marketing industry. It is estimated in the U.S. Department of Agriculture that each dollar received from exports stimulates another dollar and five cents worth of business activity for the rest of the economy. Thus, the $43.8 billion worth of U.S. agricultural exports in fiscal 1981 translates into nearly $90 billion worth of business for U.S. industries.

U.S. consumers also benefit from U.S. agricultural exports because the foreign exchange earnings permit them to purchase foreign products such as petroleum, electric equipment, and other items taken for granted in the American standard of living. In addition foreign demand for U.S. farm products keeps production high and unit costs of production down. Expanding exports reduce the need for large government outlays for agricultural price and income support programs.

Commodity Makeup of Exports

Since World War II (WW II) there has been a phenomenal shift in the commodity composition of U.S. agricultural exports. In the years immediately after WW II, a large share of our export trade

consisted of food, grains, cotton, and tobacco. Food was especially needed by many countries suffering from effects of the war. Many war-ravaged countries allocated a very large share of their scarce foreign exchange reserves for food products. Concessional food aid programs also were very important, and significantly offset the reduced agricultural production as well as the decline in export earnings of these countries.

Effective demand for high quality food products grew stronger as economic recovery took place after the war. Aid

There are many reasons for the American farmer being the most efficient grower of many agricultural products in the world. One of the most important is that the United States has highly fertile soils, such as found on this soybean and corn farm near Homer, Ill.

P. Simkin, FAO

programs such as the Marshall Plan provided assistance in helping many countries affected by the war to rebuild their economies and set the stage for sustained economic growth. Rapid economic growth after the war was most important in the growth in U.S. agricultural exports and the changing composition of trade. Citizens of the war-hit nations wanted more meat, and the revolutionary developments in American agriculture provided plenty of grain and oilseeds with which to increase their meat production. Thus, U.S. corn and soybean exports were the resources many foreign countries relied on to upgrade the diets of their population.

The situation of plentiful U.S. supplies of grains and oilseeds, and the excess labor of the major foreign importing countries, blended together to provide the catalyst to change the composition of U.S. agricultural exports. Grains and oilseeds accounted for more than 95 percent of export volume in 1979-81 compared with 90 percent in 1969-71. Most of the growth in U.S. exports of feedgrains and oilseeds to the developed countries occurred in the late 1960's and early 1970's. But this growth slowed in the late 1970's and early 1980's because of increased grain production that was encouraged by high price supports and by a slowing of demand due to high prices and a near halt in economic growth.

While the demand for U.S. feedgrains in the developed countries slowed, import demand for U.S. feeds picked up in the centrally planned countries and in the developing countries. Poor performance of the agricultural sector in the centrally developed countries was a main reason for the growth in exports to these countries. Providing more food and a better diet

were important in maintaining political stability in the centrally planned nations and led to increased imports.

Growth in our agricultural exports to the developing countries was associated with improved economic prospects for the petroleum exporting countries and the fast growing trade-oriented countries. By the late 1970's, these groups of countries had a population of 700 million with an annual increase in population growth of about 2.5 percent. In addition, per capita real income for this group of developing countries increased by over 4 percent annually.

Primary products or bulk items such as wheat, corn, soybeans, and cotton accounted for about two-thirds of our agricultural exports in calendar year 1981. The share of bulk items has increased slightly over the past two decades. Exports of the bulk commodities have increased about 19 percent annually since 1970.

Processed Products

Expansion of value-added or processed agricultural product exports has received much attention in recent years. An expansion in value-added exports provides more jobs, and generates more business activity and more profits than do exports of bulk type products. For each dollar increase in exports of value-added products, much more business activity is generated than for the bulk products.

However, some barriers exist to expanding our share of value-added exports. Nearly all livestock production — meat, milk, and poultry — is geared for the domestic market. Because of the very large U.S. domestic market, producers and processors concentrate mainly on marketing their output in the United States and don't take full advantage of opportunities available overseas. Furthermore, most importing countries have policies and programs designed to import raw products for conversion to processed or value-added items, as part of a program to promote domestic employment and industry. These policies usually are in the form of some type of trade restriction, such as tariffs or quotas, or a subsidy program to encourage exports of processed items to other markets.

U.S. exports of value-added products rose to $13.9 billion in calendar year 1981, compared with $2.8 billion in calendar year 1970. Much of the increase in value-added products occurred in grains and feeds and livestock, poultry, and dairy products. The rise in these categories was mainly in byproducts. For example, corn gluten feed increased sharply, primarily to the European Community (EC) because of high grain prices in the EC resulting from high price supports and import levies. Corn gluten feed enters the EC duty free while grains have levies amounting to around 100 percent of the world price of these items. Hides, skins, and inedible greases accounted for much of the increase in value-added exports of livestock, poultry and dairy products. They account for about one-half of total exports of the livestock group.

The U.S. share of the world market of value-added products is estimated to remain stable at about 10 percent. Although the world value-added or processed market for agricultural products has increased by 17 percent annually in the past decade, it will be extremely difficult for the United States to get a significantly larger share of this market. That is because of likely continuation of

very effective trade restrictions and probable continuation of U.S. producers and processors concentrating on the U.S. domestic market. However, if the extremely effective trade restrictions were removed, the United States would be able to compete very effectively to get a fair share of the export value-added market.

Where They Go — The United States markets its agricultural products in many countries and regions of the world. Traditionally, the major outlets have been the relatively high income countries of Western Europe, Canada and Japan. In recent years, however, a number of other countries and regions have increased in importance as foreign markets for the products of the U.S. farmers.

Western Europe accounted for roughly one-third of the value of U.S. agricultural exports in 1970 but dropped to 28 percent in 1981. The decline in the share of our agricultural commodities sold to Western Europe has been due totally to the 10-member countries of the European Community (EC) where guaranteed prices under the Common Agricultural Policy have led to sharply increased production. The Netherlands and West Germany are the two major country outlets within the EC while Spain is the leading outlet for U.S. agricultural products in the rest of Western Europe.

The Far East first surpassed Western Europe in 1979 as the major market for U.S. agricultural exports. In addition, the share accounted for by the Far East has been on the increase and amounted to nearly one-third of U.S. agricultural exports in 1981. Japan is far and away the major country market for the United States in this area, and for that matter in

U.S. exports of agricultural products, selected regions, 1970 and 1981

Region	1970 Value	1970 Share	1981 Value	1981 Share	Increase 1970 to 1981
	$Mil.	Percent	$Mil.	Percent	Percent
North America	965	13.4	4,414	10.4	357.4
Caribbean	145	2.0	801	1.9	452.4
Central America	72	1.0	370	0.9	413.9
South America	306	4.3	2,765	6.5	803.6
EC-10	2,115	29.4	9,063	21.4	328.5
Non-EC Western Europe	390	5.4	2,816	6.7	622.1
Eastern Europe & U.S.S.R.	184	2.6	3,317	7.8	1,702.7
Middle East	238	3.3	1,677	4.0	604.6
North Africa	124	1.7	1,513	3.6	1,120.2
Other Africa	133	1.9	1,323	3.1	894.7
South Asia	378	5.3	787	1.8	108.2
Far East	2,088	29.1	13,270	31.3	535.5
Australia & Oceania	51	0.7	240	0.6	370.6
Total 1/	7,188	100.0	2/ 43,333	100.0	502.9

1/ Totals may not add due to rounding.
2/ Includes $976 million in transshipments not allocated to individual regions.

the world. The value of our agricultural exports to Japan was $6.6 billion in 1981. Also, the People's Republic of China is increasingly important and ranked as our sixth major country market in 1981.

The foreign market in North America (Canada and Mexico) has been the third major regional market for U.S. agricultural exports. However, the growth in U.S. exports to this region has not been sufficient to maintain its share of our agricultural exports which dropped to one-tenth in 1981. Mexico has become an increasingly important market for the United States and exceeded exports to Canada for the first time in 1979.

Eastern Europe and the Soviet Union (U.S.S.R.) showed the fastest growth as a market for U.S. agricultural exports between 1970 and 1981. However, it is

well to keep in mind that this growth was from a small amount in 1970. Exports to the U.S.S.R., in particular, can change substantially from year to year depending on favorable or unfavorable weather which can cause wide fluctuations in crop production in the U.S.S.R.

Our agricultural exports to Africa, the Middle East, and South America also grew at a relatively rapid rate between 1970 and 1981. However, all of these increases have been from relatively small amounts in 1970. Major markets are Egypt, Nigeria, and Algeria in Africa; Saudi Arabia in the Middle East; and Venezuela and Brazil in South America. Some of these countries have benefited from increased revenue from price hikes in petroleum exports which have increased their import purchasing power for agricultural commodities.

A grouping of countries into economic-political classes provides additional information on trends in U.S. agricultural export patterns. Although the developed market economies — primarily Japan, Canada and Western Europe — continued to take the lion's share of U.S. agricultural exports in 1981, the decline from 62 percent in 1970 to 46 percent was huge. On the other hand, the share of U.S. agricultural exports going to all other groupings except low income economies showed an increase. The economic-political groupings accounting for the largest gains in share were the oil exporting economies and the nonmarket industrial economies.

We're a Major Importer, Too

The United States is a major importer, as well as a major exporter, of agricultural commodities. Our total imports of agricultural commodities rose to over $16.8 billion in 1981 (preliminary), nearly triple the $5.8 billion imported in 1970. Since U.S. agricultural exports totaled $43.3 billion in 1981, our net trade in agriculture amounted to $26.5 billion — keeping our overall negative trade balance to slightly over $30 billion.

Both *complementary* and *supplementary* commodities are important to U.S. agricultural imports. Import of items not grown in the United States — coffee, cocoa, bananas, tea and so forth — *complement* domestic agricultural production, adding variety to our diets. U.S. imports of complementary commodities have increased over time, from $2.2 billion in 1970 to $5.7 billion in 1981 ($7.0 billion in 1980). Imports of commodities which *supplement* U.S. production — items often having some unique characteristic, such as European cheeses, or meeting seasonal demands, such as fresh fruits

and vegetables, or filling a deficit in U.S. requirements — have also sharply increased. Our imports of supplementary agricultural commodities rose from $3.6 billion in 1970 to $11.1 billion in 1981 ($10.4 billion in 1980).

The United States imports agricultural commodities from many countries around the world. Over half of the $17.4 billion in imports in 1980 was supplied by 10 countries. Brazil was the largest supplier with over $2 billion. Imports of agricultural commodities from Australia, Canada, Mexico and Colombia all exceeded $1 billion while imports from Indonesia exceeded three-quarters of a billion dollars. The value of agricultural imports from New Zealand and the Philippines was around $600 million each. Imports from the ninth and tenth major suppliers — the Dominican Republic and France — were below $500 million each. Of course, some changes occur in the top 10 suppliers from year to year.

The major *complementary* commodity imported by the United States is green coffee, which amounted to nearly $2.6 billion in 1981 (a sharp decline from the nearly $4 billion in 1980 due largely to a one-fourth decline in unit value). Major suppliers were Brazil, Colombia, Mexico, Indonesia and El Salvador. Rubber (dry form and latex), valued at $770 million, was imported largely from Indonesia and Malaysia. Banana imports totaled $525 million in 1981 and came primarily from Honduras, Costa Rica, Ecuador, and Colombia. Imports of cocoa beans were valued at $466 million with Ivory Coast as the predominant supplier followed by Brazil. Cocoa butter ($220 million) and tea ($133 million) were also major complementary agricultural products imported by the United States.

U.S. exports of agricultural products, selected groupings, 1970 and 1981

Grouping	1919 Value	1919 Share	1981 Value	1981 Share	Increase 1970 to 1981
	$Mil.	Percent	$Mil.	Percent	Percent
Low income economies	587	8.2	3,138	7.4	434.6
Middle income economies	896	12.5	6,053	14.3	575.6
Developed market economies	4,433	61.7	19,506	46.0	340.0
Oil exporting economies	541	7.5	5,746	13.6	962.1
Nonmarket industrial economies	231	3.2	3,472	8.2	1,403.0
Newly industrial economies	500	6.9	4,441	10.5	788.2
Total 1/	7,188	100.0	2/ 43,333	100.0	489.3

1/ Totals may not add due to rounding.
2/ Includes $976 million in transshipments not allocated to individual regions.

U.S. imports of agricultural commodities, by value, 1970-81

Year	Total $Mil.	Total Percent	Complementary $Mil.	Complementary Percent	Supplementary $Mil.	Supplementary Percent
1970	5,769.6	100.0	2,161.1	37.5	3,608.5	62.5
1971	5,823.4	100.0	2,135.8	36.7	3,687.6	63.3
1972	6,466.9	100.0	2,182.6	33.8	4,284.3	66.2
1973	8,419.1	100.0	2,867.4	34.1	5,551.7	65.9
1974	10,247.0	100.0	3,240.0	31.6	7,007.0	68.4
1975	9,292.9	100.0	3,095.5	33.3	6,197.4	66.7
1976	10,965.7	100.0	4,709.8	43.0	6,255.9	57.0
1977	13,438.1	100.0	6,782.0	50.5	6,656.1	49.5
1978	14,804.8	100.0	7,019.8	47.4	7,785.0	52.6
1979	16,724.1	100.0	7,247.9	43.3	9,476.2	56.7
1980	17,366.1	100.0	6,992.2	40.3	10,373.9	59.7
1981 1/	16,778.3	100.0	5,697.6	34.0	11,080.7	66.0

1/ Preliminary.

The most important *supplementary* commodity group imported by the United States in 1981 was sugar and related products at $2.1 billion. Most of the imported sugar was from Central and South American countries, especially Brazil, the Dominican Republic, Argentina, and Colombia. Other major suppliers of sugar included Australia — $331 million and up sharply from $146 million in 1980 — and the Philippines.

Meats and products is the second major supplementary agricultural commodity group imported by the United States. Imports were valued at $2.0 billion in 1981. Nearly 603,000 metric tons of beef and veal were imported, with Australia the major supplier followed by New Zealand and Canada. New Zealand was also the major supplier of lamb and Canada the major supplier of pork.

Vegetables and preparations ranked third in value of supplementary imports in 1981 at $1.1 billion. Mexico is the predominant supplier because of fresh vegetables. Taiwan is a major supplier because of canned mushrooms, while Spain ranks high due largely to our imports of olives. Canada and Japan are also substantial consistent year-to-year suppliers of vegetables and preparations to the U.S. market.

Oilseeds and products was the fourth major commodity group of imports in 1981. The Philippines, People's Republic of China (PRC), and Malaysia were the major suppliers of commodities in this grouping. Imports from the Philippines was largely coconut oil; from PRC, peanuts; and from Malaysia, palm oil. The large imports from PRC in 1981 ($153 million) was most unusual (only $131,000 in 1980) and was the result of

large peanut imports due to the disastrous U.S. peanut crop in 1980.

Imports of supplementary fruits and preparations amounted to $734 million in 1981. The origins of these imports are more widely dispersed than for many other commodities but three countries — Mexico, the Philippines, Brazil — accounted for nearly half of the total in 1980. Mexico is a major supplier of many fresh fruits, the Philippines of canned pineapples, and Brazil of concentrated orange juice.

Dairy products are also a major supplementary agricultural commodity imported into the United States: over 170,000 metric tons valued at $524 million in 1981. Countries in Western Europe — Denmark, France, Finland, Austria, Switzerland, Norway, Italy, the Netherlands, and West Germany — were major suppliers of cheeses to the United States. These nine countries together accounted for three-fourths of the U.S. import value of cheeses in both 1980 and 1981. New Zealand, Ireland, and Australia — in that order — were the leading suppliers of casein and mixtures to the United States in both 1980 and 1981.

Tobacco (unmanufactured) and tobacco leaf (oriental) are important commodities imported by the United States although we are a major producer and exporter of tobacco (primarily flue-cured). Imports of tobacco and tobacco leaf were valued at $354 million and $244 million, respectively, in 1981. Turkey supplied over one-third of the unmanufactured tobacco and over one-half of the oriental tobacco leaf. Additional major suppliers of both commodities were Greece, Yugoslavia, Bulgaria, Italy, and Lebanon. Other major supplementary agricultural commodities imported by the United States include wines, malt liquors, cattle, and wool.

Problems Ahead for Exports

U.S. agricultural exports have experienced a phenomenal growth over the past several decades and are expected to show further growth in the future. Imports of agricultural products into the United States will also continue to rise. Population growth and rising per capita incomes will continue to be the primary forces behind these developments. Several events have occurred, however, which will make it difficult to expand exports for several years. In 1982, our exports are expected to decline from 1981 in view of depressed world economic conditions and the increased strength of the U.S. dollar relative to most other currencies.

Many of the developed countries are experiencing high rates of unemployment, resulting in reduced income and purchasing power. In a number of developing countries, slower growth will be necessary because of balance of payments problems. Also, a stronger dollar makes our agricultural products more expensive to the importer since he must give up more of his currency to buy a given amount of our export commodity. On the other hand, a stronger dollar makes imports less expensive to us and offsets to some extent the effects of our economic slowdown on both the volume and value of agricultural imports.

Of course, the value of agricultural trade consists of two components: quantity and price. Even though the quantity traded may increase substantially, a sharp decline in unit prices due to large supplies

may result in a decline in total value. Prices fluctuate more widely than do quantities in international trade, although the long term trend has been for both to increase.

Traditionally, Japan, the European Community, and Canada have been the major markets for U.S. agricultural exports. These areas will remain significant U.S. markets although their share of total U.S. agricultural exports is expected to continue declining. The U.S.S.R., People's Republic of China, and Eastern Europe have been major markets for U.S. agricultural commodities but some uncertainty now is attached to them. Some of the newly industrialized countries — for example, Taiwan and South Korea — are expected to continue as growing outlets for U.S. agricultural products. The high income oil exporting countries of the Middle East have sharply expanded their imports of agricultural commodities, including products from the United States. This area particularly merits increased U.S. market development efforts.

Although the United States will continue as a major exporter of bulk commodities, there is growing interest in exporting a larger proportion of our agricultural commodities as high-valued or processed agricultural products. The result would be of benefit to domestic employment and increased Gross National Product (GNP). No major changes are foreseen in the near term in the source or composition of U.S. agricultural imports. Certainly some year-to-year changes will occur as a result of supply availabilities associated with weather or possibly political factors.

World Economic Shifts Affect Agriculture, All of Us

By Jim Longmire, Arthur Morey, and John Nuttall

The world economy is vastly changed from a decade ago. Major currencies are no longer bound to the U.S. dollar. Prices for oil and other goods are much higher, as are interest rates. Economic growth rates, on the other hand, are much lower, creating fewer employment possibilities and a larger unemployed pool. These shifts have changed the nature of agricultural trade and had a large impact on the farm economy.

International economic and financial conditions are important to U.S. agriculture. A third of U.S. farm products are exported. As a result, the well-being of many U.S. farmers depends on international and general economic conditions such as overseas growth, unemployment, interest rates, oil prices and the value of the dollar. This chapter takes a general look at the changes in the world economy during the past 10 years. It places agriculture into the big picture, and shows how changes in the world economy affect U.S. agriculture in particular.

The 1970's constitute a period of major change in international economic conditions. During the past decade, real GNP (Gross National Product) increased more slowly than in the 1960's. The industrialized countries grew at just over 3 percent per annum in the seventies, compared with almost 5 percent in the previous decade. Economic growth became more variable as well. The oil price shocks in 1973 and 1979 combined with belt-tightening policies to induce two sharp world recessions. Some major industrialized countries moved into reverse gear, both in 1974 and in the extended recession still underway in early 1982. This compares with the previous two decades, when negative growth rates rarely occurred.

Foremost among the difficulties for a number of economies in the 1970's was "stagflation." Stagflation occurs when economies experience high inflation combined with low growth. The average annual rate of inflation for the world during the 1960's was 4.4 percent. For the 1970's, world inflation averaged 11 percent, or two and a half times the rate in the previous decade.

One reason for the higher inflation was an increase in growth of the money supply in the world economy. The money supply is measured by the amount of

Jim Longmire and Arthur Morey are Economists, International Economics Division, Economic Research Service.

John Nuttall is Branch Chief, Trade and Economic Information Division, International Agricultural Statistics, Foreign Agricultural Service.

cash plus assets that are readily converted into cash. An increase in the money supply without a comparable increase in production creates a situation where too much cash chases too few goods—inflation. Growth in the money supply in a number of economies was much higher in the seventies than in the previous decade. Along with the general slowdown in economic activity in the 1970's, this encouraged a general surge in prices. The availability of cheap credit also led to a surge in spending.

Another reason for higher inflation in the seventies was the success of trade unions in negotiating large wage increases. The wage increases became part of the so-called wage-price spiral. As higher wages were passed on in higher prices, so did higher prices lead trade unions to demand additional wage increases.

The average rate of unemployment in most industrialized countries doubled or trebled in the seventies. Key factors leading to the higher unemployment were the slowdown in economic growth and the two recessions. Other contributing factors included: 1) Increased wages and employee fringe benefits. 2) Rapid growth of the labor force, resulting from those born in the postwar baby boom reaching adulthood, and increased participation by women in the work force. 3) Displacement of workers by machines and new forms of technology.

Attempts are being made to combat inflation and the slowdown in economic growth. Over the past two years a number of countries have limited the money supply's growth in an attempt to control inflation. This has been associated with much higher rates of interest, as the de-

mand for money has not moderated as much as the growth in the money supply.

Supply Side Policies

Besides attempts to keep a tighter rein on inflation, more efforts are being made to stimulate productivity and investment. In the United States, these are termed supply side policies. Only time will show whether this combination of policies can overcome the inflation and economic stagnation — stagflation — which characterized the 1970's as well as the early 1980's. Effects of stagflation on the industrialized economies spilled over to most, but not all, other countries. A number of newly emerging industrial economies, most notably those in East and Southeast Asia, displayed rapid growth in the seventies. Their growth rates have begun to slow, however, as a result of the recent worldwide recession.

For the oil exporting countries, the seventies were boom times. Many development projects were undertaken by the Middle East and other oil-rich nations. Many of these economies remain heavily dependent on oil, and as shown in the early 1980's, this dependence leaves them vulnerable to downturns in the energy market. Centrally planned economies grew less rapidly in the 1970's than in 1960's, and this slowdown became even more accentuated during the early 1980's. Causes of this poor productivity growth are related to a number of factors, including poor harvests, a lack of economic incentives, and slow technical progress.

The value of one currency relative to another is the exchange rate. Until 1971, most countries tied the value of their currencies to the U.S. dollar. Problems in the fixed system of international payments led, beginning in 1971, to a change in the way currencies were related to each other. Since 1971, certain currencies have been floated freely in international foreign exchange markets. Under a system of freely floating exchange rates, international currency adjustments occur frequently and more smoothly. In general, the system has moved the focus of general economic policies toward treating the causes (money supply growth, inflation) rather than the effects (devaluing currency, trade imbalances) of exchange rate movements.

The factors shifting exchange rates over time can be broken into three categories. First are short-term factors that those in financial circles watch particularly closely. These include interest rate differentials across economies. Even the minutest differential between rates can make it profitable for banks and international investors to move assets between countries and across currencies.

Second, exchange rate movements can be caused by differences in rates of inflation between economies. As a country's rate of inflation increases relative to rates in other countries, its currency likely will devalue. For example, between 1975 and 1980 the Argentine peso devalued by an average of 120 percent per year against the U.S. dollar. Over the same period, Argentine inflation averaged about 180 percent per year, compared to about 10 percent in the United States. Because there were many more Argentine pesos than U.S. dollars in international money markets at the end of this period than at the beginning, the peso lost value.

The third reason for exchange rate movements is changes in the structure and performance of economies. Such changes affect the export and import levels of economies, as well as the flows of funds for longer term investment. For example, discovery and sale of North Sea oil and gas boosted the British pound's value above what it might have been with no discoveries. Similarly, the strong export performance of U.S. agriculture in the 1970's kept the value of the dollar higher than it might otherwise have been.

When the U.S. dollar was floated in the early 1970's, it devalued against other currencies in general, falling by almost 10 percent between 1971 and 1973. Some pickup occurred through 1977, but a general depreciation of about 12 percent occurred in the next 2 years. Since 1980, the dollar has more than recovered its 12 percent loss.

The movement of the dollar against other currencies derives from a combination of factors, one of which is the relationship between interest rates and rates of inflation. Through the last half of the 1970's, inflation outstripped interest rates in the United States. This encouraged a movement of investment funds out of the United States and into other economies where the rates of interest relative to inflation were more attractive. With much higher rates of interest in the early 1980's, funds have moved back into the United States.

Dollar Gains — Over the past 2 years, the U.S. dollar made some striking gains against certain currencies. For example, against major European currencies the dollar appreciated by some 25 to 30 percent between spring 1981 and spring 1982. A number of smaller economies continue to peg the value of their currencies to the U.S. dollar or a basket of currencies. This is usually done to try to prevent speculative flows of money from influencing exchange and interest rates. The fact that a country ties its currency to the U.S. dollar does not imply that the competitive position of agriculture in this country does not change relative to the United States. Changing rates of inflation and productivity growth can alter both the competitive position and the exchange rate vis-a-vis the United States.

Centrally planned economies do not have market rates of exchange for their currencies. Their currencies are termed nonconvertible, in the sense that they are not freely traded in foreign exchange markets. They import and export using convertible currencies such as U.S. dollars, or through barter arrangements. The ability to generate foreign currency by exporting is vital to the socialist economies. These countries need the foreign currency generated by exports to import goods and services, including agricultural commodities.

Gold, Oil, and the Ruble

For the Soviet Union (U.S.S.R.) the prices of gold and oil, two of its major exports, provide some guide as to how its exchange rate might move against the dollar. Increasing gold and oil prices effectively cause a revaluation of the Soviet ruble. Note, however, that since the Soviet currency is not freely traded, any such revaluation would be implemented unilaterally by the U.S.S.R. The strength of gold and oil prices in the 1970's enabled the U.S.S.R. to expand its grain imports during this period. In the early 1980's, declining prices of gold and oil have meant that the Soviets have had to move a greater volume of exports

to obtain the foreign exchange necessary to maintain their high level of grain imports.

The hikes in oil prices in the 1970's led to massive shifts in international payments and finance. The oil price rises forced oil importers to sell goods and borrow cash equivalent in value to all U.S. exports, just to meet this increased import bill. The oil price increases impacted most heavily on resource poor, low-income developing economies. These countries face major difficulties in obtaining the foreign exchange necessary to service increased debt, to purchase food, and to finance development. The oil price rises exacerbated their difficulties considerably, both directly with their higher import bill and indirectly by reducing prospects for trade with other economies also slowed by the oil price rises.

Declining oil prices in the past 2 years have altered the impact of the earlier price hikes. The larger amount of funds transferred to oil producers has declined significantly. This has created difficulties for a number of oil exporters, especially those whose reliance on energy exports remain high. In the 1970's, the oil exporters used surplus funds from oil export earnings for two main purposes: domestic economic development and overseas investment. Overseas investment by the oil exporting countries is known as recycling Petro-Dollars. Only by recycling the oil revenues has the international financial system been able to withstand the massive transfers of funds involved.

The problem of indebtedness remains significant for a number of developing and centrally planned economies. It is estimated that between 1970 and 1980, the total outstanding debt of developing countries expanded more than sixfold to $440 billion. Although their debt did not grow as rapidly as their exports, their borrowing from private creditors increased substantially. In addition, high interest rates during the early 1980's have further increased the burden of indebtedness for these economies.

In the 1970's, foreign indebtedness of the centrally planned economies expanded rapidly, most notably in Eastern Europe. While the Soviet Union has been able to finance rapidly growing food imports through increased sales of oil and gold, other socialist economies have faced much tighter hard currency constraints. The extent of lending to these economies in the 1970's by Western economies, with hindsight, now appears somewhat generous.

The worldwide slowdown in economic growth and the heating up of inflation during the 1970's affected farmers in a number of ways. Slowing growth is generally accompanied by decreased or stagnant consumer spending. Low growth or reductions in incomes tend to dampen the demand for beef, pork, poultry, and other livestock products. The decreased demand for livestock and products, in turn, lowers the demand for corn, soybean products, and other feedstuffs that make up a large proportion of U.S. agricultural exports. Economic slowdown reduces demand for food generally — most noticeably in developing countries. Policymakers also tend to close off market access in periods of economic slowdown, as happened recently in Nigeria.

In industries that use a large amount of energy in production, higher oil prices can lead to higher costs and lower profits. Lower profits force some businesses to cut production or shut down entirely. This business slowdown and the corresponding increase in unemployment have tended to slow economic growth in virtually every oil importing country. Business slowdowns and rising numbers of people out of work can lead to recessions that reduce income and consumer purchasing power. This further dampens the demand for goods and services, including agricultural products.

Some relief came to many low-income countries that had trouble paying for higher priced oil. Because these countries needed foreign exchange to pay for oil and because their outlays for oil imports tended to constrain their ability to import other products, including food, international and governmental agencies increased financial and food aid. This aid allowed the countries to import more food products than they otherwise might have imported.

Inflation has also affected farmers in many ways. Inflation increases the costs of materials used in farming. When the demand for farm products is strong, as it was through much of the seventies, farm prices tend to be higher and farm profits may increase. When demand is weak, as for the last year, prices for farm products may fall below production costs and farmers may lose money.

Effects of High Interest Rates
Inflation also increased the value of farmland. This has increased the net wealth of agriculture significantly, but at the same time has made agriculture a costly business to enter. Low interest rates relative to inflation boosted farmland values

in the seventies, but the now higher interest rates are having the opposite effect.

At times, farmers are negatively affected when governments adopt and implement policies designed to drive down the inflation rate. As we have seen in the United States, as well as certain other countries, such policies initially tend to cause high interest rates and lower economic growth rates. The high interest rates can, in turn, further dampen economic growth and stifle investment. In addition to dampening economic growth rates, high interest rates can lower demand for agricultural products in other ways. For example, with commodities such as cotton and soybean products, inventories are usually kept on hand to meet a surge in demand. To do this, firms often borrow money. High interest rates raise the cost of the loans, causing firms to cut down on their inventories. That reduces demand for these products both in the United States and overseas, and in this manner directly affects U.S. exports.

High interest rates also raise purchasing costs for those who buy on credit. Many countries pay for commodities over a 6 to 8-month period. For countries whose economies are in poor condition, interest rates can be prohibitively high, forcing

them to import less than might otherwise be the case.

Exchange rate movements are important in determining U.S. farm prices and export volumes. Importers of farm products have to exchange foreign currencies or export goods and services to obtain the dollars and other currencies necessary to make their purchases. If the dollar strengthens, U.S. exports become more expensive to the importer. This tends to depress U.S. farm export volumes and prices. Lower export prices, in turn, translate into lower U.S. domestic farm prices.

Only under certain market conditions are exchange rate movements accompanied by a one-to-one movement in prices. Adjustments of supplies and purchases induced by an exchange rate movement also affect prices. An example best illustrates the importance of exchange rates. Between April 1981 and April 1982, soybean prices (landed Rotterdam) fell 16 percent. However, over the same period the Dutch guilder devalued by 15 percent against the U.S. dollar. To the Dutch processor, soybean prices remained approximately unchanged. To U.S. farmers there was a significant decline.

Exchange rates similarly affect the prices of farm inputs and consumer goods. When the dollar appreciates, petroleum, fertilizers, and other inputs become cheaper in terms of U.S. dollars than they otherwise would have been. The net effect of exchange rate movements on agriculture is difficult to measure. Nevertheless, without floating rates it is doubtful the world economy would have adjusted as rapidly as it did to the major shocks to trade and payments that occurred throughout the 1970's.

The general economic changes that occurred in the 1970's have had major implications for U.S. agriculture — not all good, not all bad. Economic pressures have tightened, but new opportunities have arisen. As economies deal with those problems which have carried through into the 1980's, some major adjustments in the world and the U.S. economy will occur. Agriculture will have to continue to meet the challenge of these changes.

Inflation not only increases the cost of materials used in farming, it also increases the value of farmland, making agriculture a costly business to enter.

Tim McCabe

Tariffs, Embargoes, Other Trade Barriers

By G. Edward Schuh and Philip L. Paarlberg

World agriculture has been characterized as in disarray because of policies established by national governments. This chapter briefly examines the nature of trade policies in agricultural markets to determine their impact upon U.S. farm programs and the U.S. farmer. Purpose of these trade policies usually is to keep market forces from coming into play so as to determine where production will take place. Consequences of such interventions are that much of the world's agricultural output is produced inefficiently, and consumers have to pay more for food and other agricultural products they buy.

Why do countries trade to begin with? Presumably because they are better off with trade than without it. This means their national income is higher with trade. For trade to take place, some countries must be able to produce certain commodities at a lower relative cost than other countries. In turn, this implies that other commodities can be produced relatively cheaper elsewhere. If there are such gains from trade, why do individual countries want to intervene in trade rather than to become more specialized in producing what they do best? The reason is that while trade may benefit the nation as a whole, or particular groups within society, some groups may be harmed. In addition, policymakers may be able to benefit certain groups in society by trade interventions, even though the country as a whole may be worse off.

An important aspect of trade is that it is a two-way street. For a country to be able to export its goods and services and thereby gain from trade, it has to be willing to accept imports from other countries. Other countries must be able to sell their own products in order to have the income to purchase products from the exporting country. Current attempts to liberalize trade result from the experience with protectionism during the Great Depression. The depression prompted producer groups in many countries to ask governments to impose import tariffs to protect their dwindling domestic markets. Tariff protection curtailed world trade, which reduced the gains from trade and worsened the depression as workers in trade-oriented sectors were laid off.

Role of G.A.T.T. — Following World War II, the experience with tariffs in the 1930's prompted creation of an international organization concerned with promoting freer trade, the General Agreement on Tariffs and Trade (G.A.T.T.). G.A.T.T. has developed procedures to

G. Edward Schuh is Professor and Head, Department of Agricultural and Applied Economics, University of Minnesota, St. Paul.

Philip L. Paarlberg is an Agricultural Economist with the Economic Research Service, USDA, at Purdue University, West Lafayette, IN.

reduce tariffs and provide for settling trade disputes. It also has conducted a series of multilateral trade negotiations designed to systematically lower trade barriers. Unfortunately, agriculture has not received a great deal of attention in the negotiations. This in part is because most of the industrialized countries of the West, including the United States, have trade barriers designed to protect domestic commodity programs.

The latest round of multilateral trade negotiations was completed in 1979. Agriculture received more attention in this round, with the result that tariff reductions on a number of agricultural commodities now are being implemented. The new agreement also provides rules on the use of countervailing duties, an important means by which countries retaliate against each other for trade interventions. Export subsidies on agricultural products are permitted if the subsidies do not displace other nations' exports, or involve "material injury" in a particular market. After determining injury to an industry, a country may impose a countervailing duty on the subsidized export.

The latest round of multilateral trade negotiations reduced tariff barriers in agricultural markets. However, the pragmatism of trade negotiations within the G.A.T.T. framework has resulted in only limited gains in reducing nontariff barriers

Trade is a two-way street. To be able to export its goods and services, a country must accept imports from other countries. Here, dates from the Persian Gulf are being unloaded in Savannah, Ga.

Jim Strawser

and export subsidies. Thus, agricultural markets remain highly protectionist despite existence of G.A.T.T.

Variable Levy on Imports

For grains and livestock products, European countries — including the European Community (E.C.) — generally rely on an import barrier known as a variable levy to protect their domestic price support programs from imports. A variable levy is a tariff which adjusts daily to maintain a constant import price. For commodities subject to this form of protection, the European Commission each year establishes a minimum import price for each commodity — the threshold price. The daily difference between the threshold price and the world market price is the levy.

The variable levy has important consequences for U.S. farmers. For example, it keeps agricultural prices within the community considerably above world market levels. Hence, production by E.C. farmers is stimulated and consumption is dampened. The net effect is to reduce E.C. imports of the commodities subject to the levy, grains and livestock products, and to lower the price received by farmers in exporting countries. Thus, U.S. farm prices and production of grains and livestock products are lower because of E.C. policies. In the markets for grains, where the United States operates its own price support programs, U.S. treasury outlays are larger because of the variable levy. On the other hand, since the E.C. does not subject some products — such as soybeans and meal, manioc, corn gluten feed, and citrus pulp — to such levies, imports of these grain substitutes have expanded to meet the needs of artificially stimulated E.C. livestock production.

The variable import levy system also affects the variability in U.S. prices. Since the levy adjusts daily to changing market conditions, domestic prices in the E.C. are completely insulated from the effects of world markets. Consequently, E.C. producers and consumers do not adjust to world market price signals. This forces additional price adjustment onto other nations, such as the United States, which do not insulate their domestic markets.

Many nations continue to use import tariffs and taxes to protect their domestic agriculture from world market competition. Japan, the United States, and the European Community, for example, impose import tariffs on various types of vegetable oils. Several developing countries which are currently major markets for U.S. exports impose import tariffs. They include Mexico and Taiwan. Effects of these trade restrictions are somewhat like those of variable levies. World trade of the protected commodity is reduced, as are prices for farmers in the exporting nation.

Past rounds of multilateral trade negotiations have been successful in reducing tariff barriers. Consequently, such barriers are now less severe than in the past. In 1961, the European Community agreed to free entry of oilseeds and oilseed meals. Recently, Japan agreed to duty-free imports of soybeans, while Taiwan conceded to fix maximum duties on soybeans, corn and cotton. Other nations agreed to reduce tariff barriers on livestock, livestock products, tobacco, fruits, vegetables, oilseed products, feed grains and rice. The United States agreed to gradually reduce its import duty on palm oil.

Although tariff barriers have been reduced, nontariff barriers continue as obstacles to agricultural trade. Nontariff barriers include import quotas, import licensing, government purchasing agencies (state trading), health sanitary regulations, and other import regulations. Virtually every country has one or more of such barriers. Japan has quantitative restrictions on dairy products, livestock and meats, fruits and vegetables, and vegetable oils. Korea employs a combination quota-tariff to protect its farmers.

Restrictions by U.S. The United States also relies heavily upon quantitative import restrictions. Section 22 of the Agricultural Adjustment Act of 1933 restricts imports through duties or quotas when imports interfere with the Commodity Credit Corporation price support operations. Four groups of commodities currently are subject to import restrictions under Section 22: cotton and products, wheat and products, dairy products, and peanuts. Although not covered under Section 22 authority, meat imports into the United States are subject to quota restrictions under 1964 legislation.

One of the most common forms of nontariff trade barriers currently in use is state trading. This involves the import and export of commodities by government agencies, such as marketing boards. Typically, such agencies are granted monopoly positions in markets, with the result that they can control markets. Eastern European nations, the People's Republic of China, and the Soviet Union (U.S.S.R.) rely exclusively upon state trading. It also is used frequently by developing countries — India, Brazil, Chile, Mexico, and most African nations. Japan's Food Agency controls wheat import licenses and can also be considered a state trading agency.

State trading in wheat is so frequent that it is said the bulk of world trade has a state trader on at least one side of the transaction. State trading results in different degrees of restriction of trade, depending upon the price and import decision of the agency. Finally, state trading agencies which are large buyers, such as the Soviet Union or Japan, can potentially use their large volume to gain favorable purchase terms.

Barriers in Export Markets
Exporting nations also intervene frequently in world trade, usually to promote exports, but occasionally to limit trade and channel production to domestic markets. Trade barriers adopted by exporting countries generally can be classified as export subsidies, export taxes, state trading, and export embargoes. Here we will discuss all but the last trade barrier, export embargoes, which are considered a bit later on.

Export subsidies and export taxes are in principle the same type of barrier with opposite effects. The purpose of an export subsidy is to lower the price of the commodity to the purchaser, thereby encouraging larger exports and often gaining access to new markets or markets of competitors. Export subsidies are usually adopted in one of three situations. An important circumstance is when domestic supplies are excessive. Current examples include Japanese rice exports and E.C. wheat exports. As a result of high domestic support prices, both entities have excess stocks which they are trying to reduce by subsidizing exports. From the middle 1950's until 1973, the United States subsidized wheat exports for similar reasons.

The second situation is when a nation attempts to gain access to new markets, usually by undercutting traditional suppliers. E.C. export subsidies on wheat and Brazilian pricing of soybean meal in Europe can be viewed in this context. The policy is usually short term for it tends to create the third situation, that of retaliatory export subsidies. In contrast to export subsidies, *export taxes* are often designed to restrict exports and increase world prices. For agricultural commodities whose demand is largely insensitive to price, the result can be to increase foreign exchange earnings and hence improve the exporting country's balance of payments. Brazil, for example, once used export taxes to cause the prices of coffee to be higher for importing nations. Export taxes also can be used to keep domestic prices lower than world prices. Such trade diversion benefits domestic consumers and producers in other countries. It harms domestic producers. Many less developed countries use such policies as a means of having cheap food policies.

Just as many importing nations rely on state trading, so do many exporters. Grains exported by Canada, Australia, and South Africa are under the control of marketing boards. Centralized selling agencies give these countries market power when dealing with state importing agencies. Further, some importers — notably Mexico — prefer to deal with governmental or quasi-governmental agencies rather than with private trading firms. The degree to which export marketing boards interfere with trade varies greatly, depending upon the board involved.

Export Embargoes

A trade barrier which recently has re-

ceived considerable publicity is the export embargo. An export embargo is the prohibition of export sales generally or to a particular nation. Imposition of a total embargo means the importing nations face reduced supplies, hence the world market price rises. Meanwhile, the embargo causes excess supplies in the exporting country and prices fall. Embargoes directed towards a specific country tend to be ineffective since world trade flows adjust to circumvent the policy.

The U.S. Government has imposed four embargoes — either total or partial — since 1973. This experience with export embargoes tends to confirm what has just been said. In 1973, for example, the United States imposed the only total embargo on exports of an agricultural commodity in its recent history by embargoing the export of high protein feedstuffs. This embargo resulted from several developments in U.S. and world agriculture which caused soybean and product prices to rise rapidly. As interim measures, the U.S. Department of Agriculture (USDA) adopted several policy changes, including relaxation of set-aside restrictions and suspension of concessionary export sales of vegetable oils. Despite these policies, the combination of strong domestic and international demand continued to push prices upward at a rapid rate.

On June 27, 1973, the U.S. Department of Commerce released data showing surprisingly heavy exports. On that same day, the Commerce Department imposed a general export embargo on soybeans, cottonseed, and their products. On July 2, the embargo was replaced with a system of validated export licenses. Ultimately, 41 agricultural commodities related to the oilseed complex were placed under export control. The licensing system remained in effect until August 1, when the Commerce Department announced that licenses for shipment during September would be issued for the unfilled balance of orders prior to June 13, 1973.

Immediate impact of the export controls on U.S. and world market prices was dramatic. Soybean prices in Chicago were nearly halved, while world market prices for soybean meal rose 25 percent in a single day. The high world prices enabled Brazil to increase its exports to fill the void left by the United States. The embargo created concerns among importers about reliability of the United States as a supplier of protein feedstuffs. Japan, the E.C., Eastern Europe, and the Soviet Union continued to buy large quantities in successive years, but did purchase more frequently from other countries.

Anti-Soviet — The other export embargoes imposed by the U.S. Government were partial embargoes directed at the Soviet Union. The first was a suspension of grain sales to the Soviets in the fall of 1974. Due to poor crops in the United States, Canada, Australia, Argentina, India, and especially in the Soviet Union, by the summer of 1974 world grain supplies were extremely tight, and prices were rising rapidly. The response of USDA was to institute a sales reporting system in September 1974. With prices continuing to rise, on Oct. 4 it was announced that sales of corn and wheat to the Soviet Union were suspended until discussion between the two countries could be held. An agreement was finally reached which limited Soviet purchases.

Following the sales suspension the price of wheat in Kansas City fell. In Rotterdam, price effects of the U.S. embargo were insignificant as trade patterns adjusted. As 1974-75 progressed, the supply situation eased. In March 1975 the purchase limit on wheat was eliminated and the limit on corn was increased. However, the Soviets did not purchase any U.S. grain in excess of the October limits.

The second partial embargo occurred the following fall. The 1975 Soviet grain crop was 75 million tons below the planned level. In the second half of July, the Soviet Union bought 9.8 million tons of U.S. grain. With these purchases, U.S. grain prices began to rise sharply in speculation. In late July, USDA requested notification by exporters prior to sales to the Soviet Union. This failed to stop the runup in prices, so on Aug. 11 grain companies were asked to withhold future sales to the Soviets until U.S. crop prospects were more certain. With prices continuing to rise, Poland was included in the sales moratorium on Sept. 7. Two days later, the President proposed a U.S.-U.S.S.R. grains agreement. With conclusion of this agreement on Oct. 20, 1975 the moratorium on future sales to the U.S.S.R. and Poland was ended.

As a result of these interventions, Congress included a provision in 1977 farm legislation to reduce the possibility of future embargoes. This legislation requires that if commodities are embargoed due to short supplies, loan rates on the affected commodities are to increase to 90 percent of parity.

The third partial export embargo occurred in response to the Soviet invasion of Afghanistan. The President suspended all grain shipments to the Soviet Union in excess of the quantities obligated under the 1975 U.S.-U.S.S.R. grains agreement, cancelling 17 million tons of grain sales. This action occurred under authority of the Export Administration Act of 1977. Since the embargo was not a consequence of short supplies, the provision of the 1977 farm legislation did not apply.

USDA adopted policies designed to offset the decline in U.S. grain prices and to protect exporting firms which would have defaulted on contracts. These included direct U.S. Government purchases, placements in the Farmer-Owned Reserve, and assumption of contracts by USDA. Further, to prevent world trade patterns from shifting to offset the embargo's effects on the U.S.S.R., the United States sought cooperation of the major exporting countries. Canada, Australia, and the European Community agreed to support the United States. Argentina and Brazil did not. The embargo was ended by the Reagan Administration in 1981.

U.S. Taxpayers Suffer

Despite the agreements obtained from other major exporting countries, leakage occurred and the Soviets obtained most of the grain they needed. Successive crop failures did cause the Soviets continued supply problems. Although U.S. grain prices fell in the short run, Government purchases and additional U.S. sales to other markets helped return prices to pre-embargo levels by summer. U.S. taxpayers suffered as a result of the embargo as the Government purchased much of the embargoed grain. It appears that after three embargoes

directed at the Soviet Union, U.S.-Soviet grain trade has suffered. Following removal of the embargo the Soviets have shown restraint in buying large quantities of grain from the United States. Further, the Soviets signed a grain supply agreement with Argentina.

From the discussion of trade barriers and embargoes presented in this chapter, several general conclusions can be made. First, there is a wide variety of agricultural trade barriers, which suggests that agricultural trade occurs in a rather protectionist environment. As a result, trade in agricultural products is lower than what would occur with free trade. Farmers in exporting countries receive lower prices for their products, and farm programs are more costly. Although international organizations designed to liberalize trade policies — such as G.A.T.T. — have made progress in reducing tariffs, nontariff barriers which have remained extensive and other trade barriers have caused price fluctuations in world markets to be greater than they otherwise would be.

Total export embargoes, such as imposed by the United States against high protein feedstuffs, result in lower domestic prices to farmers and impose costs on overseas customers. Embargoes also serve to undercut importing nations' confidence in the exporter as a reliable supplier, thereby encouraging import diversification and domestic self-sufficiency programs. Partial export embargoes against a particular country have proved ineffective because patterns of world trade adjust to circumvent the embargo. Even with agreements among major exporting countries to honor the embargo, leakage is sufficient to erode most of the consequences.

Tracing Your Food Dollar Back to the Farm

By Harry H. Harp and John M. Connor

arl hesitated. The supermarket's special display of a new line of frozen entrees had caught his eye. The packages looked vaguely familiar. Picking one up, Earl noticed it was made by a reliable company. Even more interesting was the message telling him that the container could be popped into their new microwave oven. The price was a dime more than the brand his wife usually bought, he thought. But what the heck, the check he had just picked up for milk he sold through his farmer co-op was the biggest he'd seen. Remembering a nice night they had had in a restaurant in the city, Earl tossed the chicken teriyaki dinner into his shopping cart.

Earl's decision started a chain of events that eventually influenced what Earl's fellow farmers' income would be next year. This process is what economists call derived demand. The chain is a complex one, often consisting of a dozen links. Since the end of World War II, these linkages — the food marketing system — for various farm products have been broken and reforged in new forms. New information techniques now provide for quick signaling of changes in consumer preferences and supply conditions. Many of the new information systems have replaced or supplemented the major market

signals of old: prices on cash commodity markets.

As a result, the roles and functions of various market participants — farmers, processors, wholesalers, retailers, and consumers — have altered. Control over what to produce and when has shifted back and forth along the chain, as has the party bearing the risk of price changes. Finally, the postwar changes in food marketing have put in place a new, more industrialized structure of markets that is likely to persist to the year 2000.

The demand for farm commodities is a derived demand. That is, consumer purchases cause retailers to buy from wholesalers, wholesalers from manufacturers, and so on until the demand reaches the farm gate. Money and information moves backward through the food system as products move forward. As the products move forward, they change form and place; at each stage the food marketers add margins.

Vertical Integration

Over the last couple of decades, there has been more vertical integration in the food system. In other words, farm products undergo fewer changes in ownership as they move through the system. The

Harry H. Harp is acting head of the Food Price Analysis Section in the Economic Research Service (ERS).

John M. Connor is head of the Food Manufacturing Research Section, ERS.

same company performs marketing functions that used to be performed by several companies. Also, the system doesn't depend on price signals now as much as before. What to produce and when is being signalled more by new information systems. The systems coordinate product movements both within firms and between firms that buy and sell from one another. These information systems have arisen from changes in communications technology and the ability to store and retrieve large amounts of information with computers.

What Happened to $100 of Consumer Food Spending

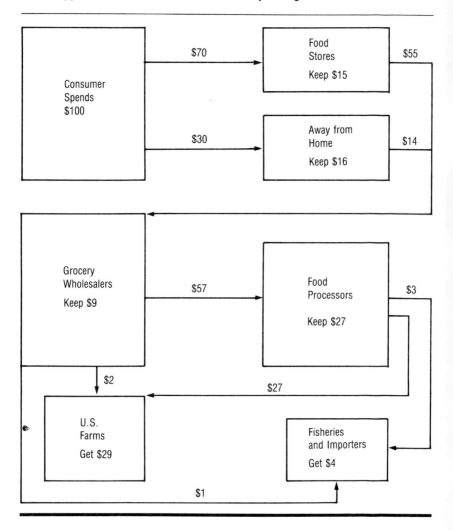

One effect of the shifts from cash-market pricing to other information systems has been that processed foods move through the marketing system faster and with less labor than a few decades ago. Because more coordination is done by private firms, it has become harder to get public information on food marketing practices.

The domestic marketing system is the largest purchaser of U.S. farm products. About four-fifths of marketed farm output is sold for consumption in the United States, of which 80 percent is used for processed foods and beverages and 10 percent (mostly produce) is unprocessed. The remainder is tobacco, fibers, and other nonfood products. Americans obtain four-fifths of their food from food stores. So the main channel of food delivery is from farms to processors to wholesalers to food stores.

Farmers are both producers and customers for products of the system. The farmer supplies crop and livestock products for conversion into the kinds of products desired by consumers. Farmers are partners with the marketing system in that they must work in tandem with the other parts of the system to produce the quality of food and fiber products needed. Together with other marketing firms, farmers must promote food in such a way as to earn consumers' favor and stimulate them to spend an appropriate share of their dollars for food.

From an economic standpoint, we depend on the system to operate a pricing mechanism that coordinates supply and demand, and transfers ownership and risk from agent to agent. Ideally, market prices signal the right production decisions needed to meet consumer demand. In practice, surpluses or shortages often develop for some commodities, causing prices to fluctuate widely. So the system carries inventories to moderate these swings. The value added in marketing is the main determinant of marketing margins of companies and the prices consumers are charged.

The organization of processing and distribution activities influences pricemaking, product allocation, and overall performance. At the same time, these factors can influence how many firms can coexist in the system. There are many channels to market, but most food flows through about 250,000 retail food stores or 275,000 eating places plus thousands of schools, hospitals, and other institutions. Over 600,000 establishments are involved in food marketing. Firms marketing cotton, tobacco, and other fiber products represent a significant addition to the number of firms in the food system.

Number of Food Firms Drops

The food system has undergone significant changes since World War II. The number of food companies has declined from about 725,000 in 1947 to about 540,000 today. The decrease has come about because of drastic declines in the numbers of food manufacturers (54 percent) and retailers (49 percent), even though the number of wholesalers and eating places has gone up in the last 30 years. This overall decline in food firms occurred at a time when the U.S. economy expanded greatly and company numbers along with it. So in relative terms the declines in the food system are even greater. In 1947 one manufacturer in five made foods, but now it's more like one in 15. Similarly, 30 percent of all retailers sold food 30 years ago,

Employment trends in the food system, 1950-1980

Sector	Year			
	1950	**1960**	**1970**	**1980**
	1/ Thousands			
Agriculture	7,160	5,458	3,463	3,364
Food and Tobacco Manufacturing	1,893	1,884	1,866	1,780
Wholesale Grocery	2/ 206	494	550	674
Retail Food and Grocery	2/ 1,478	1,356	1,731	2,386
Eating and Drinking Places	2/ 1,228	1,654	2,488	4,666
Total Food System	11,965	10,846	10,098	12,780
Total Civilian Employment	58,918	65,778	78,678	99,303

1/ Average annual full-time equivalent persons.
2/ 1948-54 average.

Source: U.S. Bureau of the Census.

but now only 13 percent do. Food whole-salers and food service companies have held their own.

Another way of looking at changes in the food system is with employment levels. Since 1950 the number of farmers has been cut in half. Food manufacturing workers remained about constant, but all other food marketing workers increased, especially food service workers. In 1950 one worker in five helped make or deliver food, but now only one in eight is needed.

Retailing. — Supermarkets (store annual sales of $1 million and up) now dominate retailer food sales. Most supermarkets are owned by chains (11 stores or more). Chains accounted for 34 percent of U.S. grocery sales in 1948 but about 60 percent today. Both store size and the number of stores per company have risen dramatically on average the last few decades. The appearance of "convenience store" chains has kept average

store size from growing faster than it did.

Food stores are the points at which consumers register their preferences most directly. Smaller food stores offer only one or two well-known national brands, but chain supermarkets often emphasize private brands, product differentiation, lots of store services, and new product introductions. In the realm of supply procurement, big chains often deal directly with producers to get much of their fruit, vegetables, and other nonprocessed food product supplies. Many large supermarket chains operate their own bakeries and fluid milk packaging and ice cream plants. Others contract with processors to supply private label milk, canned goods, and additional groceries.

Most large chains operate their own warehouses and have integrated wholesaling and retailing functions. Many independent retailers have associated themselves with wholesale suppliers to take advantage of large-scale buying of foods and advertising services and to get good advice on retail merchandising. The placement and design of the special in-store display that caught Earl's eye was very carefully thought out for maximum sales effect.

Within the last few years, supermarket operators have experimented with stores offering limited assortments, less service, and lower prices. They have attempted to reduce costs by further automating warehousing, delivery, inventory control, and checkout operations. At the same time, retailers have instituted unit pricing or open dating of products to meet consumer demand for freshness and for information for price comparisons.

Affluent Consumers

One of the most significant factors affecting food retailing has been the rapid growth of consumer income. The affluent consumer buys a wide variety of foods, many of which are highly processed, heavily packaged, more convenient, or simply "new and exciting." Earl's working wife, small family, and busy schedule are typical of the changing profile of the American consumer. Earl's willingness to try a new ethnic dish that could be used in their new microwave oven has encouraged food companies to try to exploit trends or "fads" in food tastes by offering thousands of new food items each year. Americans eat and drink 1,500 pounds per person today, the same as they did 50 years ago. But they pay an additional 1 to 2 percent per person in real dollars each year for the added value in their foods.

The away-from-home market is the most rapidly growing segment of the farm product marketing system. Consumers spent 23 percent of their after tax income on food after World War II, but that is down to 16 percent today. However, the decline has come completely at the expense of food bought to be used at home. Americans spend the same proportion of their disposable income on eating out (4 percent) today as they did 30 years ago. But today it represents a quarter or more of all food expenditures — a big increase. In terms of the quantity of food eaten, however, it accounts for about one-fifth.

The most dramatic increases have been in the so-called "fast food" establishments, such as hamburger stands, pizza parlors, fried chicken establishments, and fish places. These are being developed partly as fully owned chain outlets but much more important as franchised outlets. The emphasis in eating establishments has been strongly on reducing labor inputs. In fast food establishments, kitchen labor is greatly reduced by streamlined equipment and labor out front by self-service.

All of these changes are having a marked impact on the suppliers to the away-from-home market. The emphasis on getting labor out of the restaurant or institutional kitchens has created a strong demand for fabricators, a new type of food supplier. Fabricators are supplying increasing quantities of food in prepared and semiprepared forms, which will permit food service establishments to provide food with a minimum of labor.

Meats are being cut, wrapped, and boxed at the packing plant and delivered to the restaurant kitchen ready to go into the oven or on the stove. The restaurant operator can buy steaks, roasts, or hamburger as needed. Fabricators are going into business preparing main courses or complete meals in a fashion analogous to the TV dinners available in supermarkets. Many changes first made for food service establishments eventually get offered as new labor-saving, grocery items for use at home.

Role of Wholesalers

Wholesalers play an important role in buying, selling, storing, and transporting food and fiber. Major improvements in space arrangements and materials handling equipment in recent years have stimulated the building of new, larger, and more efficient establishments. Also, improvements in motortrucks and highways extended distribution areas served by many firms, enabling them to utilize larger facilities. Even though food retailers have integrated extensively into wholesaling, the number of wholesale companies has stayed about the same partly because of the booming food service sector.

Wholesalers transmit retail-level demand for food into production signals for processors. Earl's purchase of a frozen entree was recorded electronically at the store. His and other purchases resulted in the store reordering the item 1 week later.

Within 3 months a marketing data company had sold this information to the manufacturer. The manufacturer's brand manager then knew almost exactly how many cases of his brand were sold in about 40 cities around the country. More importantly, the manager found out how much of the other brand was sold, and at what price. This information was used to change production levels, reset prices, decide on more discounts in certain

cities, or revise the amount of local or national advertising for the product. If sales did especially well, the manufacturer might consider adding a new flavor combination to the line. If sales slipped, the manufacturer might change the formulation or packaging to stimulate sales. As a last resort, a price reduction might be considered. Years ago these decisions took manufacturers years to complete, not a few months.

Food Processors

Nearly all food and fiber products are processed in some way after they leave the farm. Processing generally involves altering the form and composition of raw farm products in some way. Processing companies have been integrating into a wide range of activities, including farming, food distribution and input supplying. In the dairy industry, for instance, some fluid milk processors have moved into operating retail dairy or convenience food stores in order to retain a place in the market. Similarly, ice cream manufacturers have established their own outlets — through soft-serve ice cream stands and ice cream that emphasize a quality product — at relatively high prices.

Contracts. Integration of farm and processing activities through common ownership has been small in total. Processors' contracts with farmers are a much more prevalent way of coordinating production and marketing. Almost a tenth of the output of crops and a third of livestock production are sold under contract to processors. Nearly all fluid grade milk is sold under contract between producers and cooperatives of proprietary handlers. Most broilers and about two-fifths of the turkeys are produced under contract with processors and firms with interests in the food industry. Virtually all the production of sugarcane and sugar beets and about three-fourths of vegetable processing also are controlled primarily by processing firms through production contracts.

Many firms have sought to broaden their product lines. Fluid milk processors, for instance, have added new dairy products and fruit juices and drinks. Major dairy companies have diversified into other food product lines, such as ready-to-eat cereals, pet foods, poultry and eggs, bakery products and synthetic dairy products. Some companies have diversified to nonfood product lines. Product diversification decreases a firm's dependence on a particular commodity and thus may put it in a stronger bargaining position relative to producers.

Some food processing companies are integrating all the way forward into food service and restaurant businesses, particularly the preparation of nearly ready-to-serve foods for the food service markets as well as retail food stores. Functions of these firms may include primary processing of products, such as fruits and vegetables near where the crops are produced, as well as further processing and preparation of meals in central commissaries for the institutional market.

Food processing companies are responsible for most of the $10 to $15 billion spent on advertising and sales promotion of foods. Though retailers and farm groups sometimes promote commodities or unbranded foods, 90 percent or more is for branded foods and beverages. Food manufacturers are also primarily responsible for developing new or improved food products. One reason food marketing firms make such an effort in this direction is that consumers have more "discretionary income." Foods today are viewed more like luxuries than necessities; there is more impulse buying in groceries. Highly processed foods usually have many ingredients, making comparisons about quality and price even more difficult for consumers.

Advertising and promotion play an important role in developing farm products, though it should be recognized that they represent only one element in the total production-marketing mix. To be effective they must be coordinated with relevant production and marketing functions. For example, advertising and promotion probably won't be effective if the product is not acceptable to consumers, if the price is beyond reason, if the product is not readily available to consumers, or if the product is not merchandised correctly. Today packaging plays a vital role in selling farm products through the modern supermarket. The color and illustrations on packages attract consumer attention and encourage purchases. Packaging also serves to inform the consumer and preserve shelf life.

Synthetics, Other Substitutes
Aside from the benefits derived from new products by consumers, new products are vitally important to farmers in maintaining their markets in the face of increasing competition from nonagricultural products.

In the United States, as well as in other countries, many agricultural products have lost substantial market shares because of the development of substitutes and synthetics. For example, new high fructose corn sirup provides a substitute for cane and beet sugar in soft drinks, canned fruits, and bakery products. Corn sweeteners together with synthetic sweeteners account for about 40 percent of all sweeteners.

On the horizon are soybean products such as tofu and imitation meat or meat extenders which may take over some of the market for meat. Processors are always searching for ways of substituting for or stretching more expensive ingredients in food products that are acceptable to consumers. Earl's "chicken teriyaki" may have been only 10 percent chicken and the rest grains and vegetables.

Consumers register their food preferences in grocery stores and restaurants. These spending patterns are transmitted back through several stages of the food system to the farm. Farm groups, retailers, and especially manufacturers try to influence consumers to spend more on their products. These efforts do slowly change the kinds of farm products produced, but rises in the total quantity of farm food products are due mainly to population increases and larger overseas shipments. The U.S. population goes up only 1 percent per year or less.

If per person real expenditures on food rise, it is mainly due to a willingness of consumers to pay more for perceived quality increases. A sizable share of present food and fiber purchases is already in the discretionary category, and in the years ahead this will be even more so. Future sales must be obtained in direct competition with television sets, automobiles, household equipment, utilities, travel, interest on debts, and thousands of goods and services which are shouting louder and longer for a greater share of the consumer's dollar.

Farmers and marketers can keep sales for their products growing by supplying consumers with what they want at reasonable prices and stimulating those wants. This means creating acceptable new products and improving old ones in terms of quality, nutrition, variety, uniformity, and "built-in maid service." It means development of more efficient processing and marketing methods by manufacturers. It means shifting farm production to products for which there is a growing market. One opportunity will be to step up cooperation between farmers and marketers in educational and promotional efforts to reach those groups in the domestic and world population whose diets are below good nutritional standards.

Public food programs expand U.S. markets for farm products. A series of programs are carried out to raise food consumption levels among underconsuming groups: low-income families; inmates of institutions; and children in schools, summer camps, and child care centers. These programs create a substantial market for food in commercial channels of trade and furnish a constructive outlet for foods in large supply. Perhaps the most lasting benefit is the formation of good food habits acquired by children eating well-balanced nutritious lunches. Under this program many children are exposed to foods such as apricots, pineapple, honey, sweetpotatoes, and ethnic foods containing beef or turkey for the first time.

Section II.
Farm Marketing in a New Environment

William E. Carnahan

The $200 Billion Job of Marketing Our Food

By Alden C. Manchester

*W*heat in an elevator in Kansas is of no use to the housewife in Atlanta who wants to make rolls for dinner. Cattle in a Texas feedlot are not steaks in New York. Potatoes in a field in Idaho are not french fries on the table at McDonald's in Los Angeles. The goods that farmers grow and sell must be stored, transported, processed, and delivered — and in the form consumers want, when they want them, and to the places where consumers are.

Farmers in an earlier day often sold directly to customers. Some still do. But specialization is the general rule today. Each function between the time the farmer first offers products for sale and the final purchase is performed by firms or persons who have a particular advantage or skill. Specialization — the division of labor — creates a series of activities in the market process. As the process becomes increasingly complex, as more and more steps come between the farmer and the buyer, agencies or individuals appear whose only business is to facilitate exchange of ownership: commodity exchanges, brokers, commission houses, auction companies.

Even though soil and climate in places in Louisiana and a few other States are most favorable for growing early strawberries, no farmer there could afford to produce on a commercial scale if the farmer had to carry the strawberries to Pittsburgh and peddle them from house to house. Adapting farm production to the various possibilities of soil and weather over our vast country depends chiefly on adequate transportation and on handling and sales agencies that do the job at reasonable cost.

Or if early strawberries are too narrow an example, consider any of the major commodities — oranges, which need the climate of the South; the great corn and livestock business built upon the rich soils and temperate climate of the Corn Belt; or the volume, methods, and location of wheat production in the Great Plains. Existence of such types of agriculture, organization of the farms within the areas, and year-to-year changes in farmers' decisions as to what to do rest on a highly geared marketing system made up of thousands of separate activities, each essentially independent but together one closely knit, flexible system.

Elevators, packing sheds, canneries, tobacco warehouses, cotton gins, local buyers, assemblers, auction markets; trucklines, railroads, and airfreight companies; commission houses, brokers, organized exchanges, credit institutions; packing plants, flour and textile mills, cigarette factories; wholesalers, jobbers,

Alden C. Manchester is Senior Economist in the National Economics Division, Economic Research Service.

exporters, converters, factory sales representatives; supermarkets, convenience stores, fast food outlets, drugstores, restaurants — those are the kinds of activities that move farm products to consumers over the United States and the rest of the world.

Most of our food comes from U.S. farms; 89 percent of the value and 94 percent of the quantity. Since fish and imported foods bring higher prices per pound than the average of our farm foods, they account for 16 percent of the value of food consumed but only 7 percent of the quantity. Home food production, both farm and nonfarm, accounts for about 3 percent. A significant portion of the U.S. food supply goes abroad: 25 percent as much as is consumed at

home. Less than 1 percent goes to nonfood uses. (These figures include only the food use of feedgrains such as corn and oats. Most of those grains are used as animal feed, including substantial quantities exported.)

About 72 percent of U.S. food is consumed at home, although away-from-home eating takes 38 percent of the food dollar since restaurant prices are considerably higher than grocery store prices to cover the cost of the additional services. Most food for use at home comes from the supermarket — 66 percent, up sharply from 37 percent in 1958. Convenience stores account for 4 percent and other grocery stores for 16 percent. Home delivery, mostly of milk

About 72 percent of U.S. food is consumed at home.

and bread, is now less than 1 percent, compared to 5 percent in 1939. The away-from-home market has grown rapidly in recent years, primarily with the growth in sales of fast food establishments, which now account for 30 percent of eating-out dollars, compared to 6 percent in 1958. Sales at restaurants, lunchrooms and cafeterias are down from 56 percent of away-from-home sales in 1958 to 41 percent today.

How It All Adds Up

U.S. farmers received $85 billion for the food which went to American consumers in 1981. The job of marketing that food cost $200 billion. The different functions break down like this: Processing, $76.2 billion; Transportation, $15.1 billion; Wholesaling, $23.4 billion; Retailing, $38.0 billion; Food service, $47.1 billion.

Looked at the other way, the costs of marketing cover: Labor, $87.9 billion.

Packaging materials, $23.0 billion. Transportation, $15.1 billion. Energy, $10.3 billion. Corporate profits, $12.0 billion. Other, $51.2 billion.

The marketing system for agricultural products is much more like other parts of the economy than it was 30 years ago, but there still are major differences. Crop output cannot be closely controlled like, say, steel output because of the vagaries of weather. Many agricultural products are bulky, and production is widely dispersed and distant from consumers. There are long, fixed lags between the decision to produce and actual output, differing for annual crops such as wheat and corn, perennial crops such as apples and oranges, and livestock products like meat or milk. There are lags in industrial production too, but a somewhat higher degree of control. Most crops mature once a year — they cannot be produced continually. Many agricultural products

Fast food restaurants now account for 30 percent of eating-out dollars, compared to 6 percent in 1958. These young people are enjoying fried chicken in a fast food restaurant.

are highly perishable, such as milk and fresh fruit.

These differences mean the agricultural marketing system must deal with: Widely varying production from one year to another. The marketing system must accommodate these variations by storage or other means. Prices in any year are the result of these mismatches of supply and demand, so they send poor signals to farmers about future production plans. Prices may be way above costs or below them. Efforts to reduce risks through individual actions (contracting, forward selling, etc.), through group actions (bargaining and cooperative marketing), or through public efforts to change the system must also be dealt with in the marketing system.

Agricultural processing and distribution are characterized by large-scale corporate economic units. The 100 largest food and tobacco processing companies accounted for 52.5 percent of U.S. shipments of food and tobacco products in 1975. Another 100 companies accounted for an additional 11 percent. These 200 companies are broadly diversified. U.S. sales of processed foods, alcoholic beverages, and tobacco made up only 52 percent of their business.

Branding. Outputs of U.S. food manufacturers are either consumer food products or intermediate products used in their manufacture. Consumer food products are largely branded, many with strong brands that differentiate them from others. Manufacturers engage in a continual process of new product development and promotion as they seek to maintain or improve their own positions in the marketplace. A minority of brands belong to retailers or wholesalers, but the great majority are processor brands. Branding provides the basis for consumer identification of packaged food products and helps food manufacturers differentiate their products from those of other manufacturers. Constant attention to product development and differentiation provides a food manufacturer with a partially protected place in the market with somewhat higher returns.

Numbers of farmers and of marketing firms are declining as individual firms grow. In the broadest sense, changes in the structure of farming and of the marketing system are caused by the same set of forces. Technological change is one of the major forces creating pressures toward larger farms. It also has been a major contributor to the growth and size of food manufacturing and distribution plants and firms.

Changes in transportation technology have an obvious effect. Introduction of the motortruck made it possible for farmers to greatly expand the area where they might look for buyers of their products, at the same time increasing the area from which an assembler or manufacturer of agricultural products could economically purchase. This made larger, more efficient manufacturing plants possible and the numbers became fewer. Larger plants could exert more buying power but at the same time farmers could go farther to market, so the number of alternative outlets available to a typical farmer did not decline as fast as the total number of buyers.

Terminal Market Decline

Changes in farm product marketing to gain transport and handling economies led to new forms of trading. The rise in direct buying by processors and distributors brought about a decline in terminal markets, which once were great nerve centers for pricing and price information. Grain terminals, stockyards, wholesale poultry and egg markets, and fruit and vegetable markets brought together competitive forces over a wide area. Prices were openly established and news of price changes were spread widely by press and radio. These markets have been largely, but not entirely, replaced by direct dealing between the parties who used to meet in the markets.

Many of the organized markets of an earlier day have disappeared. Small farmers who brought their products for sale in these markets have either grown larger or gone into other lines of work. Small retailers who were the principal buyers in many of the markets have grown, gone into other lines of business,

or found less time-consuming ways of buying products for their stores. Livestock auctions that once provided an outlet for the farmer with one or a few head of livestock to sell are much less important than they used to be, because there are many fewer farmers with a few head of livestock as a sideline. Livestock production is largely a specialized business, and specialized producers deal directly with the meat packer. Specialized buying firms which assemble small lots of livestock are much fewer in number than they once were.

As buying and selling arrangements changed, pricing systems have adapted. Terminal markets for livestock and wholesale markets for fresh fruits and vegetables are no longer the dominant pricemaking institutions they once were. The focus of pricemaking has moved

The motor truck has made it possible for the farmer to expand the area in which to look for buyers of his products. This 18-wheeler from North Carolina unloads at the Maryland wholesale produce market.

William E. Carnahan

back to the shipping point for fresh fruits and vegetables, but wholesalers still supply the majority of fresh produce. Pricemaking for livestock has been dispersed and now occurs mostly in private negotiations by telephone between producers and packers and between packers and large retailers.

The pricing system that has emerged for farm products has been shaped by inherent characteristics of farm products, needs and character of the modern processing and distribution sectors, and economics of the pricing systems themselves. The food and fiber marketing system includes big, highly rationalized businesses, often requiring a steady supply of particular farm products — vegetables, fruits, cotton, etc. Where there is little assurance of supply, such firms have actively generated a supply by entering into contracts with farmers or sometimes by direct ownership of production resources. A large firm may find it easier to coordinate economic activity via internal command rather than a price system, and decisions once made in the marketplace may shift to the firm as the nature of firms change.

As wages and salaries rose relative to the cost of capital, incentives grew to move away from time-consuming negotiation of prices for each transaction. Economies are gained, in many cases, by negotiating a general pricing formula and then placing specific orders by telephone. The formulas often rely on prices established on wholesale markets as base prices. Formula pricing is increasingly questioned, partly because of the thinness (small volume) of trading on wholesale markets, which suggests the possibility of

Livestock auctions are much less important today than they were many years ago, because there are fewer farmers with only a few head of livestock as a sideline. The Polled Hereford being auctioned here is at Senatobia, Miss.

David F. Warren

abuse, and partly because of the difficulty of reporting prices in a market that is so widely dispersed, perhaps offering differential advantages to some marketers.

Toward a Better Way

Hope for improving agricultural pricing systems lies in several directions. Physical presence of the commodity when buying and selling occur is unnecessary and can be wasteful. As long as the product can be described to the reasonable satisfaction of traders and delivery, payment and redress of grievances can be assured,

satisfactory exchange can occur. Indeed, the commodity need not even be in existence when the transaction occurs. It is in this context that techniques for forward trading, futures trading, and electronic marketing can be understood and evaluated.

For some agricultural commodities, particularly those produced on a lot or batch basis for processing, little or no production is undertaken without a contract between producer and processor. Most of the broiler industry in the South was

built on this basis. Vegetables for processing are largely produced under contract.

Exceptions include perennials and crops which may be used either for processing or fresh market. Most asparagus, a perennial, is purchased on the open market for processing. The same varieties are used both for processing and fresh market. A number of varieties of potatoes are used both for processing and fresh market. Contracting accounts for a significant share of such production.

Frequently the processor sorts potatoes received from the grower, sending top grades in selected size ranges to the fresh market and the remainder to processing.

Most other vegetables for processing are produced only under contract. In the majority of cases, contracting and production of such vegetables started together. In the early days, processors specified very tightly the product to be delivered and the terms and conditions. They often supplied seed and other inputs. As growers became accustomed to requirements of the buyers, contract terms became less detailed.

Marketing contracts, written or verbal, have been the usual way of selling continuously produced products such as milk and eggs for many years. Such contracts provide a method of setting prices and other terms of trade for commodities that move from farm to market every few days. Contracts where the contractor owns the hens have come into increased use for eggs in the last 20 years. Marketing contracts (forward selling) for staple commodities — grains, oilseeds, and cotton — came into use during the seventies. They are far from the dominant way of doing business for these commodities. They permit growers to shift some of their price risks and buyers to remove some uncertainties as to supply.

Another way of shifting the risk of price change is through futures trading. The number of agricultural products for which

David F. Warren

Wholesale markets for fresh fruits and vegetables are no longer the dominant price-making institutions they once were. However, wholesalers such as these in Maryland still supply the majority of fresh produce.

active futures trading exists has increased. It now includes spring wheat, hard winter wheat, soft red winter wheat, corn, soybeans, soybean oil and meal, oats, cotton, shell eggs, potatoes, fed steers, feeder cattle, slaughter hogs, iced broilers, sugar, and orange juice.

Salesmanship. To good salespeople, the American market is big, exciting, different. It is up to them to make the most of it, to catch the consumer's attention, to sell. Their efforts lead to advertising and the development of new services and products in an attempt to get a larger part of an established market and to enlarge the total market. Farm products and commodities processed from them — food, clothing, industrial materials of many kinds — get their share of this selling effort.

Ever since exchange gained a place in economic affairs, some form of selling effort has been a necessity. The producer and/or the vendor of a commodity or service was faced with the need to inform potential buyers of its availability and to persuade them to buy. Immediate interests of food processors, textile manufacturers, and others like them, and of those who wholesale and retail the products, are closely related. Advertising and sales activities of manufacturers and retailers are closely tied together.

The average American consumer expects the marketing system to keep goods flowing continuously into the handiest retail outlets, preferably at prices that allow a rising level of living. That goal requires just as much of the farmers as it does of the marketing system. American farm products also move into foreign markets. In them, too, despite an intervening web of trade difficulties that sometimes can considerably modify free-market demand, the basic marketing function is to find and serve the final user.

Facing this large and complex marketing system, what can a farmer do? What choices does the farmer have? Obviously, the farmer does not have as wide a range of options as, say, a manufacturer of household appliances. But the farmer does have a number of choices which will be discussed more fully in later chapters in this section.

While not having the same freedom in product design as the toaster manufacturer, farmers can affect characteristics of their products by choice of crop variety or livestock type and by decisions about some production practices. For example, the livestock feeder must decide how long and what to feed cattle and thus determine marketing weight and affect the grade. Acting as a group, farmers can have some influence on the demand for their products through advertising and other promotional efforts. Farmers must decide where to sell their products, a choice which affects the price received and the costs of selling.

Generally speaking, farmers are price takers — not price makers. But some choices are available: Sell at the current price (the spot market); Store and sell later; Deliver now but defer setting the price; Fix the price before delivery by a contract; "Lock in" a price on the futures market; Sell through a cooperative which pools all its members' sales and pays each the average price; Contract for a service payment not dependent on the market price, as in broilers. No one farmer has all these choices, but most have more than one.

Links That Make Up the Marketing Chain

By Edward V. Jesse

One way of viewing the U.S. agricultural marketing system is to look at the physical services — transformations in time, space, and form — provided by the system: Corn harvested in central Indiana in October becomes the bowl of cornflakes eaten by a New York City schoolboy in January; tomatoes picked in the San Joaquin Valley in California in August become catsup for a Memorial Day hotdog in St. Louis.

Marketing functions such as these can be identified and located according to when they occur as food and fiber moves from farm to consumer. The sequence of functions is known as a marketing chain; each function is a link in this chain. The three major marketing functions are assembly, processing, and distribution. The relationship among these functions can be depicted as a pair of funnels joined at their spout.

In the assembly stage, raw agricultural products are "funnelled" into centralized locations. Production from many individual farms and ranches is concentrated into larger amounts for processing (represented by the spouts of the two funnels), where processing includes such functions as grading and packaging as well as physical transformation (manufacturing). Processed products are subsequently dispersed in the distribution stage of marketing. Finished goods are moved from central processing locations to consumers throughout the United States and much of the world.

The number and complexity of operations performed as part of these three major marketing functions differ widely among commodities — and even for the same commodity — depending on raw product characteristics and end uses. Some marketing chains are very complex and long, with many individual steps comprising each function. Others are simple and short: for example, strawberries sold from "pick your own" farms. It might seem that no marketing functions are performed in this direct marketing case. But assembly, processing, and distribution still take place, all performed by the farmer and the consumer instead of the "middleman."

Raw product assembly, or collecting products of the farm for processing, is the first link in any marketing chain. Assembly primarily involves transportation from farms to buyers. However, storage either onfarm or at collection points such as country grain elevators may also occur as part of assembly. Perishable crops like fruits and vegetables are assembled immediately after

Edward V. Jesse is an Agricultural Economist with the Economic Research Service, USDA, at the University of Wisconsin, Madison.

harvest. On the other hand, nonperishable crops (grains, potatoes) are often stored by farmers and released gradually into the marketing system over the year. Livestock products like milk and eggs move off the farms continuously.

Assembly, or receiving, points for farm products are many and varied. The first receiving point may be a processor, or the raw product may be assembled and reassembled several times before reaching processors. Grain, for example, often moves from farms to country elevators to terminal elevators at milling or export locations.

Transportation from farm to first assembly point is usually by truck, the exception being some hauling by farm tractors and wagons when distances are short. Refrigerated bulk milk tankers, fiberglass gondolas to haul processing tomatoes, and self-unloading grain hoppers are some of the specialized vehicles

used. Transportation from first to subsequent assembly points may be by truck, rail, barge, or even air for highly perishable, high value commodities.

The past 30 years have witnessed major improvements in transportation, and elimination of some raw products assembly functions. More and more farm deliveries are direct to processors rather than to intermediate buyers who assemble larger sized quantities from several farms. Livestock auction markets are being replaced by direct farmer-to-packer sales. Local assembly points are giving way to regional assembly.

This shortening of the marketing chain at the assembly stage is due mainly to the changing structure of farming. Increasing farm size, decreasing farm numbers, and production specialization have greatly reduced the need for assembly intermediaries. A feedlot shipping several truckloads of cattle each week does not need

to use an auction market — it is cheaper and more efficient for the farmer to deal directly with packers.

The Finished Goods Stage

Raw agricultural commodities become finished goods in the processing stage of the marketing system. Processing may be as simple as removing culls and packaging fresh produce. Or it may involve numerous complex mechanical and chemical processes for products like sugar, corn sirup, and vegetable oils.

Some raw agricultural products go through several substages within the processing stage. A number of processing functions create only consumer goods, others only intermediate products that are inputs to subsequent processing, others both. Wheat is a good example where flour is basically an intermediate product. Some wheat flour, of course, is packaged and sold to consumers for home baking. But most of the flour

milled is used by commercial bakers and manufacturers of refrigerated dough, pasta, and blended mixes.

Some dressed pork reaches the consumer as fresh cuts. But pork carcasses are also an intermediate product in processing, curing, and sausage-making. In contrast, separate and distinct processing functions often occur for the same farm commodity, depending on what finished good is to be produced. Raw grade A milk may be bottled fresh or manufactured into butter, cheese, or other products. But bottled milk is not an intermediate product like flour or pork carcasses. Similarly, fruits and vegetables destined for the produce counter are processed separately from those to be canned or frozen.

Storage may also occur within the processing stage. Firms manufacturing semi-durable finished goods from annually harvested crops (such as cereal products, sugar, and canned fruits and vegetables) must carry inventories in order to service distributors throughout the year. Usually stocks of finished products are held, but some processors (for example, potato chip manufacturers, flour millers, sugar beet processors) also hold raw product inventories.

6,000 Dairies Shut Down

Changes in the number and size of food, fiber, and tobacco processors have paralleled changes in the number and size of U.S. farms — numbers are fewer and size is larger. All categories of manufacturing establishments for major farm

Transportation from farm to the first assembly point is usually by truck. These trucks wait to unload their wheat at a farmer-owned cooperative in Stockton, Kans.

John White

product groups between 1958 and 1977 show substantial reductions, ranging from 16 to 76 percent. The largest absolute change was in fluid milk and dairy products — more than 6,000 dairy plants ceased operation. (These figures do not include processing plants like produce packinghouses, tree nut and peanut shellers, cotton gins, and dry bean cleaners which do not involve manufacturing procedures as defined by the U.S. Bureau of the Census.)

Over the same 1958-77 period, per capita consumption of agricultural products was fairly stable (except for cotton and wool use, which declined as consumers switched to synthetics), while population grew from 174 to 216 million. The net result, compared to 25 years ago, is a substantially smaller number of plants processing a substantially larger quantity of raw agricultural products. Part of the reason for this change in the structure of the processing industry (decrease in plant numbers and increase in size) is technological. Improvements in transportation and processing techniques made large-scale plants far more efficient, and thus survival of smaller plants became impossible.

Structural change in processing has been especially pronounced for highly fabricated food products that can be differentiated in the minds of consumers through advertising. Sellers of lesser known brands have frequently been unable to attract enough buyers to remain in business, even by offering lower prices. For example, in 1977 the four largest dry cereal manufacturers accounted for 89 percent of ready-to-eat cereal sales in the United States compared to 68 percent in 1935.

The distribution function is the final link in the marketing chains of agricultural commodities. Distribution involves wholesaling and retailing, with transportation and storage embedded within both. Wholesaling is the reverse of raw product assembly. Wholesalers buy in volume from processors and parcel out smaller quantities to grocery stores, restaurants, and other firms servicing consumers. Wholesaling is a buffer between the needs of the retail trade and the supplies of processors. Physically, wholesaling arranges for transportation from processors to city distribution centers; receives and breaks loads; stores, processes buyer orders; and transports small lots to retailers.

Some food wholesalers are full-line, providing grocery stores with a complete assortment of grocery items. Others specialize in specific products or in servicing specific clients. Some perform limited processing functions, such as preparing salads or pressing hamburger patties. Some distribute products under their own brands. Some are operated as cooperatives with grocery stores as members.

Chains Take Over

The number of independent wholesalers has diminished with the growth of supermarket chains and processors. Most chains are large enough to efficiently operate their own distribution centers: they purchase food products directly from large processors, store them at regional warehouses, and distribute them to individual retail outlets. The wholesaling function is still performed in this case, but it is done by the retail chain itself rather than by an independent wholesaler.

Number of Establishments Processing Agricultural Products in 1958 and 1977

Agricultural Product Category	Establishments		Percent Change
	1958	1977	
Meat Products	5,528	4,534	−18.0
Dairy Products	9,879	3,731	−62.2
Preserved Fruits & Vegetables	2,920	2,379	−18.5
Grain Mill Products	3,484	3,043	−12.7
Bakery Products	6,319	3,386	−46.4
Sugar, Confectionery Products	1,588	1,198	−24.6
Fats and Oils	3,588	869	−75.8
Beverages	5,558	3,104	−44.2
Misc. Food, Kindred Products	5,244	4,412	−15.9
Tobacco Products	504	228	−54.8
Weaving Mills, Cotton	496	314	−36.7
Weaving & Finishing Mills, Wool	469	165	−64.8

Source: 1958 and 1977 Census of Manufacturers-General Summary.

For some food products, the wholesaling function is performed by brokers. Unlike wholesalers, brokers do not purchase products for subsequent resale. Rather, they line up buyers and sellers and coordinate shipments without physically handling goods. Brokers are especially important in export trading, where communication between buyers and sellers is difficult and expensive.

The Retailer — Retailing involves final disassembly of farm-produced goods. While we tend to think of food retailing in terms of grocery stores, only about half of the U.S. consumer's food dollar is spent there. Another 15 percent is spent in specialty food stores (like butcher shops), convenience stores, drug and department stores, and at roadside or farmers' markets. This leaves about 35 percent of retail food sales for away-from-home eating. These retail outlets include conventional sit-down restaurants and burger stands, as well as vending machines, school cafeterias, and hotdog wagons in the park.

The away-from-home or food service component of food retailing expanded through the 1970's as a percent of total retail food expenditures, due mainly to increasing family incomes and more working wives with less time to spend in the kitchen. (Less favorable economic conditions in recent years have contributed to a reversal of that trend.) Among the retail food service outlets, those characterized as "fast food" have expanded most rapidly.

More than 60 percent of retail food purchases for home use are made at supermarkets — grocery stores with more

142

than $1 million annual sales. Most supermarkets are affiliated with grocery chains (firms with 11 or more stores) like Safeway, Kroger, and A&P. Over the past 25 years, chains have consistently increased their share of retail grocery sales, rapidly replacing single-store independent grocers.

Now that we've examined what goes on within the three stages of the marketing system, let's look at some specific examples of marketing chains — for potatoes, corn, and beef cattle. Each has very different characteristics.

Potatoes may move directly from farmers to packinghouses or processors, or they may also move through onfarm or commercial storage. Unlike many other vegetable crops, potatoes are dual-purpose: the same varieties are suitable for either fresh market or processing.

Fresh potatoes move from packinghouse to retailers either directly or through wholesale markets in major cities. Wholesalers handling fresh potatoes usually specialize in produce, and supply food service retailers and small grocery stores. Potato processors produce a wide assortment of dry and frozen potato products. These may be branded and packaged in consumer-sized units or delivered in bulk to the food service trade. (Imagine McDonald's french fry bill!)

Corn and Feed — Much of the corn grown on farms in the United States does not leave home; it is consumed by

Away-from-home eating includes hotdog stands like this one near the U.S. Department of Agriculture in Washington. About 35 percent of retail food sales is at away-from-home outlets.

livestock on the same farms. Moreover, a good bit of the corn sold off-farm is also used for livestock feed, either directly or as part of a feed mix. Hence, some corn marketing chains connect back to farms rather than extending to consumers. Corn is also one of our major export items with nearly $8 billion sold overseas last year. (Japan, Russia, and Mexico are our biggest customers.) Through assembly, the marketing chain for exported corn is the same as for corn used in the United States. There are three basic processing methods for corn used as food. All three result mainly in intermediate products that are further processed into consumer goods. Corn products ultimately used by consumers bear little resemblance to the product harvested by farmers.

Cattle for beef products are assembled from three distinct sources: confinement feedlots, dairy farms (cull milking cows), and livestock farms and ranches. Auctions at stockyards in major meatpacking centers and in producing areas are still important in cattle assembly, but as noted earlier, most cattle now move directly to packing plants.

Following slaughter, carcass-halves may be sold to retailers (direct or through meat wholesalers) for cutting and trimming by butchers in specialty stores, restaurants, and grocery stores. Or these functions may be performed by meatpackers. Some large meatpackers today sell boxed beef, carcasses broken down into "primals" (major cuts like shoulders and loins) to meet individual specifications in retail outlets. Beef carcasses are also an intermediate product used by other food manufacturers to make products like canned beef, sandwich meats, sausages, and TV dinners.

Marketing Chains for Selected Farm Commodities

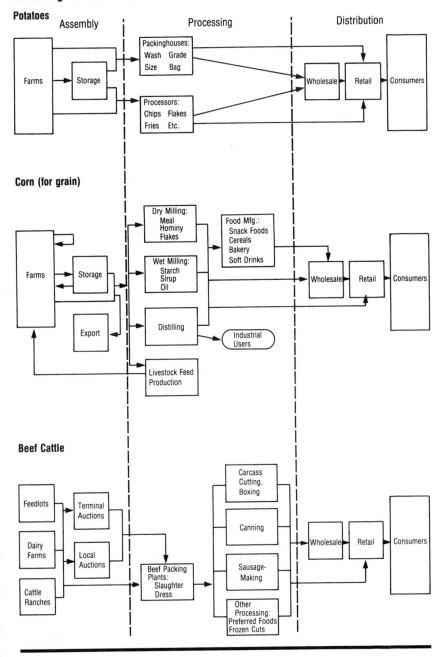

Potatoes

Assembly — Processing — Distribution

Farms → Storage → Packinghouses: Wash Grade Size Bag; Processors: Chips Flakes Fries Etc. → Wholesale → Retail → Consumers

Corn (for grain)

Farms → Storage → Export → Dry Milling: Meal Hominy Flakes; Wet Milling: Starch Sirup Oil; Distilling; Livestock Feed Production → Food Mfg.: Snack Foods Cereals Bakery Soft Drinks; Industrial Users → Wholesale → Retail → Consumers

Beef Cattle

Feedlots; Dairy Farms; Cattle Ranches → Terminal Auctions; Local Auctions → Beef Packing Plants: Slaughter Dress → Carcass Cutting, Boxing; Canning; Sausage-Making; Other Processing: Preferred Foods Frozen Cuts → Wholesale → Retail → Consumers

Who Does What in the Marketing Field

By Joseph N. Uhl

While the functional approach examines the "what gets done" in food marketing, the institutional approach emphasizes the "who does it." These are complementary but somewhat different ways of viewing food marketing. This approach focuses attention on the unique types of firms and agents that have evolved to perform the food marketing tasks.

A marketing institution is any organization, group, or agency which is directly involved in the food marketing process or influences the process in some way. Institutions organize economic activity. They assist in making decisions about the what, when, where, and how of producing and distributing the Nation's food supply. In our economy the marketplace is the key institution for efficiently allocating resources. Institutions are to the economy as organs are to the body, serving as command centers that power and guide food marketing decisions. The food marketing system is a complex set of institutions designed to efficiently deliver an abundant, wholesome, and fairly priced food supply to American — and increasingly worldwide — consumers.

Individual firms such as brokers, wholesalers, processors, and grocers are the most familiar and conspicuous food marketing institutions. These firms perform the day-to-day tasks of altering farm and food products in time, form, and space. But numerous other institutions influence food marketing. These include government laws, regulations, and agencies; trade associations; commodity and farm organizations; as well as research and educational institutions. In addition, of course, food marketing is affected by the legal, social, cultural and economic institutions of the society in which it operates.

The sum total of these various agencies constitutes the institutional structure of food marketing. All these institutions are important in the food marketing process. The institutional approach examines the nature of the various agents and how they work together in the marketing system. How well they perform their jobs influences how well we eat and what we pay for our food. Careful study of this institutional structure can provide a number of insights into the changing food marketing system.

The institutional approach to food marketing highlights the interrelationships between the various marketing agents. Each institution contributes in different ways to the food marketing effort. Coordinating these agencies is a major task. Inefficiencies anywhere in the system can reduce total marketing performance. It is

Joseph N. Uhl is Associate Professor, Agricultural Economics, Purdue University, West Lafayette.

important that all the marketing agencies work together toward the goal of efficient delivery of food from farmers to consumers.

Forces of Change — The institutional approach also focuses attention on the forces of change in food marketing. Obsolete firms and marketing methods are continually being displaced by more efficient operations. The food marketing system is in a constant state of flux as institutions adjust and adapt themselves to technological, economic and social changes. Institutional survival and adaptation are studied using this approach. Why do some marketing firms survive while others fall by the wayside? Why did the supermarket make the Ma and Pa corner grocery store obsolete? How have food wholesalers, displaced by market decentralization, survived? The competitive marketplace continually tests and retests institutions for their contributions to economic goals.

This approach is also valuable for viewing the role of public policy in food marketing. Market policies are the instruments by which society conditions the performance of market institutions. New laws, regulations and policies may alter food marketing institutions and the performance of food marketing firms. At any point in time, the institutional structure of food marketing is a product of technological possibilities and public policies. By the same token, changes in the institutional structure of marketing are frequently the occasion for changes in public policies toward the food marketing system.

The institutional approach draws our attention to the human element in food marketing. Individuals operate the marketing machinery. Institutions change in response to managers' decisions. Nothing gets done in food marketing until someone makes a decision. Managerial decisions energize the food marketing process.

Types of Middlemen

A large number of diverse firms are involved in marketing the Nation's food supply. These firms can be classified in a variety of ways: 1) by marketing functions performed (such as storage, processing, transportation, etc.), 2) by market levels (retail, wholesale, etc.), 3) by ownership patterns (proprietorship, cooperatives, corporations), or 4) by com-

Assemblers are middlemen operating in farm production areas, buying directly from farmers. Country grain elevators like these are an example. Their function is to collect large volumes of farm supplies from many farmers and prepare them for shipment.

146

modities handled (grain, livestock, produce, etc.). The institutional approach is concerned with the changing types of food marketing middlemen and trends in the marketing system's organizational patterns.

Assemblers are those middlemen who operate in farm production areas, buying directly from farmers. Examples are country grain elevators, livestock auction markets, and shipping point brokers. Their function is to collect large volumes of farm supplies from numerous farmers and to prepare these for forward shipment. Like most food marketing firms, their numbers are declining as their size increases. Many farmers participate in assembly operations through cooperative organizations.

Wholesalers are largely located in the cities. Their job is to receive shipments of farm and food products from assemblers, farmers, and food manufacturers and to inventory a diverse market basket of products for retailers. Examples are commission agents, brokers, car-lot receivers, and jobbers. Their numbers also are declining as food retailers operate their own wholesaling operations.

Food manufacturers specialize in adding form utility to farm products. Many of these now buy direct from farmers, and several own farm operations. They also frequently perform their own wholesaling functions. While there are several large, well-known food processing firms, such as Kelloggs, General Foods, Pillsbury, and Kraft, there also are many smaller processors.

Earl R. Baker

147

Food retailers are the most familiar food marketing institutions to consumers. They represent the last stage in the food marketing system. Grocery stores, restaurants, and institutional feeding operations are examples. The number of food retail operations has declined in the past 50 years while the average size has grown. Familiar names here include Safeway, A&P, Kroger, Von's, Jewell, and Standard. Although the Ma and Pa corner grocery store is rare today, a number of independently owned foodstores and smaller chains compete with the giant firms.

Related Institutions

Other institutions operate in the background of food marketing. "Facilitative organizations" assist middlemen in per-

Food retailers like this new one in Laurel, Md., are the most familiar food marketing institutions to consumers. They represent the last stage in the food marketing system.

William Carnahan

forming their marketing functions. They grease the wheels of the marketing machinery. These include organized commodity exchanges, such as the Chicago Board of Trade and the Chicago Mercantile Exchange. Transportation and communication agencies also facilitate the food marketing process. In addition, there are a number of public and private sources of agricultural and food marketing information. For example, the U.S. Department of Agriculture's Agricultural Marketing Service provides a wide range of market news reports which contribute to efficient production and marketing decisions.

Government agencies also influence the efficiency and fairness of food marketing. The U.S. Department of Agriculture (USDA) oversees a wide range of marketing activities through such regulations as the Meat Inspection Act, the Packers and Stockyards Act, the U.S. Warehouse Act, and the Perishable Agricultural Commodities Act. The Food and Drug Administration and Federal Trade Commission also regulate important aspects of food marketing. These public institutions develop market rules and policies intended to insure that the marketing system performs in the public interest.

USDA also administers several enabling laws and regulations which assist farmers in creating new marketing institutions. An example is the Capper-Volsted Act, permitting farmers to organize and market their products collectively. Marketing orders which provide farmers with the tools for more orderly marketing of their products are another example, as are bargaining associations.

Educational and research organizations are sometimes overlooked as marketing institutions. The Land-Grant College Act (1862), along with the Smith-Lever Act (1914), established an extensive system of public higher education and adult education for agriculture. The Research and Marketing Act (1946) broadened the mission to include marketing as well as production problems. Today's food marketing system depends upon a continuing stream of new technologies and educated manpower from these research-educational institutions.

Trade associations, commodity groups and farm organizations also are heavily involved in food marketing activities today. Several trade associations gather industry statistics, disseminate market information, conduct educational programs, and participate in development of marketing policies. Farm organizations are active in formation of marketing policies, as it has become clear that these can affect farm prices and incomes as much as or more than traditional farm policies.

Evolution of the System

All of this constitutes an extremely complex and sophisticated food marketing system. Why do we have such highly specialized food marketing firms and so many supporting institutions? Are they all necessary? And how do they affect our food bills? Food marketing was less complex in earlier periods. It would be possible to market our food in a simpler fashion without middlemen and these other agencies. Farmers can and do sell directly to consumers at roadside and farmers' markets without the services of market intermediaries. Other countries manage to market their farm products with a much less elaborate marketing system.

However, marketing institutions are products of economic development. Higher income, urban consumers demand more marketing services. Farmers in the industrialized economies for the most part prefer to specialize their activities in food production and leave marketing to the middlemen. And rising standards of market performance in affluent societies result in greater public regulation and assistance to the food marketing sector. Specialized marketing middlemen evolve where they can perform the marketing functions more efficiently than farmers or consumers. Many food marketing activities are subject to scale economies whereby costs fall with increased volume. As a result, specialized food marketing firms have assumed an increasing role in the food industry.

Policy Questions — There are several important trends in the institutional structure of food marketing. These affect farmers, middlemen, and consumers. In turn, they raise public policy questions. The tendency toward fewer and larger sizes of marketing firms concerns many observers. This means farmers are selling to larger, more powerful buyers. One response on the part of farmers has been an attempt to gain countervailing power through new farm marketing institutions, such as cooperatives, bargaining associations, and commodity promotional programs. Concerns with the trend toward fewer and larger firms have taken the form of public policies limiting the size and activities of certain food middlemen. What kinds of institutions and new marketing arrangements does today's farmer need? Will the institutional arrangements of the 1970's serve the farmer well in the coming years?

Diversifying — Another institutional trend has been the diversifying of food marketing firms. Food retailers have extended their operations to the wholesale and processing levels. Food processors engage not only in wholesaling but also in farming activities. Many food marketing firms are now owned by nonfood companies, and several of the major food manufacturers have diversified into nonfood product lines. Implications of these trends are not fully understood, but they clearly are resulting in a food industry which differs from traditional patterns.

Decentralization and integration into agriculture are other trends altering the institutional structure of food marketing. They have been accompanied by development of new trading patterns, demise of traditional institutions like the central terminal markets, and growth of new firms. These trends have raised public policy issues in the areas of farmer bargaining power, market information, and pricing arrangements. Also influencing food marketing institutions are the changing geographic location of agriculture, growth of the away-from-home food market, and the 1970's spurt in international trade of agricultural products.

Conclusions — The food marketing system is a complex set of institutions which exists to efficiently market the Nation's food supply. Key questions being asked today are: Do we have the appropriate institutions for the food marketing system of the 1980's and 90's? What set of public policies, firm types, and other institutions will insure optimum performance of the food marketing system in the coming years? How should the institutional structure of food marketing be changed to accommodate needs of farmers, middlemen and consumers?

How Markets Coordinate Decisions

By Wayne D. Purcell

oordination of economic activities from producer to consumer is important. If what is produced is not consistent with what is being demanded by consumers, valuable resources are not used in the best way. Producers, consumers and middlemen could benefit from changes which brought improved coordination. A market system is like a complex assembly line. The farmer starts the process by producing the basic raw material.

As the raw material moves up through the system, it is processed to meet demands of the final consumer. *Form utility,* where utility equals satisfaction, is being created by changing the product to make it acceptable to the consumer. The amount of processing varies among commodities, but consumers are increasingly willing to pay for the services required to create form utility. Ready to cook broilers are acceptable to consumers — a live chicken is not.

Market systems also create *place* and *time utility.* The processed food or fiber product is moved to a place where it is readily accessible to the consumer. The modern supermarket, with its wide array of products, emerged because the consumer looks for convenient access to products and services. Storage of the nonperishable product and canning, freezing and other methods of making perishable products available throughout the

year create time utility. The consumer wants the product on a yearround basis. If the consumer is willing to pay for them, the market system will provide the time-related services.

If the market system offers the consumer a product form inconsistent with consumer demand, the "assembly line" is not working very well. The optimal level of coordination between production and consumption is not being achieved. Changes need to be made. How the changes are prompted depends on the way the system is organized. For most commodities, the production-marketing system is characterized by separate ownership of each stage of economic activity. Negotiated prices become important. Price signals come from buyer-seller negotiations along each interface where two stages of economic activity merge. It is these price signals that bring coordination.

Consumers can start the process by buying more aggressively a particular product or quality within a product line. As consumers compete for the available supply, price gets "bid up." Retailers bid higher prices to wholesalers in an attempt to get more of the product which is moving well. Wholesalers bid higher to the processors from whom they buy — and the process is continued until the price signal, a *price premium* in this instance, reaches the producer. Theoreti-

Wayne D. Purcell is Professor of Agricultural Economics, Virginia Tech, Blacksburg.

cally, the producer reacts to this price signal by reallocating resources and producing more of the preferred product or the preferred quality. Coordination between what is demanded by consumers and what is provided is restored. *Price discounts* reverse the process and encourage producers to offer less of a particular product or quality.

Obstacles — The process is obviously more complex than a simple assembly line which has an overseer to observe the level of interstage coordination being achieved. Price signals follow a long and complicated path and there are obstacles along the way. Among those obstacles which have been identified in the research literature are: Goal conflicts at the interface where buyer and seller must interact; absence of any perception of a total system; inadequate grades and related descriptive terminology; and lack of competition on a price basis.

Buyer and seller have a most legitimate conflict of interest. Sellers want high prices, buyers want low prices. But the goal conflicts encountered sometimes go beyond the legitimate arena. For example, producers will often try to maximize output — yield per acre, weight per head at weaning time, etc. This may or may not meet the needs of the processor who is looking to the producing sector for a timely flow of raw material of a certain and consistent quality. If processors could control what is being done at the producing level, they would often do it differently.

Participants in the production-marketing system often do not perceive of themselves as part of an overall system. They do not see the "assembly line" at work and do not see what they are doing as a

"work station" in that assembly line. Thus they do not see interstage coordination as something they should worry about, and make no attempt to work with others in the system.

Cutability and Competition

If a system of price signals is to be effective, the available grades or descriptive terminology used in negotiating prices must be adequate. All significant and discernible differences in value must be identified and categorized by grades and the grades must be widely used by all buyers and sellers. A price signal cannot be attached to a product attribute which is not identified.

As an example, consider the situation in the beef complex prior to the initiation of yield grades. Quality grades (Prime, Choice, Good, etc.) were being used as a measure of palatability. But within the Choice grade, beef carcasses of comparable weight could vary significantly in value because of different ratios of lean and valuable cuts to total carcass weight. Price signals could not be expected to motivate changes toward high cutability cattle (high ratio of lean to total carcass weight) by producers when cutability was not being brought into the pricing process. A set of grades which allows all important value-related product attributes to be brought into the pricing process is a necessary condition to high levels of coordination between what is being produced and what is in demand at the consumer level.

Today's supermarket has a wide array of products that are available on a year-round basis.

Absence of competition on a price basis can block transmission of price signals. For example, a wholesaler might recognize the higher bid from a retail chain for a particular commodity and simply absorb it in the form of a wider operating margin instead of passing it to his supplier. A high level of competition, which encourages the "passing on" of the price premium, is important.

The cutability issue in cattle provides an interesting illustration. Since 1975, all beef carcasses which are quality graded must also be yield graded (or vice versa). Yield grade 1 is attached to carcasses with the highest ratio of lean cuts to total carcass weight, and yield grade 5 identifies low cutability carcasses. Yield grade 3 is the average or "par" carcass. The market is currently attaching a price discount, often substantial, to yield grades 4 and 5. But there is little or no visible evidence of a premium being paid for yield grades 1 and 2 — and there are usually as many 1's and 2's in a pen of cattle as there are 4's and 5's. There is room for an hypothesis that the level of competition is not adequate to "force" the paying of premiums for 1's and 2's.

The price system is actually a communication system. If high levels of vertical coordination are to be achieved, the system must "communicate" effectively to producers. The price mechanism must be an effective overseer of the systemwide assembly line. Economic incentive in the form of price signals must replace the verbal communication the overseer of an assembly line uses to make sure inter-stage coordination is achieved. Achieving effective levels of communication is no small assignment. Even if all other obstacles are overcome, the organizational structure of most food and fiber systems often gets in the way.

Along the vertical continuum from producer to consumer, tremendous differences in the economic structures prevail. The modern retail chain is part of an industry sector organized as what economists might call an oligopoly. There are a few large firms. These firms tend to compete by spending huge sums of money on advertising. A particular firm reacts to the competitor's price specials by also running price specials to "offset" impact of the other firm's advertising program. You can be sure the manager of a supermarket in a particular market keeps a close eye on newspaper ads of the competition.

Sticky Prices Fail to Do Job

Except for this type of retaliatory price competition in the newspapers, retail prices tend to be "sticky" and slow to change. Changing prices is costly to the supermarket and irritating to the final consumer, so retailers hold the line on prices and let them go up over time in a stairstep fashion. Such an approach does not do much to help the probability that price signals will turn out to be effective messages in a communication system.

"Middlemen" tend to operate in a similar organizational structure. There are a few, large firms in any particular market area. There is price competition, but these large firms (flour mills, cotton merchants, grain exporters, vegetable processors, meat packers, etc.) have at

Wheat hauled to a local elevator, such as this one in St. John, Wash., brings the posted bid price for that day with premiums or discounts for protein level, moisture, foreign matter, etc.

least a degree of market power — the capacity to influence price or other terms of trade. The goal is often the realization of a certain gross margin per head, per ton, etc.

When a limited supply of raw material forces the processor's procurement cost up, this might simply mean taking a smaller margin than desired for a few weeks. But when raw material is in abundant supply, the large processor tends to "get even." Operating margins are allowed to increase, at least for a limited time, as the price of the raw material is forced lower. Any price signals which enter this operating arena from higher up in the system may be totally concealed or even reversed in the short

run as the firm wields an element of market power. Needed resource reallocation is blocked or slowed.

Price Takers — Skipping down to the producer level, the operating structure changes completely. The norm here is many small producers, approaching conditions economists call pure competition. The individual is a *price taker*, not a *price maker*. Price is determined at the aggregate level by interaction of demand and supply and the producer sells, on any particular day, at the prevailing price. A truckload of wheat hauled to the local elevator brings the posted bid price for that day with premiums or discounts for protein level, moisture level, foreign matter content, etc.

Earl R. Baker

Price for raw material at the producer level is a derived price, reflecting essentially value at the consumer level less the sum of the operating margins of all middlemen. And since the middlemen have at least some element of market power, the price to the producer does not and will not vary directly with changes in value at the consumer level. Add to this the complicating influence of extreme price variability at the producer level and it is easy to see why some researchers have questioned the effectiveness of the price mechanism as a communication system. If there is concern about the effectiveness of that communication effort, then there must be concern about the level of vertical coordination being achieved.

Contracts Supplement Signals

Relying on the communication processes of the price mechanism is not the only way to get vertical coordination. The alternatives range from approaches which supplement the price mechanism to vertical integration, a way of organizing which replaces price signals with management directive. Contracts can be used to supplement price signals. Say a processor is having difficulty getting a consistent flow of high quality raw material. Contracts with producers which specify quality standards, indicate time of delivery, and offer appropriate economic rewards for compliance can help. Such approaches are widely used throughout agriculture, but are especially prevalent in the fruits and vegetables sector. How

effective this approach will be in prompting alinement between what is produced and what is demanded depends on ability of the processor to interpret what is needed at the consumer level, get this reflected in a contract, and offer an incentive which will motivate producers to change.

Buying and selling by description can enhance the effectiveness of price signals. The emerging electronic marketing systems, where buyers bid or buy over computerized or other electronic systems, must consistently use a complete and detailed set of grades or other descriptors. Insofar as price differences are clearly related to differences in identified product attributes, the producer is better able to "sort out" and see the message inherent in the prices because of the increased visibility and importance of grades.

Almost all broiler production is in the hands of integrated firms. Chickens are hatched, fed, processed, packaged, and made ready for retail by one firm. These broilers are feeding on a special formulated and mixed feed in Mississippi.

Vertical integration is at the other end of the continuum from the open exchange systems. A type of vertical coordination, it involves the bringing of two or more stages of economic activity under the ownership and control of a single business entity or management. Management directive replaces price signals as a means of coordination. Management in the processing arm of the business simply passes the specifications for raw materials back to the producing arm of the business. Within technological and cost limitations, quality and timing of product flow are controlled and there are no visible, negotiated prices. Vertical integration is not unusual in fruits, vegetables, and grains. And almost all broiler production is in the hands of integrated firms. The chickens are hatched, fed, processed, packaged, and made ready for retail display by one firm.

Types of Efficiency — In discussing implications of various ways of achieving vertical coordination, it is useful to recognize that analysts of marketing systems talk about two types of efficiency. *Technical efficiency* deals with the cost of doing a job. The ratio of useful output to inputs gives a mental picture. Other considerations equal, a higher level of technical efficiency would be desirable. There is evidence in the research literature that the vertically integrated system can achieve higher levels of technical efficiency than an open market exchange system. This is consistent with the opportunity to specify raw material attributes and control the flow of those raw materials.

The second type or form of efficiency is *pricing efficiency*. High levels of pricing efficiency suggest that what is being produced is consistent with what is demand-

George A. Robinson

157

ed by consumers. Pricing efficiency, therefore, is a measure of the system's communication effectiveness. In a vertically integrated system, the ability to "match" what is produced with the demands of consumers is constrained only by management's ability to decipher those consumer demands, by the available technology, and by the cost-benefit ratio of making changes to maintain alinement with consumer demands. But this does not mean society would necessarily benefit from moves to vertical integration.

The net benefits of vertical integration are perhaps impossible to measure. Since price negotiations are effectively eliminated, what are the implications to society of the disappearance of previously observable prices? And if integrating means larger size and the possibility of increased market power, what are the implications to society? Leaving these issues for another forum, this chapter will focus attention on the current and pending interplay between open exchange systems and vertically integrated systems. For purposes of discussion, it is useful to hypothesize that failure of the price mechanism, in an open exchange system, to achieve high levels of vertical coordination will prompt moves to vertically integrated systems. Let's look at some reasons why this might occur.

Short and Long Run Impact

In the short run (within a year), failure of the marketing system to achieve high levels of interstage or vertical coordination are costly to society in general and to the individual firm. Consumers are denied access to preferred products and/or qualities at the levels and with the consistency they would prefer. Impact on the individual firm is best seen by con-

sidering the position of a processing firm. If the system does not generate a consistent flow of raw materials of acceptable quality, the firm has a difficult time meeting orders from its customers. A variable flow of raw materials is sure to increase the per unit costs of processing. Labor, for example, is either overworked or underworked depending on the flow of raw materials into the plant. In the short run, therefore, failure to coordinate can mean poor alinement between what is produced and what is demanded by consumers and increased costs of the final product at the consumer level.

Over a longer planning horizon, failure to coordinate has significant cost implications. Continuing to use the processing firm as an example, the type of plant which is planned and constructed will vary with anticipated problems in raw material flows. If a hightly variable flow is anticipated, the plant must be flexible in terms of daily or weekly quantity it can handle. A flexible plant will be less efficient in a technical sense than a plant which can be designed for a particular operating volume and a stable flow of raw materials into the plant. Over time, the reduced efficiency and higher costs get passed on to the consumer in the form of higher product prices.

In a short and long run context, there are economic incentives for higher levels of vertical coordination. If the exchange system and the price mechanism do not generate acceptable levels of coordination, pressures for vertical integration emerge. Everyone, from producer to consumer, has a stake in what type of system we will see and the level of coordination realized. More widespread understanding of how markets coordinate decisions would help.

Grades and Promotions in the Food System

By Mary C. Kenney

Upon returning from a relaxing vacation, we may be struck by the amount of noise and confusion which is part of our everyday life. It might occur to us that much of this noise consists of people telling us what they think we ought to know. Many messages of different types are beamed directly at us. We pay attention to messages that interest us and ignore the rest. We have learned to filter out information we feel will not benefit us. In fact, if we were unable to extract messages which have a personal meaning, we would be victims of information overload; we wouldn't know much about anything.

In general, messages about certain products or groups of products are likely to reach a small audience. Since most of us are not likely to purchase a 20-carat diamond necklace, descriptions of such an article probably won't interest us. Similarly we are not apt to pay much attention to messages persuading us to purchase this kind of luxury item, since even if we wanted to buy it, our pocketbooks would prevent us from doing so. On the other hand, some products we are certain to consume and likely to purchase on a regular basis. Because of our direct interest in food, we are apt to pay attention to food messages of many types. Many people believe that reading food labels helps them decide what food to buy. Some

may listen to television food advertising for the same reason.

This chapter will explain the value of commodity grades which send messages to many traders in the food system, but which are unlikely to be apparent to many consumers as they shop in retail grocery stores. Nevertheless, consumers are better off because commodity grades are used by other buyers and sellers in the food marketing system. By properly identifying agricultural commodities at various levels of the system, grades can save time and money. Grades can facilitate message sending and increase economic efficiency. In fact, consumers pay less for food than they would in the absence of a commodity grading system.

Besides the two-way communication between producers and consumers which grades can provide, we will discuss messages sent by producers to consumers through generic promotion programs, why producers support such efforts, and what we know of their effectiveness.

Until the early part of this century, most people in the United States lived on farms. Much of the food consumed was produced nearby. The food closely resembled agricultural commodities as they were produced. There was little need for a formal system to provide for identifying

Mary C. Kenney is Division Economist, Livestock, Meat, Grain, & Seed Division, Agricultural Marketing Service.

food. Today, most of us live a considerable distance from the source of the food we eat. Much food has been processed and packaged to the extent that it is difficult for us to visualize the ingredients as they were sold for the first time, and how they arrived at their present form. We could, of course, find out these things for ourselves. However, we spend our time earning a living, going to school, or pursuing other interests in our spare time. Further, there is no need for each of us, independently, to search for the information we need to make food purchase decisions.

Because consumers care about the quality of the food they eat, and reward those who provide high quality food by paying more for it, professional buyers and sellers at all levels of the food marketing system have developed product descriptions which convey such messages from producers through food handlers, manufacturers, wholesalers, retailers, to consumers. The system also permits consumer preferences to be revealed to agricultural producers.

We know the goal of the marketing system is to match food supplies with consumers' preferences as they are revealed by demand. However, professional commodity (and food) buyers do not have to personally inspect products in order to provide quality assurance to consumers. Instead, those who buy and sell agricultural commodities and food products substitute trading by description for personal inspection.

Economic Efficiency

Trading by description can contribute to economic efficiency. This means consumers will benefit from lower food prices as reduced trading costs at earlier stages of

marketing (closer to the farm) are passed on by food retailers. It may be, however, that retailers themselves do not benefit from efficiencies from selling by description. But to the extent that markets are competitive and sellers are required to pass on cost savings in order to remain viable competitors, consumers will benefit from all efficiencies in the food marketing chain, whatever the trading level.

Some buyers and sellers deal with one another on a regular basis and develop a system of their own whereby product descriptions may mean the same thing to both of them. Sometimes, however, such descriptions are inadequate for trading purposes because they fail to convey essential information. In such cases, a standardized system of commonly understood terms is required.

Usually, professional buyers in the food system purchase commodities from many sellers, and deal with each seller rather infrequently. They do not take the time to develop a sufficient understanding of the way the other uses words. It would probably be a poor use of their business time, anyway. One might say that the opportunity cost of their time is too great, that economic efficiency in the entire system declines as product identification becomes unnecessarily personalized.

Grade Standards — The Federal Government has provided uniform trading terms called grades. Grading refers to the sorting of a commodity into relatively standard classes which reflect acceptability on the part of the buyer. The U.S. Department of Agriculture (USDA) develops grade standards for meat, cattle, wool, poultry, eggs, dairy products; fresh, frozen, canned and dried fruits and vegetables; cotton, tobacco, spirits of turpentine and rosin. Because use of grading is voluntary in most cases, those who receive the service generally pay for it. State departments of agriculture often cooperate with USDA in carrying out grading work.

Wholesalers, manufacturers, and people who buy for retail stores are much more likely than consumers to rely on grades as they trade. Most of these people purchase large quantities of product at a time, frequently from a distance. The purchase usually involves a lot of money. Losses in such transactions are apt to be significant if the product is not what the buyer believed was ordered.

In fact, accurate grading can lower transportation costs for the entire marketing system by indicating, along with price information, which products are likely to bring a sufficiently higher return at the next point of sale to justify shipping costs. Grading can reduce spoilage by separating high quality product from that likely to deteriorate more quickly. Marketing costs decline as raw commodities from many producers can be commingled for sale according to grade; farmers are paid based on returns from the lot.

Some Tests for Grades

Do the grades assigned to a commodity convey the same information to all traders who use them? If not, the descriptive terms may be confusing or inadequate. Quality assurance in the marketing system would be enhanced through modifying and/or explaining the descriptive terms to suit traders' needs. Are the grades based on factors obvious to buyers and sellers as they negotiate price? The ability to verify product classification through personal inspection

makes a grading system more useful.

Do the grades reflect differing needs of buyers as they purchase products for various uses? The grading system should reflect significant differences in demand while not being too complex or costly to utilize. Do the grades accurately describe significant variations within the product? If not, buyers whose purchases are based on grades will be uncertain about actual characteristics of the product. To be most effective, the number of grades assigned should correspond directly to the number of quality categories buyers feel are important.

If the number of grades assigned is greater than the number of buyer categories, buyers may not distinguish between grades. To differentiate through grade names when buyers are indifferent about products falling into two or more grades creates confusion in agricultural marketing. On the other hand, problems can arise when users perceive distinct quality differences within one assigned grade. If this happens, adding one or more grade categories to coincide with the number of classes which consumers recognize will enhance pricing efficiency.

Are the grades based on standards which can be measured reliably at a reasonable cost? How accurately can commodity graders assign grades? For example, backfat measurement is crucial in determining pork grades. Presently it is not practical to measure backfat of live animals, so we must substitute estimates for actual measurement as hogs and other animals are sold. USDA is now conducting research to develop an electronic instrument to measure the backfat of live animals which can be applied easily at a reasonable cost. (The role of sound waves in indicating fat is being studied along with other approaches.) Technological advances of this type have great potential for improving the present system. Instrument grading of live hogs could provide a check against carcass measurement of backfat when there are substantial inconsistencies between live prices and the carcass value of pork. Because most hogs are sold on buyer estimate of quality, it could also provide farmers with important information about the hogs they sell.

Since it is common for packers to pay farmers according to average price, those who produce high yielding hogs claim they are paid less than the actual carcass value warrants. Some sellers of lower quality hogs may receive higher prices than consumer preferences would indicate because variations from average quality are not adequately considered by packers.

Getting the Pork Message

To understand how grading issues such as these are considered by USDA and industry as they search for the most appropriate grading system, let's look at the pork carcass grades. We noted earlier that commodity grades are found less frequently in retail grocery stores than at earlier stages of the food marketing chain. Because grades for pork carcasses do not indicate meat quality to consumers, but rather the total amount of lean meat contained in the carcass, retail pork is not graded.

Meatpackers and those who purchase for sale in retail establishments use the carcass grades as a way of estimating returns from the final sale of pork. Together with the related grades for live hogs, the grades make it possible to pay

the hog producer according to the ultimate value of his or her product. Although the information exchange between retail pork buyers and hog producers is indirect, and the pork grade unknown to consumers, the pork grades permit messages to be sent between farmers and consumers through professional commodity buyers.

We know that when commodity grades indicate value, they can promote efficient marketing. Since most of the retail value of pork comes from sales of the four lean cuts of pork (hams, loins, picnics, Boston butts), pork grades are based on the ratio of the weight of the four lean cuts to total carcass weight. This ratio is called the "yield." More than 53 percent of the carcass weight of a U.S. No. 1 pork grade consists of the four lean cuts (or has a "yield" of greater than 53 percent); packers can expect less than 47 percent of a U.S. No. 4 grade carcass to be sold as lean cuts. To estimate yield, meat graders determine the length (or weight), measure the amount of backfat, and evaluate the degree of muscling.

As the length (or weight) of backfat thickness and degree of muscling of a pork carcass are recorded, the related grade can be determined by using these measurements. Longer, heavier carcasses with less backfat and more muscling will be graded more highly; the highest possible grade is U.S. No. 1. At the present time, we have ample evidence that expected packer returns differ significantly between carcasses which fall in adjacent grade categories. So we can conclude that there probably are not too many grades of pork, based on buyers' perceptions.

However, the U.S. No. 4 grade, the lowest yield category, is hard to find these days. As consumers have expressed their preference for a leaner product, hog farmers have raised far fewer fat hogs, and there have been fewer and fewer U.S. No. 4 carcasses sold in recent years. In any case, buyers and sellers are probably not confused by existence of a No. 4 grade; they just don't use it very much.

We noted earlier that problems arise when the grading system fails to distinguish differences which buyers feel are important. This could happen if many buyers were willing to pay a significantly higher price per pound for one shipment of pork carcasses than another, based on the differences in average yield, when both of the shipments carry the U.S. No. 1 grade. In fact, meat and animal researchers recently weighed the four lean cuts derived from many U.S. No. 1 carcasses. They found that yields of the four cuts ranged from slightly more than 53 percent to nearly 70 percent. Since a range of 17 percent is considerably greater than yield differences between the highest and lowest grades under the present system, these results raise questions about the need for one or more additional grades.

How Grade Changes Come About

Problems of this type are typical of issues which USDA and industry must consider as they work to maintain the best grading system practicable. Together with industry feedback, research results which indicate a change in the quality of agricultural commodities are often used as a basis for studying the need for a change in commodity grades. If, after considering all

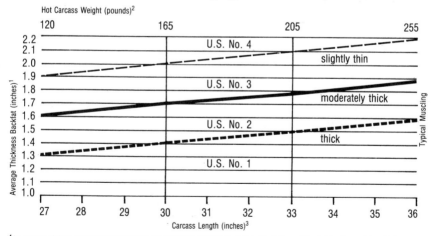

Relationship Between Average Thickness of Backfat, Carcass Length or Weight, and Grade for Carcasses with Muscling Typical of Their Degree of Fatness.

[1] An average of three measurements including the skin made opposite the first and last ribs and the last lumbar vertebra. It also reflects adjustment, as appropriate, to compensate for variations—from—normal fat distribution.

[2] Carcass weight is based on a hot packer style carcass.

[3] Carcass length is measured from the anterior point of the aitch bone to the anterior edge of the first rib.

relevant issues (in addition to the few highlighted in this chapter), USDA determines that a grade change would improve marketing conditions for a particular commodity, USDA proposes a modification which experts have determined to be the most useful, considering ease and cost of utilization.

The proposal describes other alternatives which were considered, and the reason for selecting the one being proposed. The proposal is published in the Federal Register, and news releases are distributed. The public is invited to comment. Written comments and views expressed in public hearings are weighed heavily. Often the proposal is modified, published in its modified form, and the public given additional opportunities to comment. The final decision of whether to change a grading system or how to modify it is the result of a great deal of thought by many people.

We have discussed how, by identifying quality differences, a commodity grading system can assist farmers in determining what level of product quality will be the most profitable for them to produce and sell. By being responsive to consumers' preferences, farmers can increase their income. We noted that agricultural commodity grades, while not messages in the usual sense, can transmit messages from consumers to producers. As they sort commodities into appropriate groups, grades provide buyers and sellers with a valuable marketing tool.

By replacing product descriptions which tend to vary and be ambiguous to traders with standardized terms that are commonly understood, grades promote economic efficiency. If the cost of using a grading system is less than the benefit to a firm, there will be sufficient incentive to

pay for grading services. When the entire system performs well, farmers will expand production in areas where rewards are greatest according to consumers' purchasing patterns. In this sense, farmers respond to consumer tastes as they have been shaped.

Advertising — There are, however, means available to sellers in the food system, such as advertising and promotion, whereby preferences themselves may be altered. Advertising messages as well as grades promote economic efficiency in the marketplace through product identification. We remarked earlier about the confusion and complexity of everyday life. We know consumers rely on food messages to guide them in their purchasing decisions. Because individual tastes are flexible and change over time, consumers can be influenced by product information and/or persuasion to purchase certain food items instead of others.

People are better off when they can exercise product choices over a wide quality and price range. Without some outside help, however, it would be very costly for consumers to undertake the personal search necessary to satisfy their preferences. Objective product information conveyed through advertising can assist them in making better choices. Image conscious sellers who advertise have an incentive to assure food shoppers that their products are of acceptable quality. In this way, the risk of dissatisfaction can be reduced for consumers.

Food manufacturers lead all other manufacturing groups in expenditures on advertising. In 1979 these firms accounted for about 25 percent of total advertising outlays by all manufacturers. Grocery stores also spend more money to convince people to patronize their establishments than any other group of retailers. Continued willingness of these firms to devote significant resources to such efforts (at least $5 billion in 1979) is an indication of their belief in the effectiveness of these programs in influencing consumers' food purchase decisions.

Push and Pull Strategies

About one-half this money is spent on mass media messages sent through magazines, billboards, and local and national television and radio; newspaper advertising amounts to about 20 percent of the total. Firms also utilize discount coupons and incentive premiums. Strategies of this type which are designed to influence consumer choice directly are called "pull" promotion or advertising. "Push" promotion, on the other hand, includes allowances given food retailers, sales efforts at conventions, in-store food displays, and advertising in the trade press. About $3 billion was spent on "push" promotion of food during 1979.

Agricultural producers are aware of the potential benefits available from food promotion and advertising. In contrast to food manufacturers, who want to influence consumer choice in favor of their brands, farmers are interested in generic advertising designed to increase peoples' preferences for certain commodities, such as citrus products or milk. We know it is difficult to convince individuals to alter their consumption patterns in a fundamental way. Nevertheless, some farmers find compelling reasons to support commodity promotion efforts.

While the number of large farming enterprises has increased substantially in the past few decades, many producers still find themselves at a bargaining disadvantage as they negotiate with buyers. For one thing, producers typically have fewer sales outlets than buyers have sources of supply. This is especially true because central markets, where many buyers and sellers come to trade, are no longer very active. Direct purchasing of agricultural commodities, in which terms of trade are individually negotiated, is much more common these days.

Perishability of many farm products, which places some farmers under pressure to sell before the commodity deteriorates and loses value, is another factor which precludes the farmers' equal standing with buyers in some cases. Lack of supply control for most agricultural products also has an adverse effect on many farmers. Historically, farmers produce more of a commodity the year following a profitable selling season for the product. As long as total supply is not restrained, farmers find it difficult to maintain sufficient profit margins. They look to increasing consumer demand as a solution to the depressed prices and profits they may experience during high production years.

Of course, increased supplies will always be purchased for storage or will be consumed. However, as long as consumer preferences for the product do not vary, increased consumption will be accompanied by much lower prices. Hence selling additional product will not increase total revenue to farmers when consumer demand is unchanged, as the demand for groups of agricultural commodities is quite unresponsive to price.

Amount Constant — The amount of food consumed from a product group is quite constant in most peoples' diets. Much lower prices are required to entice people to alter their dietary patterns in order to save money as long as their incomes are stable and their tastes as well as prices of other products remain the same.

Because lower retail prices mean lower prices at the farm gate, some agricultural producers are willing to spend money to convince retail shoppers to shift their preferences in favor of certain commodities or food items made from their products. If the advertising and promotion efforts are successful, shoppers will purchase greater amounts of the advertised product at a given price than they would have prior to the program. This is what is meant by an outward shift in demand.

Because individual farmers often suffer during recurring periods of expanded supply, they would like commodity promotion programs to shift demand so that prices during such times will not be so low. Of course, farmers only benefit from increased consumer demand to the extent the system translates retail price changes efficiently to the farm gate.

In contrast to agricultural producers, food manufacturers may find it profitable to differentiate their product in consumers' minds without necessarily aiming to increase demand for it. Decreased price sensitivity by retail shoppers, as they perceive that a given food product has fewer acceptable substitutes, can increase revenue to the manufacturer, since the firm has control over the amount of product supplied to the market. Such a strategy would have an adverse impact on commodity revenue during expansionary years.

Producer Promotion

Sometimes, farmers join cooperatives or other voluntary producer groups. How

effectively products can be promoted through voluntary arrangements depends upon how large contributions are, how effectively they are expended, and how stable the funds remain over time. There is a tendency for some producers to withhold contributions to voluntary efforts because they feel the product advertising and promotion activities undertaken by program participants will increase their receipts at no expense to them. Other farmers contribute when marketing conditions are favorable and withdraw as profits are squeezed, often on a cyclical basis.

Because of the difficulty of maintaining effective advertising and promotion programs under these conditions, farmers have sought participation in organizations established by law. Federal regulations to permit research and promotion activities are appealing to producers who want to increase demand for their commodity and are willing to contribute to the effort. Under Federal auspices, once a program is approved by a required majority of eligible voters, it is binding on all but the very smallest producers. While refunds are available upon request under some programs, each operation affected must initially contribute its share to the program. Shares are usually directly related to the size of the production enterprise or history of production.

Through the Agricultural Marketing Agreement Act of 1937, Federal regulations permit advertising and promotion for 14 fruits and vegetables; commodity handlers are assessed. At this time, milk producers contribute to six advertising and promotion efforts under the Federal Milk Marketing Order Program. As with all provisions of marketing orders, authority for research and promotion activities must be approved by the Secretary of Agriculture and by producers in a referendum before becoming effective.

Legislating — If members of a commodity group feel that Federal legislation authorizing research, promotion or advertising activities for their industry is desirable, they must seek the support of a member of Congress in introducing appropriate legislation. If the bill is reported out of committee, passed by both houses of Congress, and signed by the President, industry members may propose an order to implement the legislation. The order must be submitted to all eligible industry members for their approval or disapproval through a referendum.

Separate Federal laws have been passed to permit research and promotion for the following commodities: cotton, potatoes, eggs, wheat, wool, lamb, mohair, beef, and floral products. Following are federally legislated commodity research and promotion programs active at this time. In all cases, USDA is required to monitor

activities authorized by the boards to ensure that whatever is done is consistent with the intent of the laws.

The Cotton Research and Promotion Act of 1966 provides for collecting $1 per bale from first buyers of cotton. The money is used for research and promotion. Producers may request and receive refunds of their assessments. Net collections under this program amounted to about $20 million for the 1981-82 crop year.

To strengthen the egg industry's market position, the Egg Research and Consumer Act of 1974 authorizes a program whereby egg producers may finance research and promotion projects through the Egg Board. At this time, producers are charged 5 cents per 30 dozen case of eggs sold, and may pay 7.5 cents, if that amount is approved in a referendum to be held shortly. Producers who have fewer than 3,000 laying hens and those whose egg production is primarily for breeding are exempt. The Potato Research and Promotion Act of 1971 pro-

The first buyer of this cotton will pay $1 per bale under provisions of the Cotton Research and Promotion Act of 1966. The money is used for research and promotion of cotton.

Ford Tractor Operations

vides for a National Potato Promotion Board to collect an assessment of 1 cent per hundredweight on all Irish potatoes sold for food and seed. Producers may request refunds. Those who farm less than 5 acres are exempt.

Wheat, Wool, and Beef

The Wheat and Wheat Foods Research and Nutrition Act of 1977 authorizes research and nutrition education activities which are directed by the Wheat Industry Council. End-product manufacturers, primarily wholesale bakers, are assessed according to the amount of processed wheat they purchase. Those who notify the Council that they would like to reserve the right to request refunds may do so. During Fiscal Year 1982, the second year of the program, net revenue is expected to be about $700,000. This money will be used to select and train individuals who will speak to the nutritional merits of wheat-based foods.

The National Wool Act of 1954 authorizes advertising, promotion, and market development for wool, mohair, sheep, and goats. The programs are financed through deductions from price support payments to wool and mohair producers. When average market prices exceed the support levels, no payments are made to producers. Hence, there is no money available for promotion purposes. Currently, the deduction is set at 2.5 cents per pound of wool marketed. If a sufficient proportion of producers approve a 4-cent level in a referendum this year, the American Sheep Producers Council will be overseeing greater expenditures for generic wool and lamb promotion.

Legislative authority for beef promotion now is available through the Beef Research and Consumer Information Act. A board is authorized to collect assessments from producers to improve and develop markets for cattle, beef, and beef products through research and information activities. Since the order failed to gain approval of the required percentage of producers who voted, in order to activate a program the industry would have to propose another order and secure approval in a referendum.

The Floral Research and Consumer Information Act of 1981 also authorizes research, consumer and producer education as well as promotion. However, this Act will not be effective until the industry requests a public hearing and obtains approval of a sufficient number of flower and plant producers.

Sales Studied — Although generic promotion and advertising expenditures are small relative to dollars spent on all food advertising, there have been several serious attempts to determine whether commodity advertising has increased sales. Some studies indicated higher sales in the short run as food shoppers respond to advertising messages. We do not know, however, what the long term effects of permanently changing preferences may be, or to what extent commodity advertising has the potential for changing food preferences over time.

The problem of effectively isolating the role of commodity advertising, as it influences sales, from other factors which affect demand, has plagued most analysts. Although we do not have definitive information concerning the magnitude of sales response to advertising messages, some of the work sheds light on the possible pattern of response. It appears to take several months for advertising to achieve its maximum effect. There is also some evidence that the residual effects of advertising efforts are evident for as long as 8 months after the expenditure.

While a few studies have attempted to estimate the optimal level of promotion and advertising expenditures, the results are presented cautiously. Further, the studies emphasize the need for analysts to consider unique commodity characteristics as well as significant differences between markets which make inter-product and inter-market generalizations inappropriate.

Size Factor — Firms have the potential to capture operating efficiencies from advertising. However, there appears to be no empirical evidence to support the notion of economies to scale in production. It may be that there are substantial pecuniary advantages to size. We don't know, however, if agricultural producers could benefit to the same extent as food manufacturers. Whether or not firms have a greater incentive to innovate because of advertising is another interesting question.

We recognize a potential for increased efficiency overall from advertising. However, many studies which have explored this relationship have been based on broad industry-level data. In fact, it is necessary to allow for differences in firm strategies and product characteristics when examining the competitive effects of advertising. People who have studied the persuasive power of advertising agree that a superior product image cannot be created in the minds of consumers by product differentiation or advertising alone.

Some Programs May Be Effective

Because product identification is obvious, generic promotion and advertising programs on behalf of commodities sold to consumers in fresh form may be quite effective in increasing sales. Brand or regional identification, too, serves to convey the notion that there is something special about these products. When production is constrained to a limited geographic area, promotion efforts have a greater potential for increasing sales receipts than they may for commodities whose supplies can expand more easily. Regionally produced commodity programs are also more apt to be guided by tight organization and coordination.

Those who have analyzed sales response to advertising have not addressed the distributional issues. From a societal view, it would be useful to know how the benefits from advertising are distributed between different groups, consumers, producers, commodity promotion boards and advertising agencies, for example. Do lower income food shoppers benefit more than those in higher income groups?

Do producers benefit according to size of their enterprise? Is the sales increase for the farmer enough to offset assessments under the commodity promotion program? Does a favorable commodity profit situation due to advertising in one season lead to such product expansion in the following season that profits to individual farmers are lower than if there were no commodity promotion and advertising program? Even if food shoppers make better purchasing decisions as a result of the information conveyed through advertising messages, are there more effective ways of providing information to them?

Timing Sales for High Returns

By Gene A. Futrell and Robert N. Wisner

P rice variability is a characteristic of most agricultural commodities and products. It can result from a number of things — short-term changes in market supply or demand conditions, developments that might impact on longer term supplies or demands (such as weather, government policies, international developments, economic conditions), seasonal supply and demand patterns or tendencies, and year-to-year or cyclical changes in production. While prices have long been somewhat variable, they have become more volatile in recent years.

A greater international dimension to agricultural markets has made crop and livestock production around the world increasingly important market factors, along with world economic conditions, trade policies, and any other factors that might affect U.S. exports. Demand growth, variable weather conditions, and smaller world stocks of grains (relative to usage) have made markets more sensitive to changes in supply/demand influences and have contributed to price volatility. Some of the variation in price is fairly predictable, some is not. From whatever the source, price changes can have a big impact on cash receipts and on bottom line results in the farm busi-

ness. Timing of pricing and selling is an important part of marketing management and one of the keys to success or failure in modern farming.

Effective use of market news and outlook information can help improve the timing of marketings and aid in managing price and financial risks. Understanding and making appropriate use of marketing and pricing alternatives, including forward pricing options, can add some flexibility to the timing of sales. An understanding of seasonal production and price patterns and of cyclical production patterns for some commodities also provides useful guides to production, storage, and marketing decisions. Some things to consider in timing sales of both crop and livestock products are discussed in this chapter.

In a normal marketing year, prices for most major U.S. crops show distinct seasonal patterns. Lowest prices of the year usually occur at or near harvest, when supplies are abundant. After storable crops have been moved into storage facilities, farmer marketings usually diminish and prices begin an uptrend that frequently continues until 2 or 3 months before the next harvest. For fall harvested crops, the uptrend may temporarily halt in late winter and early spring as farmers

Gene A. Futrell is Professor of Economics and Extension Economist in Marketing and Livestock Market Analysis, Iowa State University, Ames.

Robert N. Wisner is Professor of Economics and Extension Economist in Grain Marketing and Analysis at the university.

expand sales from the previous year's crop to meet income taxes, farm payments, and spring planting expenses.

Many crops also exhibit price strength at planting time, when farmer marketings slacken as growers place top priority on getting the crop seeded. Planting time price strength is most noticeable for crops such as corn, cotton and soybeans, but often is less noticeable for wheat. Price strength during the U.S. winter wheat planting season may be tempered by sales of newly harvested U.S. and Canadian spring wheat. Conversely, price strength in the spring wheat planting season may be tempered by the approaching winter wheat harvest in the Southern Plains.

Storage Expenses

In taking advantage of seasonal price patterns to increase returns for storable crops, farmers should keep in mind both the costs of storage and their individual ability to bear the risk of declining prices later in the marketing year. For most crops, one of the largest costs of storage is interest on the value of the crop inventory. For 8 months' storage, interest costs can easily amount to 20 cents per bushel of corn, 30 cents for wheat, and 50 cents per bushel of soybeans. These costs occur either through interest expenses that could have been avoided by selling the crop at harvest and paying off operating loans, or through potential interest earnings from the money invested in crop inventories. Other storage ex-

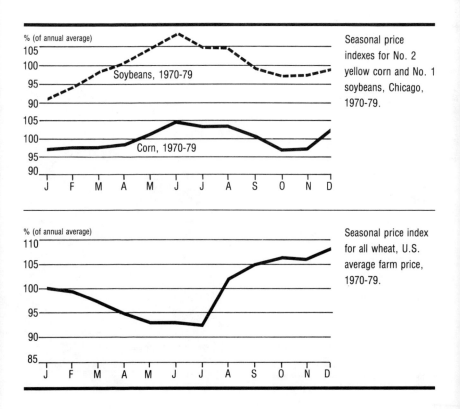

Seasonal price indexes for No. 2 yellow corn and No. 1 soybeans, Chicago, 1970-79.

Seasonal price index for all wheat, U.S. average farm price, 1970-79.

penses include extra handling and drying costs to make the crop safe for longer term storage, and commercial charges if production is stored off the farm.

In years of normal U.S. crop production, risk of declining prices is low during the first few months after harvest. However, market risk increases substantially after about 6 or 7 months of storage. Sharp downward price adjustments often occur in the last month or two before harvest as domestic and foreign users cut inventories to minimal levels in anticipation of lower cost new-crop supplies.

In years when adverse weather reduces U.S. production below anticipated market requirements, crop prices generally follow a contraseasonal pattern. In this case the highest price of the marketing year often comes at or near harvest, with gradually declining prices as the season progresses. High early-season prices reflect aggressive bidding by users for the limited supplies. Ample storage space and limited farmer marketings may also contribute to price strength at harvest in years of short crops.

A good rule in crop marketing is to store when crops are large, and to sell a significant part of your production at harvest when the U.S. crop is short of expected market requirements. In years of short crops, favorable forward pricing opportunities may also be available for delivery later in the year and for pricing the next year's production.

Perishables — Seasonal price patterns

Vegetable prices are under pressure at harvest time because of the perishable nature of production and the need to encourage increased use to avoid spoilage. Lettuce, which is being harvested here in California, is among the most perishable.

for perishable crops such as fruits and vegetables are similar to those for readily storable crops, except that price movements may be greater. Prices are under pressure at harvest time because of the perishable nature of production and the need to encourage increased utilization to avoid spoilage. Where possible, harvest-time prices also encourage processing and storage activities. Later in the year when prices rise enough to cover processing and storage expenses, these supplies are returned to the marketplace.

In the last 25 years improved handling, processing and storage technology, and

more uniform demand throughout the year have tended to reduce seasonal variation in crop prices. But these developments likely have been offset by high interest costs on product inventories, which tend to be reflected in increased seasonal price movements for storable commodities.

Crop Cycles — Unlike livestock, it is difficult to find longer term price and production cycles for major U.S. crops. In the last 2 decades, world demand for most U.S. crops has trended steadily upward, with production varying from year to year as a result of weather, government farm programs and relative prices

for various crops. One objective of U.S. Government farm programs has been to reduce year-to-year variations in commercial supplies, thus tending to remove cyclical tendencies that might otherwise be present.

Since the late 19th century, grain prices have traced out what might be considered a 26- to 28-year cycle from peak to peak. Every 26 to 28 years since the 1890's a period of high and volatile grain prices has occurred, and has been followed by a return to lower and more stable prices. But this pattern is due primarily to the influence of wars, inflationary periods, and other world events rather than

Christopher Springmann

to biological or economic characteristics of agriculture. With only three such periods in this century, statisticians have limited evidence for projecting that prices will follow a similar cyclical pattern in the years ahead.

Production of most livestock and poultry products is at least somewhat cyclical. Periods of increased production in response to favorable profits are eventually followed by production downturns when prices become unprofitable. Production cycles may range from 2 years or less on some products to 10 years or more on others, depending in large part on how quickly increased production is biologically possible.

The production cycle for beef cattle has been quite regular and is typically 10 to 12 years from peak to peak. The hog cycle is less consistent but often varies from 3 to 5 years in length. Production cycles tend to be shorter for eggs and

turkeys and are usually about 2 years from peak to peak. Broilers, milk and sheep production have not shown a regular cyclical pattern but have been dominated more by longer term production trends. Some livestock and poultry products have fairly regular seasonal variations in supplies and prices. These patterns generally reflect either seasonal changes in costs of production or the technical or biological efficiency of production.

Hogs, Cattle, Eggs
Hog prices are typically lowest during late winter-early spring and again during the fourth quarter. Prices at these times reflect seasonal increases in slaughter, resulting from larger farrowings during both the late summer and spring months. Smaller farrowings in December-February result in a seasonal decline in third quarter pork supplies which usually bring higher prices. Slaughter cattle prices show less seasonal variation than hogs,

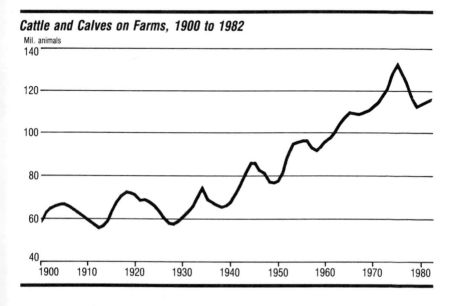

Cattle and Calves on Farms, 1900 to 1982

Mil. animals

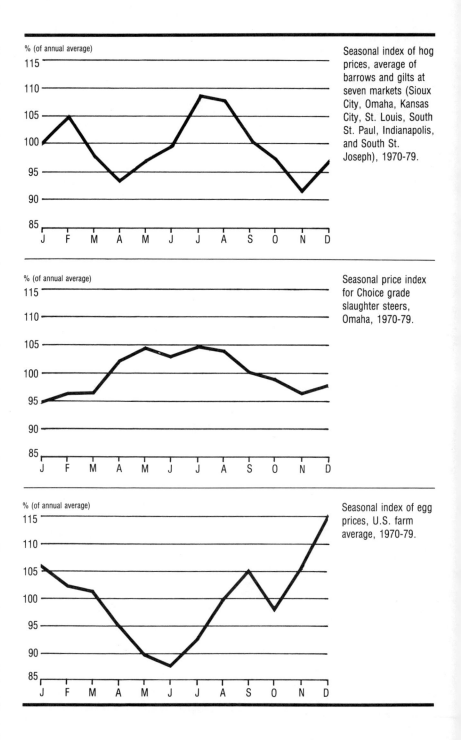

% (of annual average)

Seasonal index of hog prices, average of barrows and gilts at seven markets (Sioux City, Omaha, Kansas City, St. Louis, South St. Paul, Indianapolis, and South St. Joseph), 1970-79.

% (of annual average)

Seasonal price index for Choice grade slaughter steers, Omaha, 1970-79.

% (of annual average)

Seasonal index of egg prices, U.S. farm average, 1970-79.

and the pattern is less predictable from year to year. But prices do tend to be somewhat higher in spring and summer than at other times of year. Egg prices are typically lowest during peak production in spring, then rise seasonally in summer and fall as production declines.

Seasonal price tendencies and the cyclical stage of production for a particular product can be useful as general guides to timing pricing or sales. In some cases these patterns may also be a major consideration in production decisions, such as when to farrow sows, purchase feeder livestock, or buy replacement chicks or turkey poults. Seasonal price patterns also can be used in decisions on the weight at which to market livestock.

Normally it would not be advisable to carry cattle or hogs to heavier-than-normal weights during months when the seasonal tendency is for prices to decline. But heavier than normal weights may be warranted when prices are rising seasonally. These decisions, however, should also consider the expected cost of additional weight gains in relation to the expected selling price.

While seasonal and cyclical patterns are fairly consistent for some livestock products, there's no certainty that every cycle will be the same or that the seasonal pattern will be "normal" every year. These patterns can only be starting points and each year must be examined for any evidence of unusual conditions. In some years cyclical changes in production may offset normal seasonal price tendencies. At other times, weather or other influences on production or weight gains may moderate seasonal patterns. Or unusually high or low feed prices, high interest rates, or other cost factors may alter a production cycle from the typical pattern.

In developing a sales or pricing plan for any particular year, keep well informed on domestic and foreign production, general demand conditions and prospects, governmental policies that may affect markets, and day-to-day developments in livestock markets. How is slaughter or production running relative to earlier periods and to usual seasonal patterns or expectations? Are there unusual factors on the demand side of the market such as abnormally large or small supplies of competing products or new sources of demand? Keeping up on current market conditions and prospective price developments requires lots of information: market news reports, crop and livestock production estimates, and market analysis and outlook information. Careful use of this information can help guide production decisions and sales strategies.

Getting, Using Market Information

The U.S. Department of Agriculture (USDA) is a major source of information and data needed to guide decisions on timing of marketing. The market news network for collecting and disseminating information on market supplies and prices, often through cooperative Federal-State programs, provides information needed for day-to-day marketing and pricing decisions. Price information from the Nation's major commodity futures exchanges is also an important source of current market news. USDA programs in crop and livestock data estimating, and economic and commodity analysis, provide benchmarks used worldwide in forecasting prices for agricultural commodities. The USDA system provides current estimates and projections of U.S. and world crop and livestock supplies and utilization several times during the year.

USDA is a major source of information and data needed to guide decisions on timing of marketing. Here at Chicago's fruit and vegetable market, a USDA market newsman (right) interviews one of the commission merchants.

Jack Schneider

Season average price forecasts for most major crops and quarterly livestock price forecasts from this network are available through outlook and situation reports and USDA newsletters. These forecasts can be used by farmers in evaluating current cash prices, in setting annual price goals for their production, in making decisions about forward contracting or hedging through use of futures markets, and in deciding whether to store their crops.

For example, if current prices are moderately below the season average price forecast, growers might decide to store their crops and wait for higher prices. Cash prices or contracting prices for later delivery that are moderately above the predicted season average price would be a signal to sell at least part of the production and reduce exposure to price risk. Listings of various USDA outlook reports, crop estimates and livestock production reports, and information on how to obtain them, are available from USDA in Washington, D.C.

Other Sources — In addition to USDA outlook reports, economic newsletters and other materials are regularly published by many land-grant universities. These sources of outlook information provide more localized market conditions and prices that relate more closely to a producer's own area. Other sources of market outlook reports include commercial advisory services, farm magazines, farm management firms, and commodity brokerage companies. Types of reports and services available from these sources vary widely in content, depth of analysis, and cost.

Some advisory services offer specific recommendations on the percentage of production to be sold at various times during the year. In using these recommendations, farmers need to judge how their costs, financial risk-bearing ability, and production risks differ from the average producer and to make appropriate allowances for such differences.

Marketing Orders, Agreements
Marketing orders and agreements are tools used primarily in marketing dairy products, fruits, vegetables, and nuts to improve the level and stability of producer prices and incomes. Marketing agreements are voluntary agreements between producers and handlers of a commodity and the Secretary of Agriculture which specify how the commodity will be marketed. Most marketing agreements are supported by marketing orders. A marketing order is established by majority vote of producers of the commodity and becomes binding on all producers and handlers of the commodity covered by the order. Marketing orders and agreements usually cover the flow of the commodity to market including the timing and quality specifications, and sometimes involve pooling or averaging of returns to producers, marketing allotments, providing of market information and product advertising.

Many marketing orders operate in conjunction with marketing cooperatives. The Secretary of Agriculture is required to authorize and supervise marketing orders, and has responsibility for seeing they meet the public interest. Authority for marketing orders and agreements has its origins in the Agricultural Adjustment Act of 1933 and the 1937 Agricultural Marketing Agreement Act. Use of these tools is specifically prohibited for several major commodities including grains, soybeans, and livestock.

Selecting the Best Market Alternative

By V. James Rhodes

hat shall I do? Shall I sell my cattle to the packer buyer who has just made an offer or send them tomorrow to an auction market? Shall I sell my hogs today at the local buying station or wait another week? Would it be profitable to erect a roadside market for selling my apples and peaches? Shall I sign a contract to produce so many acres of green beans or shall I put that land in soybeans this season? Shall I contract some of my expected wheat crop before harvest, or sell it all at harvest to my local co-op?

Those questions suggest the nature of market alternatives for farmers. Alternatives involve outlets or buyers. Also important are the various conditions of sale. Some of these conditions can be classified by type of market outlet such as an auction, buying station, feedlot sale, or roadside stand. Other market alternatives involve the market options provided. These market options include the time relationships of sale, delivery and pricing; schedule of premiums and discounts, and other factors.

What criteria do farmers consider when selecting their best market alternatives? Highest net returns is likely to be at the top of the list. Net returns are the take-home pay after all marketing expenses (transportation, commissions, time spent in selling, pricing, and delivery) are deducted. Clearly, net returns are more important than gross price.

Other criteria are also important in choosing the best market alternative. A national sample of hog producers recently mentioned the following characteristics of a preferred market outlet (not listed in rank order): Top price. Proximity. Competitive bids. Daily market with price established early in day. Adequate demand (can take any quantity offered and also can take nonstandard sizes and qualities along with the typical sizes and qualities). Honesty in weights, grades and condemnations. Friendly personnel who are willing to handle fairly any mistakes or misunderstandings. An appropriate set of premiums and discounts for quality and size (farmers vary greatly as to what they consider "appropriate"). Variety of options for timing and pricing and selling. Conditions of delivery (is there congestion at the docks or 3 inches of manure to wade?).

Reworded slightly, this list could apply to producers of many farm commodities. The relative importance of market characteristics will vary among farm commodities and even among producers of a particular commodity. Hence the best market outlet for one producer may not be the best for another.

V. James Rhodes is Professor of Agricultural Economics, University of Missouri, Columbia.

Haul 400 Miles or Quit

The market characteristics of proximity and competitive buyers have been growing more important in recent years. A declining number of processors and of other outlets for many commodities means that markets are fewer and farther away. Transportation costs for many commodities can rapidly erode net returns. No farmer wants to haul hogs or sugar beets or vegetables 400 miles to market. Numerous producers in various areas have been faced with the unpalatable alternatives of haul that far or quit production. But growers in the Red River Valley banded together to buy the American Crystal Sugar Company when it threatened to close the only beet factories in the area.

Vegetable growers in California have rather regularly been forming cooperatives to buy processing plants that are being closed by the large processors. Recently a packing plant in New Mexico was purchased by a group of West Texas hog producers who had no other major market outlet within 400 miles. In other commodities and in other areas, the same story is repeated of producers banding together to preserve a market outlet. Usually, their organization becomes a cooperative, although it is sometimes an investor-owned firm (IOF).

A farm cooperative is a special kind of business firm owned and operated by an association of farmer-members for their mutual benefit. When organized as a corporation, a co-op has the usual corporate attributes of unlimited life, limited liability, and freedom to contract as an artificial person. A cooperative differs in significant ways from the ordinary IOF. A cooperative's member-patrons (customers) control it via democratic voting procedures. Operation is at cost with the savings refunded to members in proportion to their volume of business with the co-op. A cooperative may have capital stock, as in an IOF, but the stockowners do not have voting control of the co-op nor do they receive more than limited returns.

Cooperatives may provide bargaining and/or marketing services to their members. A bargaining cooperative, in fruits and vegetables for processing or specialty crops or milk, represents its members in working out marketing agreements on terms of sale with individual processors. Capital requirements are small because a strictly bargaining co-op is not involved in the physical functions of marketing. Bargaining, as a way of discovering price and other terms of the transaction, is particularly useful when commitments are needed before planting time as to what is grown and who will process it. Likewise the highly perishable characteristics of fluid milk have made cooperative bargaining a useful way of reducing market uncertainty and transaction costs. Market access and adequate demand are necessary characteristics of milk markets.

A marketing cooperative requires significant capital to finance the inventories and the physical facilities essential to buying, assembling, storing, processing and shipping agricultural commodities. To understand why farmers will commit scarce time and capital to cooperatives, we need to look at the reasons that farmers consider co-ops a potentially useful market alternative.

Assured Market Outlet

Farmers value co-ops as an assured market outlet. While that value is absolute when there are no other accessible outlets, co-ops are still important as a competitive yardstick when few other outlets exist. Sometimes, concentration of ownership in a particular region may greatly limit rivalry among IOF buyers. Farmers may also expect the co-op to achieve some marketing channel leadership and even market power in its dealings with processors or retailers. For example, cooperatives in grapes, walnuts, almonds, oranges, and cranberries have expanded markets through channel leadership and market development. Perceiving themselves as weak price-takers facing positions of concentrated market power, many farmers believe they can strengthen their market position through a bargaining co-op or an aggressive marketing co-op.

Why do farmers often feel more assurance of a continuing market outlet with a co-op? Because a co-op is tied to its farmer-members and their interests in a way that an IOF is not. The IOF, responsible to its owners, is expected to quit processing soybeans or sugar beets or tomatoes if its capital will yield more return elsewhere. The co-op owned by beet growers has a specific purpose — beet processing. No thought is given to switching its capital into flour milling or oil drilling. The co-op must meet market competition, of course. If a co-op simply cannot compete in beet processing, for example, it eventually must close its doors. Thus market outlet assurance can never be absolute, but generally a co-op provides more assurance to farmers than an IOF does.

Farmers value co-ops as an assured market outlet. Workers in this Haines City (Fla.) Citrus Growers Association packing plant examine every orange and reject those that do not make U.S. Grade No. 1. Losers go to the juice plant.

Like most other things, cooperatives have been growing larger. Several have sales that rank them in Fortune's list of the 500 largest industrial corporations. A recent U.S. Department of Agriculture tabulation reports that U.S. co-ops in 1979 marketed farm commodities worth nearly $42 billion. In value terms, about 28 percent of all farm commodities at the first handler level were marketed by co-ops. The co-op share was much higher in dairy, 68 percent, but was quite low in certain areas including livestock, 10 percent.

Uses of Contracts. Contracts are becoming a more important part of market alternatives. While buyers often have been more aggressive than producers in seeking contracts, many producers have found contracts useful. Producers use contracts to fix a price they like or to reduce risk. Producers may use a contract to assure market access or to participate in pooling. In a few markets such as broilers, market access is impossible without contracts. In some cases producers without marketing contracts find credit very difficult to obtain for producing that commodity.

Contracts vary in nomenclature around the country. One classification distinguishes between marketing and production contracts. A marketing contract is a simple forward sale of a growing crop or growing livestock or an existing inventory. The marketing contract provides for later delivery and may fix price or provide for pricing later. A production contract provides for a commodity to be

produced and involves the "buyer" in the production process in terms of providing specifications and inputs. Broilers are the prime example of production contracting although some turkeys and eggs, a few hogs, and some vegetables for processing are also included. There is generally a different sharing of risks and returns in production contracts than in marketing contracts. From the general perspective of this chapter, both kinds of contracts are considered as market options.

Time Options — Another important market characteristic is the set of options provided for the timing of sale and delivery. Selling, establishing a price, and delivery of possession are separate acts that may or may not be consummated

Farmers selling their wares at a farmers market is an example of simultaneous Sell-Price-Deliver. This farmers market in Washington, D.C., attracts farmers from several neighboring States and is sponsored by the Cooperative Extension Service.

simultaneously. As farmers search for new ways to manage market price risks and to time sales for high returns, they are testing options that frequently involve a separation in time of pricing, selling, and delivery.

The traditional, simultaneous sell-price-deliver (SPD) time spectrum is still likely the most used market option. Sale of livestock in an auction or terminal market, or sale for cash of grain delivered to an elevator, are examples of simultaneous SPD. Other examples include farmers selling their wares at roadside markets, or producers selling cotton for cash at the gin.

A rather similar option is to sell and price simultaneously with delivery later. The "later" may vary from the next day to several months. Delivery usually occurs at harvest or when the livestock are ready for market. This SP—D option includes various production and marketing contracts in which price is fixed at the time of contracting. Examples include not only the commodities produced on production contracts described earlier, but also marketing contracts for hogs, cattle and various crops. Generally producers are most interested in fixing prices through marketing contracts when they have pessimistic price expectations. This very general use for many commodities of an option separating SP from delivery indicates its perceived usefulness to farmers and/or buyers.

William E. Carnahan

183

A third time option is to sell at delivery with price set later. Ordinarily price is set according to a formula. The simplest case of SD—P is perhaps grade and yield selling of livestock, in which a specific set of prices for various quality characteristics is agreed upon with the actual characteristics (and hence prices) determined later during processing. The pricing delay is necessary to the postslaughter measurement of quality. A more striking example is grain or soybeans sold to an elevator on a deferred pricing plan, in which the seller eventually picks the day for pricing and price is determined by formula. The formula may relate price to the current offer price of the elevator or the price of a nearby futures contract. In the grain example, the producer gains time to achieve what he or she hopes to be a better price. One disadvantage is the producer has given over possession of the commodity without payment and thus depends for some period on the buyer's financial solvency.

A fourth time option is to sell now with both delivery and pricing postponed until later. A major example of S—DP is dairy producers who contract to market all milk for the coming year to their co-op, or to an IOF, with prices determined later through some process such as co-op bargaining.

Pros and Cons of Pools
Pooling is another example. To pool is to allow your commodity to be sold along with that of other producers by a cooperative or other pooling firm. Generally most agreements to pool are made pre-harvest. The eventual price received by the pooling producer is determined by the average net pool receipts for the qualities sold by that producer. An expert pool manager may be able to secure a better pool price than many farmers would obtain on their own. However, the farmer has to wait a year for part of the final payment and has to yield the selling decisions to the pool manager. Pooling is common in rice and milk markets, and is used a bit in soybeans, wheat, and some other crops.

When soybeans are sold to an elevator on a deferred pricing plan, the seller eventually picks the day for pricing and the price is determined by formula. Here soybeans are delivered to a Missouri elevator.

One of the biggest changes in use of market outlets for a big ticket commodity has been the decline of terminal markets for livestock. At the beginning of this century they were the dominant method of livestock marketing. It isn't clear that the terminals will survive until century's end. Much the same decline occurred earlier for the "produce" markets (fruits, vegetables, poultry, and eggs). As open, public markets, the terminals were widely praised for their pricing efficiency. Even yet, the easily gathered prices at terminal livestock markets are dissemi-

nated quickly as important market news.

The terminals' decline stems from two weaknesses. Terminals are operationally inefficient because they generally have higher transportation and transfer costs than direct shipment from seller to buyer. Terminals generally lack SPD flexibility; their operations are geared to simultaneous sale, delivery, and pricing. Farmers rather generally prefer to have the sale closed before delivery, because they retain no negotiating power once delivery has been made to the terminal.

Bill Marr

Auctions are the most viable element of the open, physical-assembly markets. In livestock, auctions offer outlets for the smaller producers and for odd lots, breeding stock, etc., of the larger producers. Auctions are also important for feeder livestock. In these instances where some off-farm physical assembly is necessary, the auctions are not operationally inefficient. Auctions are also the way that tobacco is sold. Otherwise, auctions are seldom used as market alternatives by farmers.

Electronic Markets

The appeal of the electronic commodity markets (ECM) is that they combine pricing efficiency of the old terminals with the operational efficiencies of direct seller-buyer shipment. Moreover, an ECM tends to enlarge the market for farmers because more distant buyers can compete when transaction costs are lower. Thus some price enhancement can be expected from the development of an ECM provided that volume is sufficient to keep market costs low. USDA has financed experimental operation of computerized ECMs in slaughter hog and feeder cattle marketing. Sizable volumes of lambs and cotton are being marketed on computerized ECMs. Large quantities of feeder pigs are being marketed by tel-auction, a simpler version of ECM.

The attractiveness to farmers of selling the commodity while on-farm was commented on previously. In fact, most market alternatives do involve that characteristic. The main exceptions would be auctions, terminals, and such actions as the shipment of hogs to a packer or a packer buying point with no prior packer commitments to purchase.

The larger the producer the more likely that he or she sells through individual negotiation, or what is often called private treaty. On the buying side, the larger the potential purchase the more attractive to buyers and thus the more buyer competition. On the selling side, the larger the potential sales, the more effort that a seller can devote to obtaining market information and to becoming a skilled seller. The full range of SPD flexibility is readily available, of course, to individual negotiators. Hence, individual negotiation of either cash or contractual transactions is used frequently for numerous commodities including livestock, poultry, eggs, fresh fruits and vegetables, cotton, grains and oilseeds.

Direct marketing of farmers to consumers is a specialized and growing market alternative. While not important in the aggregate for all farm commodities, direct marketing — roadside markets, U-pick operations, and farmers' markets in cities — is very important to some farmers, especially those in the Northeast. The major sales are in fruits, vegetables, melons, floral and nursery products.

Let's return to the general theme. How do farmers select their best market alternatives? Sometimes there is little choice — so little that farmers develop co-ops or even roadside markets to obtain market access. Sometimes there may be a confusing plethora of market options. Generally, however, farmers do have several options as to timing and several competing buyers. Thus, they may array alternative outlets and options in terms of the market characteristics they deem important in order to make their choice or choices.

How to Minimize Marketing Risks

By T. Everett Nichols, Jr.

*A*mong the more notable trends in American agriculture during the 1970's was the decision by the Federal Government to become less involved in production and marketing decisions. Acreage constraints were removed, price supports reduced, and farmers encouraged to operate more efficiently and market their crops more wisely. A consequence of this action is that management decisions are left up to the individual producer, and returns to proper management are increasing. Learning to cope with the political, economic, and technological changes in agriculture and managing the risks emanating from these changes is a major challenge for today's farmers.

In its simplest terms, risk can be defined as the degree of uncertainty which surrounds the outcome of a particular decision. Risk management is then the development of strategies where the chance of loss is at the lowest level acceptable to the farmer. Producers attempt to manage two major types of risks in agriculture. One is biological or yield risk which arises from variability in output levels due to weather, pests, disease, and other factors. The second type is market or price risk which results from widely fluctuating product prices at the time of harvest or sale.

Risk management in farming involves

making decisions concerning the amount of risk one is willing and able to take. Once the level of risk exposure is determined the producer can then seek the package of production practices, marketing strategies, and portfolio of insurance programs which will provide the most protection against losses. Farmers typically attempt to reduce their risk exposure through one or more of the following methods — insurance, diversification, flexibility, liquidity, or by use of contracts.

Insurance involves substituting a small known loss (insurance premium) for the possibility of a larger but uncertain loss. In purchasing insurance against losses due to weather hazards, insects and disease the farmer incurs a cash expense. But the farmer shifts the risk of large losses to other persons or insurers (government or private). They in turn spread their risk over a large number of farmers thus enabling them to absorb the risk of loss on individual farms.

Some farmers prefer self insurance plans to paying insurance premiums to others. Enterprise diversification enables farmers to spread the risk of loss by producing more than one commodity which reduces the risk of disastrous loss to the entire farm. Double cropping soybeans behind wheat is an example of diversification. This practice permits producers to even

T. Everett Nichols, Jr., is Professor of Economics and Business, North Carolina State University, Raleigh.

out seasonal distribution of income and reduces the possible effect of changes in prices during the year.

Flexibility Protects Farmer

If farmers are uncertain as to what conditions might occur several months in the future, a flexible production and marketing program may provide risk protection. Swine producers, for example, may choose to market their top hogs early if prices are falling or feed to heavier weight if prices are rising. Farmers who contract for new construction or purchase new machinery may choose designs and models that have more than one use. Leasing land instead of purchasing it can help reduce price and production risk, especially for young farmers. The advantage is that the producer can walk away after the lease ends if not satisfied with the arrangement, the weather, or the profit.

Maintaining a cash balance or other as-sets which can be readily changed into cash provides producers with liquidity and the ability to absorb risk. Since land and equipment cannot be converted readily to cash, it is useful for farmers to have access to some liquid assets. Managing these assets to get the maximum returns can be very time consuming but also very profitable.

Shifting Risk — With increased price volatility and income variability prevailing in today's economy, some producers have chosen to shift price risk to the buyer. This can be done with simple management and marketing tools using forward price contracts. Forms of these tools include: A) Cash contracts (agreements on cash price and delivery terms before product delivery) for grains, poultry, livestock and processing fruits and vegetables, and B) Futures contracts (selling a futures market contract and buying it back at the time of product delivery) for grains, livestock, cotton,

This Carroll County, Md., farmer is practicing a type of risk management in "double cropping," soybeans behind barley. The soybeans are being planted as the barley crop is harvested. This practice spreads the risk of loss by producing two crops on the same land and harvesting them at different times of the year.

Tim McCabe

poultry products and potatoes.

A sound marketing program is one of the basic elements in risk management. By forward pricing a commodity in the cash or futures market the farmer can remove some of the speculation from production by fixing the selling price before the product is produced or delivered. The farmer's decision whether to forward price a particular commodity or to speculate on market prices being favorable at sale time depends on two factors.

First, how much risk does the farmer want to assume? If growers are financially independent, can take risks and survive if prices fall, then they might prefer to price their crops or livestock at delivery. They simply produce and sell at harvest or store production for future sale. Storage provides greater flexibility and increases the number of marketing alternatives. However, placing a crop in storage and holding for an unknown price can be disastrous if prices drop substantially.

Hedging Your Production

Many farmers prefer to be risk averters. They are either unable because of financial commitment or unwilling because of temperament to assume the risk of adverse price changes. Instead, they hedge their production by locking in a desired profit with cash or futures contracts to avoid adverse price movements. New or young farmers especially need marketing security in order to make payment on debts, and have sufficient income for family expenses and capital for expanding their businesses. Hedging takes some of the risk out of farming and places them in a better position to successfully manage the capital required for the future.

Some producers use cash contracts or futures contracts to cover only their variable or cash costs of production or storage. Once these expenses are covered they speculate on higher prices for the remainder of their crop.

The second factor influencing the decision to forward price is the farmer's pricing objective. If farmers desire the top price for cattle or hogs, and want maximum flexibility to store their grain and second-guess the market, then they usually do not want to forward price their crop and livestock. But if farmers wish to lock in an acceptable profit, meet financial obligations and obtain credit easier, they probably should consider forward contracting some part of their crop.

The Market Plan — Successful marketing requires a marketing plan including knowledge of production costs, market price offerings, cash flow analysis, and marketing strategies designed to achieve business objectives. These important elements need to be determined well in advance of production, and the plan put in writing to prevent emotions from altering it later in the year. A good marketing plan includes four basic steps:

1) Calculate your breakeven price. The price at which a producer is willing to sell is the breakeven price. It should cover all production costs, including returns to risk and management. The breakeven price helps producers determine when to begin contracting a sales price for their products. In most years pricing decisions and delivery decisions must be separated to obtain the most profit. Without knowledge of production costs and breakeven prices, producers cannot know when the market is offering a profit or loss.

2) Determine market offerings. Once the breakeven price is determined, pricing options can be examined. This involves a look at futures markets and cash forward contracts to determine what the market is offering. Local market prices can be computed by using futures prices adjusted for the basis. The basis is calculated by taking the difference between central market prices and local market prices. Basis may be either negative or positive, depending upon the local market conditions and time of year. If the market price equals or exceeds the breakeven price, then producers can decide whether to produce (store) the product and whether to hedge or leave it unpriced depending upon their preference for or aversion to risk.

3) Project cash flow. A cash flow can be projected once production costs are estimated and a decision made regarding the number of acres or head to be produced. Expenses and income are projected in a monthly or quarterly cash flow statement for the year. The difference between cash inflows (marketings and borrowings) and cash outflows (expenses and purchases) reveals anticipated cash shortages or expenses. A cash flow helps the producer in planning sales and purchases to minimize credit needs, and shows the lender how much credit is needed, when it is needed, and when it can be repaid.

4) Pace marketings. It is generally good strategy for most producers to cover cash flow requirements as soon as market prices equal breakeven prices. This reduces the worry that prices will fall below production costs. It also reduces the danger that loans cannot be repaid. There are many strategies which producers can follow in pricing their products.

All can be priced at once or they can "scale up" their sales as profit opportunities occur. For example, they may forward price only 5 to 10 percent of their production initially. As prices move higher they may lock in additional amounts (say 10 percent) until they have 50 to 60 percent of their production priced. Forward pricing protects against risk of low prices but not against low yields. Forward pricing an excess amount of anticipated production may leave the producer unable to deliver the amount specified in the contract.

Picking Market Service Firms

In recent years bankruptcies of marketing firms buying products or providing marketing services to farmers have added additional risks and concern for the farmer. There are no "fail-proof" methods for identifying firms that might become insolvent and cause financial losses.

To avoid problems, farmers should seek to do business with only those firms that are financially sound, well managed, and operated efficiently. They should avoid firms that offer prices substantially higher than competitors in the same area and firms with a history of slow payment, bad checks, or recurring financial problems. It also is desirable for farmers to understand the risks associated with various contracts and verbal agreements, and to follow good business practices to protect against unnecessary risks. There is a very high payoff to knowing as much as possible about the manager's integrity, business operation, credit record and economic condition. In short, select only those firms which are properly financed, managed and operated in such a way as to merit your business.

Fair Treatment in the Marketplace

By Thomas M. Walsh and Everett O. Stoddard

One of the persistent and overriding goals of farmers and agricultural producers, seemingly unachievable at times, is to secure equitable treatment and avoid unfairness in marketing their products. There is little doubt that the Nation's agricultural community — its farmers, growers, and livestock producers — are susceptible to unfairness, deception, and sharp dealing. We should not, however, lose sight of the fact that despite the thousands of transactions which take place each day, and the infinite variety of potential difficulties and uncertainties, agricultural marketing transactions proceed with a remarkable absence of friction.

Nonetheless, vexing problems crop up, producers' reasonable expectations are not realized, and substantial financial damage — even economic ruin — may result. There is much, however, that the alert, prudent producer can do to obtain fairness, both on his own and with the aid of Federal and State regulatory statutes enacted to foster honest dealing and to prevent practices which hamper the market's smooth functioning.

Agricultural production is unique. Virtually every major production decision is made by the producer, based only upon an estimate of the market conditions which will prevail at time of sale. Agricultural production is a batch process, and each farmer or cattleman ends up with fixed amounts of product on hand which must be disposed of irrespective of the market's response to aggregate output. These characteristics highlight the vital importance of foresight, common sense, and close attention to detail in connection with the marketing transaction and the concomitant loss of physical control over one's production.

At the very core of the marketing transaction is the contract to sell, which simply defined is a *promise* or *agreement* enforceable by law. The Uniform Commercial Code (UCC), enacted with some variation in virtually every State and which governs most sales of agricultural commodities, defines a contract more elaborately as "the total legal obligation which results from the parties' *agreement.*" It defines an agreement as "the *bargain* of the parties in fact as found in their *language or by implication from other circumstances including course of dealing or usage of trade or course of performance.*"

Contracts may be oral or written. It is indisputable that far too many contracts involving the sale of agricultural commodities from the farm are concluded orally

Thomas M. Walsh is an Attorney with the Office of the General Counsel, USDA.

Everett O. Stoddard is Deputy Director, Industry Analysis Staff, Packers and Stockyards Administration.

with only a nod of the head or a handshake, and that a written contract is to be preferred. Contract documents need not be complex. In every marketing transaction, three terms are of vital importance: price, quantity, and quality. A simple straightforward agreement setting forth the terms can and often does prove invaluable in heading off subsequent problems including the failure of a party to deliver or to accept, unexpected adjustments in price because of claimed deficiencies in quality or quantity, and significant alteration of contract terms by one of the parties to the agreement.

Oral Pact Risky — More than one farmer has been dismayed to find that the value and enforceability of his oral agreement may be at grave risk under the law. Every State has adopted some variation of the statute of frauds. The UCC contains such a provision which, in substance, requires a sale of goods for $500 or more to be evidenced in writing signed by the party against whom enforcement is sought.

Such provisions, which date back to 17th century England, are intended to protect not only against fraud, dishonesty and deliberate overreaching, but also the most innocent, good-faith misunderstandings between the parties concerning terms of their agreement. By virtue of its longevity (its provisions have after all existed in some form for over three centuries), the statute of frauds should serve both to encourage producers to reduce their agreements to writing and as a reminder of the importance of the legal obligations undertaken.

If the price, quality and quantity terms of an agreement are put down in writing, the statute of frauds requirements will usually be satisfied and will, in most cases, substantially strengthen the producer's position. Disputes may still occur, however, where one party to the written agreement contends the document is incomplete in that there were additional terms not reduced to writing.

If the dispute must be litigated, evidence of promises and assurances made during the negotiations and of other material terms agreed to prior to executing the written document may be worthless in proving that what is expressly set forth in the contract is not in fact what was agreed upon. The lawbooks are replete with tales of disputes involving oral and written agreements which by their very numbers reinforce the proposition that the rules of contract place a premium on completeness and specificity.

Nonpayment is one of the most serious risks faced by agricultural producers in selling or contracting to sell their production. In recent years, several graphic examples of nonpayment resulting from the buyer's insolvency and inability to pay have been highly publicized.

167 Packers Go Broke

From 1958 to 1975 some 167 packers failed, leaving livestock producers unpaid for over $43 million worth of livestock. The largest packer failure was that of American Beef Packers which went bankrupt in January 1975, leaving producers in 13 States unpaid for a total of over $20 million in livestock sales.

In more recent years, grain farmers were outraged at the consequences of grain elevator bankruptcies. In 1978, Arkansas farmers who had sold $1 million worth of soybeans to Riverport Terminal, Inc., received worthless checks in payment. Not long after, Riverport Terminal filed for bankruptcy. That financial disaster was followed by the bankruptcy of several Arkansas and Missouri elevators owned and operated by the James Brothers. The situation quickly degenerated into chaos and resulted not only in nonpayment for crops sold and delivered, but legal entanglement in the bankruptcy proceeding of those farmers merely storing their grain in the James' facilities.

Most packers, grain elevators, and processors are reasonably sound, well-managed and well-operated firms. However, under the current economic conditions such factors as price volatility, adverse basis movements, and high interest rates can easily lead to insolvency. But it is possible for producers to achieve a more protected position and to minimize the risk of non-payment in marketing transactions.

Best Safeguard — The producer's best protection is a reasonable investigation prior to sale, storage, or other loss of physical control of his or her commodity. It is vital to know your market and your buyer. It is imperative to be alert to outward signs of financial difficulty and to inquire into the buyer's financial condition.

Knowledge of the applicable laws, State and Federal — particularly those which require or provide for licensing, registration or bonding — can be invaluable. Producers should deal only with persons or firms that have complied with those statutes. Above all, demand accurate weights and grade. Whenever possible, observe the weighing and grading. Insist on receiving scale tickets, an accurate accounting, and complete documentation for every transaction.

Packers and Stockyards Act

Three Federal statutes are particularly relevant. The Packers and Stockyards Act (P&S Act), enacted in 1921, is a comprehensive regulatory law designed to assure fair competition and fair trade practices in the livestock marketing and meat packing industries. One of the main objectives is to provide an enhanced measure of financial protection to farmers and ranchers against receiving less than the true market value of their livestock.

The P&S Act makes it unlawful for any packer, live poultry dealer, market agency or dealer to engage in or use any unfair, unjustly discriminatory or deceptive practice. Enforcement of the act is administered by the Packers and Stockyards Administration, U.S. Department of Agriculture (USDA). Under overall direction of the Administrator, the Washington staff and 13 regional supervisors and their specialists administer provisions of the act throughout the United States.

Under Title III of the act, market agencies and dealers engaged in buying and selling livestock in commerce are required to register with the Secretary of Agriculture. Civil penalties are provided for failing to do so. Key enforcement provisions confer authority on the Secretary to issue cease and desist orders, and to assess civil penalties against packers, market agencies, and dealers who are found, after notice and hearing, to have violated the act. The Secretary is empowered to suspend registrants for reasonable specified periods for violations and to suspend registrants who do not meet financial requirements of the act. The test of insolvency utilized under the act is a current ratio test, that is, current liabilities in excess of current assets.

Pursuant to the P&S Act, the Secretary has required by regulation that all market agencies and dealers (except dealers employed by a packer to purchase livestock for slaughter) maintain a bond or bond equivalent to secure performance of their obligations in livestock transactions. Persons seeking to claim on a bond must file a timely claim in writing with either the surety, the trustee on the bond, or the Administrator within 120 days from the date of the transaction on which the claim is based.

Custodial Accounts Required

In 1980, terminal stockyards and country auction markets together handled approximately $22 billion in livestock. Market agencies selling livestock on a com-

mission basis at these public markets are required to establish a separate custodial bank account for shippers' proceeds. Proceeds collected from the sale of consigned livestock are trust funds and must be deposited to the custodial account. In addition, the market agency must reimburse the account within specified time limits for proceeds which have not yet been collected.

In 1976 several major amendments to the P&S Act were enacted, substantially increasing the financial protection afforded livestock producers — particularly in connection with their sales of livestock to packers. The amendments imposed stricter prompt payment requirements on packers, market agencies and dealers un-

less prior to the transaction an express written agreement in conformity with the regulations is entered into. The new section provides that without such an agreement, the buyer must wire transfer funds to the seller's account or deliver to the seller a check for the full amount of the purchase price before the close of the next business day following the purchase and transfer of possession.

The amendments also empower the Secretary of Agriculture to require a packer found insolvent to cease purchasing livestock while insolvent or to specify the conditions under which purchases may continue, and authorizes the Secretary to require bonds of packers whose average annual purchases of livestock exceed $500,000.

Trust Provision — Perhaps the most significant addition to the P&S Act, however, was the provision establishing a packer statutory trust for the unpaid cash sellers of livestock. Packers whose average annual purchases do not exceed $500,000 are exempt.

The trust provision was developed in large part in response to a series of packer financial failures, in particular the American Beef Packers bankruptcy. It provides that all livestock purchased by a packer in cash sales, and all inventories, receivables and proceeds from meat and livestock products derived from that livestock must be held in trust for the benefit of the unpaid cash sellers. Unpaid cash sellers claiming on the trust must give written notice to the packer and file the notice with the Secretary of Agriculture.

By the Food Control Act of 1917, Congress vested in the President wide powers of control over fresh fruits and vegetables, and other foods. In cooperation with growers, shippers, and receivers, the Food Administration issued regulations in 1917 instituting a comprehensive regulatory scheme which included standardized grades, an inspection service, prohibition of undesirable business practices, and the requirements of a license for all handlers. With the end of World War I, that plan lapsed. In the agricultural depression after the war, complaints of unfair dealings by receivers of perishable agricultural commodities and counter-complaints by receivers against shippers and growers persisted.

Livestock, like these in a Texas stockyard, are bought and sold under provisions of the Packers and Stockyards Act. The Act is a comprehensive regulatory law designed to assure fair competition and fair trade practices in the livestock marketing and meatpacking industries.

Fred Witte

PACA Enacted in 1930

Ultimately Congress enacted, in 1930, the Perishable Agricultural Commodities Act (PACA). Although many unfair practices aimed at by PACA were also violations of contract or tort law, for which an injured party could seek a remedy in the courts under existing State law, proponents of the bill emphasized that a lawsuit was not a satisfactory answer. Individual losses were small, and buyers and sellers were often thousands of miles apart. The commodities were highly perishable. Litigation was expensive and slow, and the hope of recovery often clouded with doubt.

The Perishable Agricultural Commodities Act is administered by USDA officials assigned to the Regulatory Branch, Fruit and Vegetable Division, Agricultural Marketing Service. The Regulatory Branch is headquartered in Washington, D.C., and has regional offices in Chicago, Fort Worth, Los Angeles, and New York City.

Major emphasis is placed upon the prophylactic value of the statute's licensing system. The PACA licensing scheme is comprehensive and requires all commission merchants, dealers, and brokers to be licensed by the Secretary of Agriculture. Licensing fees finance the statute's administration. The Secretary must refuse to issue a license under a variety of conditions specified in the statute. Violations of the licensing provisions may result in imposition of civil penalties, and the statute provides for injunctive relief to prohibit any person from continuing to engage in business without a license.

Section 2 of the act specifies a variety of unlawful trade practices which include any deceptive practice in connection with weighing, counting, or determining the quality of a perishable commodity, the unreasonable rejection of a commodity by a dealer or the failure to deliver without reasonable cause, and the failure to accurately account or make full payment in connection with any transaction. PACA provides authority for termination, revocation and suspension of licenses.

Persons complaining of a violation of section 2 may avail themselves of the reparation procedure established by the act and set forth in regulations promulgated by the Secretary. Complaints must be filed in writing within 9 months after the cause of action accrues. Complaints may be formal or informal. In appropriate circumstances, the regulatory officials will attempt mediation and settlement of the disputes.

Warehouse Act Under AMS

The United States Warehouse Act, enacted in 1916, established a Federal program under the Secretary of Agriculture to provide a measure of protection for farmers delivering crops for storage to public warehouses, and to facilitate financing arrangements for stored grain and other agricultural products. The Warehouse Division, Agricultural Marketing Service, administers the examination and licensing scheme established by the act.

As originally enacted, and continuing until Congress amended the statute in 1931, the Federal regulatory scheme did not supplant State regulation of warehouses licensed pursuant to the act's provisions. The 1931 amendments made clear that the Secretary's authority was to be exclusive with respect to licensees and their operations regulated by the act. The United States Warehouse Act program is, however, a voluntary program and participation by eligible warehouses is not required.

2,000 Licenses — While the act's provisions apply to any agricultural product, regulations have been issued and licenses are currently issued only for storage of grain, cotton, tobacco, wool, and several other products. As of May 1982, approximately 2,000 licenses were in effect, of which 1,710 were in effect for grain warehouses, and 200 for cotton warehouses. These licenses are for approximately 40 percent of commercial grain storage capacity and 60 percent of commercial cotton storage capacity.

Warehousemen desiring to apply for a license must meet certain qualifications. The Secretary of Agriculture is authorized to issue a license only if the warehouse facility is found suitable for proper storage of the product for which the license is sought, and the warehouseman agrees to comply with the act and regulations issued under it. Applicants for licenses must meet the minimum net asset requirements set forth in the pertinent commodity regulation.

Every applicant for a license must furnish a bond to secure the performance of his or her obligations as a warehouseman operating under the act and the regulations. In addition, the bond must secure any additional obligations which the warehouseman may assume by contract with the depositors of products in the warehouse. This bond coverage has been construed to cover stored grain represented merely by scale tickets, rather than warehouse receipts as required by the act.

The U.S. Warehouse Act requires that warehouse receipts be issued for stored products, and specifies in detail the required contents for the receipts. Valid warehouse receipts are in effect written storage contracts which define the rights and responsibilities of the parties involved. The value of a receipt over a scale ticket cannot be overemphasized, and will provide greater protection in event of the elevator's bankruptcy.

All fungible (interchangeable) products stored for interstate commerce in a licensed warehouse must be inspected and graded by a person licensed under the act. Licensed warehouses are required to keep separate the depositors' stored products except fungible products such as grain which, if of the same kind and grade, may be mixed pursuant to trade practice or agreement. Licensed warehousemen are required by the act to deliver stored products upon demand of the depositor if the demand is accompanied with an offer to satisfy the warehouseman's lien, a surrender of the receipt, properly endorsed if negotiable, and a readiness to acknowledge delivery.

Affect Millions — The three Federal statutes described earlier establish programs which affect the financial well-being of millions of farmers, growers, cattlemen, and livestock feeders. Each focuses on and seeks to assure that the financial integrity of agricultural marketing systems will be maintained and that honesty and fair dealing will prevail. Together with other Federal statutes, and numerous State laws which supplement and complement them, they provide invaluable protection to the agricultural community.

Exploiting New Marketing Opportunities

By James L. Pearson and Harold S. Ricker

New marketing opportunities come about as the result of developments that impact producers, marketing firms, and consumers. These changes may be caused by introduction of new technology, significant shifts in the costs of resources and services such as energy and transportation, or new products and uses. As these developments occur, actions to take advantage of the changed relationships are initiated by entrepreneur producers and marketers. Thus, it is important that recognition be given to the inevitability of change in order to exploit the benefits.

The application of computer technology in food marketing is coming of age. Development of many computer software packages to perform specific marketing functions, along with refinements in mini-computers, have made computer applications feasible for more farmers and marketing firms. All segments of the marketing channel are being changed by computer applications as firms strive to improve the timeliness of market information and the efficiency and objectivity with which many marketing operations are performed.

Since the U.S. Department of Agriculture (USDA) conducted the first public evaluation of an optical scanning and checkout system in 1971, there have been dramatic changes in computer applications in food marketing. For consumers, the noticeable change is placement of the rectangular set of black and white lines (the Universal Product Code) on most all of the packaged items that are purchased in the local supermarket.

But behind the scenes a revolution in information processing is taking place. Scanners combined with minicomputers have enabled store managers to conduct special analyses of their store operations. For example, one store manager analyzed his soft drink aisle and discovered that half the items could be removed with minimal effect on store sales, and he could use the space for other items with greater consumer demand.

By analyzing sales of specials, one can assess whether a new product's sales are sufficient to justify adding it to the 12,000 items presently stocked. In addition to improved checkout operations, stores are using scanner data for improving work scheduling, courtesy card and check validation, and several other functions including inventory control. Eventually they will be linked with their wholesale supplier for automatic computer ordering to replenish stock.

James L. Pearson is Director, Market Research and Development Division, Agricultural Marketing Service.

Harold S. Ricker is Deputy Director of the Division.

Food manufacturers are getting more timely information on their product movement and the effectiveness of their promotion efforts as determined by product sales. New product performance can be determined quickly in test markets where stores have computerized checkout operations. Sales reports can be available to the manufacturer in a few days as opposed to the former quarterly reports provided by sales auditing firms.

Uniform Communication System

Computer-to-computer linkages are being established between manufacturers and distributors to reduce the redundancy of paperwork in processing routine business sales and order transactions. This has required industry agreement on a number of standards such as message formats and data definitions. In the future this Uniform Communication System (UCS) is expected to improve productivity by expediting the receipt of invoices and purchase orders. Besides improving production scheduling and inventory management, UCS will reduce errors in ordering and invoicing.

At the same time, efforts are being made to improve communication between the processor/manufacturer and the farmer

There have been dramatic changes in computer applications in food marketing in recent years. For consumers, the set of black and white lines on packaged items like this loaf of bread is probably the most noticeable change.

William E. Carnahan

or assembly point market through computerized market information services and electronic marketing systems. Farmers in some sections of the country can sit in their homes and view the latest market information on their TV. For example a farmer can review commodity prices on the Chicago Board of Trade, while they are changing and the market is in session, to determine whether to participate. Since this program is for information only, the telephone would be used to make a transaction on commodities such as wheat, corn, oats, soybeans, and soybean meal. Other information available includes reports of selected markets for cattle, hogs, and grain, market analyses, world weather, planting intention reports, crop production reports, and livestock on feed reports. These reports help the farmer to make better informed planning and marketing decisions.

Electronic Marketing — Electronic mar-

keting is a further extension of the information system that enables farmers and others to participate directly in markets for specific commodities through computerized trading. Buyers and sellers access the system through computer terminals at remote locations. Products for trade are listed on the terminal by description which is usually based on U.S. Department of Agriculture (USDA) grades and frequently supplemented with other descriptive information. A major

advantage of the system is that it enables farmers and buyers to have access to a broader market.

Historically, farmers have hauled their livestock to a market to sell and if the price offered was low, they either have to accept it or take the animals back home. With electronic marketing one can offer livestock for sale and have a good chance of several buyers competing for it. An example of this is in fed cattle. In the Plains States, where large feedlots are located, 10 or more buyers frequently visit a feedlot each week to inspect and bid on its offerings. However, in the Midwest, where feedlots tend to be small and located on individual farms, the owner frequently has difficulty getting even one or two buyers to come to inspect and bid on the cattle when they are ready to slaughter.

An advantage of the electronic marketing system is that all trading information is instantaneously captured in the accounting system and made available to all trading participants. This is a significant improvement over the market information system currently available for most agricultural products. However, while tests have been conducted on slaughter hogs, feeder cattle, lambs, wholesale meat, and eggs, only the lamb and eggs electronic trading systems are still operating.

TELCOT Trading System Success

A commercially successful electronic trading system is TELCOT, developed

Computers are being used widely in marketing for inventory management and for expediting the receipt of invoices and purchase orders. This computer center in a semi-automated dry grocery warehouse determines the placement of every item under the warehouse's 16.5-acre roof.

David F. Warren

by the Plains Cotton Cooperative Association in 1975. It offers bales of cotton from member cooperatives to textile buyers representing exporters and textile mills. The cotton in this Southwest area is of short fiber length used to produce heavyweight textile products. For the 1979-80 season, TELCOT had 40 textile offices and nearly 270 gins on the system with an expected trading volume of 1.7 million bales. TELCOT has succeeded because it met the producer's and gin's needs for more flexibility in marketing, and the buyer's need for better descriptions of cotton and an ability to buy large volumes faster and more economically.

Slipsheets — Moving large volumes at less total costs are productivity goals of efforts to introduce slipsheet handling of grocery products in transportation. A slipsheet is a flat sheet of material, usually fiberboard or plastic, with tabs on one or more sides, used as a base on which to assemble, store, and transport goods as a unit load. Present methods of transporting groceries involve either individually handstacking cases of product or utilizing 40 by 48 inch wooden pallets to hold approximately 66 cases of groceries (a unit load). Slipsheets are lightweight, while empty pallets weigh about 75 pounds and are 6 inches thick. Slipsheets

Slipsheets—flat sheets usually made of fiberboard or plastic—save labor, space, and money. Here a specially designed "push-pull" forklift truck grips a slipsheet by the edge and pulls the merchandise off the stack for reloading onto a wooden pallet for warehouse storage.

also can allow 10 to 12 percent more payload in a shipment because they use less cubic space.

A recent USDA study estimates cost savings of $45 to $48 per trailer load of grocery products utilizing slipsheets. Based on an estimated 3.4 million trailer loads of groceries shipped from suppliers to wholesale warehouses annually, industry savings might approximate $160 million. A major grocery manufacturer has just announced a program to provide a $60 per truckload allocation to companies that accept slipsheeted loads and unload them in a 2-hour allotment period. While this example focuses on groceries, experiments are underway to test unitized shipments of food products such as fruits and vegetables and other perishable products, using slipsheets made of materials that are impermeable to moisture.

Adjusting to Change — Change usually impacts producers and marketing firms differently. Some developments give one geographic area an advantage over another area. Adjustments must take place. Some firms gain significantly but others lose. Following are examples of adjustments to change.

Cotton Production — Dramatic shifts have taken place in the location of cotton production. Some Southern States witnessed a decline in their production while substantial gains were made in Southwestern States. Many factors contributed to this, but of major importance was new production-related technology. The mechanical cotton harvester enabled conversion from labor intensive to capital intensive production. This development, along with improved varieties and cultural practices, enabled the enormous expansion in production to take place in several South-

western States that found their circumstances improved relative to a number of Southeastern States.

Major adjustments in the production and marketing sectors took place in the westward movement of cotton production. This affected both the losers and the gainers. Losing States expanded production of row and forage crops and beef cattle. Demands for marketing services shifted to service new enterprises as the need for cotton gins and related cotton services significantly declined. In Western States, where cotton production expanded, the need for new marketing facilities and services brought a response. Many growers joined together and formed cooperatives to help market their cotton. By integrating forward into ginning and merchandising cotton, they received the added returns from the ginning and volume selling.

Cattle Feeding Revolutionized

Before 1950, cattle feeding was largely associated with Corn Belt farms. Most farms fed out fewer than 100 head per year and a small number exceeded 1,000 head. Conditions changed in the 1950's, and economies in large feedlots revolutionized cattle feeding. This development triggered a substantial concentration of cattle feeding in the High Plains States, Arizona, and California.

Over half of all fed cattle now are fattened in feedlots ranging in capacity from 1,000 head to more than 100,000 head. Most of the cattle in the large lots are in response to the growth in demand for beef over the last three decades. In 1964 less than 1 percent of the feedlots had a capacity over 1,000 head, but produced 40 percent of the fed cattle marketed. Marketings from feedlots with capacities over 1,000 head increased to 73 percent in 1981. Total number of all feedlots was down more than half, but large feedlots increased in number by 37 percent by 1981.

These specialized feeding operations achieved their lower cost per pound of gain due to several factors. Local availability of feed was an important but by no means dominant factor because additional grain must be transported from grain surplus areas. Other contributing factors were economies in large purchases of feeder cattle and feed, new knowledge about feeding cattle, technology for feed handling, and the ability to utilize ingredients in feed mixes that provide lower cost rations but maintain high gain rates. Also important to the success of large feedlots is climate. The western climate places less stress on cattle in feedlots than the climate in most other areas of the country including the Corn Belt.

These developments offered new marketing opportunities to feeder cattle producers and farmers producing surplus grain and forage. Meatpacking plants to slaughter the cattle had to be built. By contrast, the small feedlot operator has experienced increased competition in selling fed cattle. This is further complicated by the declining number of meatpackers. The consequence: Fewer buyers are available to bid on the small-lot operator's cattle.

Alternatives — This situation points up the need for alternatives in marketing cattle from small feedlots. Increased use of specialized marketing services through commission agents or a cooperative is one method of improving market access and buyer competition. Electronic marketing may be feasible since it provides an efficient means of selling with in-

creased buyer competition, description selling, reduced assembly costs, and accessibility by all sellers. Other opportunities for cattle feeders to improve their marketing dilemma include vertical integration into cooperative meatpacking and the selling of meat at wholesale.

Shifts in Vegetable Areas — The United States depends on Florida and Mexico as its primary suppliers of fresh vegetables during winter months. Climate prevents vegetable production in these months in U.S. areas outside Florida. During other seasons of the year, vegetables can be grown in most areas. Nevertheless, economic advantages have dictated the primary fresh vegetable supply points and excluded other potential sources. Two developments are eroding some advantages of the distant supply areas and favoring suppliers closer to population centers. They are increasing costs of transportation and an apparent increase in demand for locally grown and fresher produce.

More than 60 percent of nutrition conscious shoppers indicated they now buy more fresh fruits and vegetables than previously. The increasing concern of many people about diet and health has opened up new markets through salad bars and expanded other sales opportunities for fresh fruits and vegetables. Excluding potatoes, per capita consumption of U.S. fresh fruits and vegetables has increased 10 percent over the period 1975 to 1980. Per capita consumption of lettuce rose 5 pounds between 1970 and 1980 to 27.4 pounds annually. Similarly tomatoes, peppers, carrots and spinach have all shown per capita consumption jumps, with the most pronounced increases in the late seventies. Thus, changing dietary habits and shifts in tech-

Consumer interest in fresh fruits and vegetables and their availability have resulted in increases in per capita consumption for nearly all produce, including peppers like those being harvested here in North Carolina.

Warren Uzzle

An apparent rise in demand for locally grown and fresher produce has increased the emphasis on direct marketing such as this farmers market in Washington, D.C.

William E. Carnahan

nological costs have brought about shifts in farm production of fresh fruits and vegetables to the benefit of local farmers and consumers.

Efforts are underway in several States to capture more of their local demand for produce. This is being handled in two ways: 1) emphasis on direct marketing through farmers markets, roadside stands, etc., and 2) organizing growers by cooperatives or other means for marketing their produce in pooled lots. The latter is for the purpose of getting adequate product volume to satisfy the specification buying of wholesalers and food chains. While these developments are not likely to displace the major fresh vegetable supply sources, they do offer local farmers some advantage in gaining new marketings for their farm products. Reliability will be a key determinant of their success in competing. They must demonstrate an ability to supply adequate volume of uniform quality produce on a timely and regular basis.

Integration — Market coordination is the process of achieving an efficient functioning relationship between stages of production and marketing activity. One way to accomplish this is through integration by means of ownership and/or management of two or more stages in the production-servicing-processing-marketing system for a commodity or group of commodities. Hence vertical integration is 1) ownership-participation in two or more stages of the marketing system, or 2) joint management without ownership of the units. It is a way for producers and marketers of agricultural products to improve their business enterprises.

Broilers — There are many agriculturally related examples of improved coordina-

tion through vertical integration. One of the most notable is the boiler industry. This industry began integrating both vertically and horizontally (combining similar functions) after World War II. By 1959, it was approximately 50 percent integrated and it's about 99 percent integrated today. The primary integrators were feed suppliers and broiler processors.

Usually an integrated broiler firm includes feed manufacture and distribution, broiler production, processing, and wholesaling. Frequently it will include related activities such as a hatchery. Feed mixes are varied by age and sex of broilers to achieve a 3½- to 4-pound broiler in 6 weeks versus 8 weeks a few years ago. Vertical integration for broilers is accomplished by ownership and contracts. The broiler production component is predominantly contractual. Integration in the broiler industry has provided a high degree of coordination between production, processing, and sales. Instability in the supply of broilers has been reduced considerably.

Boxed Beef — Traditionally, most beef was shipped from the meatpacker to the wholesaler and retailer as carcass beef. In transit it was hauled as hanging beef, as opposed to being packaged in some manner and stacked on the vehicle's floor. On receipt of the carcass beef at the destination point it was broken down into quarters, primals, and subprimals for delivery to retail stores.

Much of this has changed today as meat packers have vertically integrated forward and ship less carcass beef. Meat packers break their carcasses into primals and subprimals which are then packaged and sold as "boxed" beef. Some meat packers are even going beyond that and further processing or fabricating into consumer portions. The latter is particularly used in servicing the hotel, restaurant, and institutional trade. Approximately half the beef sold by packers is in boxes.

These developments have increased economic efficiency in marketing beef and reduced the net price to wholesalers and retailers. This has resulted in closing of meatcutting facilities at many locations as boxed beef received from the meatpacker is distributed from the warehouse to the retail outlet. Boxed beef has enabled the meat industry to better coordinate the flow of product through the marketing system's stages. It allows bone and fat to be more economically separated from meat in the production area, as well as reducing transport costs. The wholesaler and retailer can be more selective in purchasing beef cuts that best meet demands of their trade.

Milk, Juice Storable on the Shelf

Yes, there now is milk that can be stored on the shelf and not in the refrigerator. Development of new processing and packaging technology and its approval by the Food and Drug Administration has opened the door for many new products. Aseptic milk, which made its U.S. debut this year at the World's Fair in Knoxville, is a recent example. Half-pints of aseptic juices — such as orange, grapefruit, apple, and cranberry juice cocktail — are already being marketed in the new cartons.

The aseptic process involves heating Grade A milk to 280° for a few seconds, then cooling it rapidly to 70°, and hermetically sealing it in sterile, laminated containers that shield it from heat and light. The five-layer carton, containing plastic coated foil and heavy paper, costs more than traditional cartons. However, eliminating refrigeration expenses should result in costs similar to regular pasteurized milk. Development of the approximately half-pint carton has opened up new outlets for fruit juice in the soft drink market. With a small straw attached, the carton is ideal for soft drink vending operations where impulse buying is an important factor. Dairymen are hoping for similar success with milk and milk products with flavors such as strawberry, banana, chocolate, vanilla, and maybe coffee.

A main advantage is improved shelf-life of the milk product, reported to be 3 months without refrigeration and 9 months with refrigeration. Aseptically packaged fruit juices are good for a year. The process promises to save considerable energy as the products can be shipped in unrefrigerated trucks, and stored in nonrefrigerated areas. Only when desired for drinking, or after opening, does a carton need refrigeration. Replacement of expensive cans and bottles is also an important advantage.

Sales of juices packed in cartons have increased from a 20 percent share of the market to a 60 percent share. Aseptic milk has been selling well in Europe and Canada, and American dairymen are hopeful it will help offset declining per capita milk consumption in the United States.

Corn Sweeteners — The average American now consumes almost 126 pounds of sugar and sweeteners a year. That's a staggering 35 teaspoons a day. Most of it (75 percent) is in baked goods, soft drinks, and other processed foods. However, with greater health consciousness, attention to diet, and a smaller portion of the population in the sugar-craving ages of 10 to 25 years, our consumption of sweeteners appears to have stabilized. Feeding America's demanding sweet tooth are highly competitive industries — the wet corn milling and the sugarbeet and sugarcane industries.

Corn sweeteners, and specifically high fructose corn sirup (HFCS), are the new products that have made dramatic inroads into traditional markets for sugar. Today corn sweeteners represent over 33 percent of the country's 28.9 billion pound nutritive sweetener market, compared with only 10 percent in 1970. Over 1.4 million bushels of corn per day are processed into corn sweeteners. This represents 4 to 6 percent of the U.S. corn crop. After domestic feeds and exports, the corn sweetener refining industry has become the third largest user of corn.

HFCS substitutes for sugar in a variety of processed food products. Market acceptance has been dramatic since its commercial introduction in 1967, with sales increasing steadily to over 6 billion pounds in 1982. Per capita consumption has risen from .7 pound in 1970 to an estimated 29 pounds in 1982, and is projected to 38 pounds in 1985.

HFCS represents a good example of where technology has helped create a new domestic industry. And if foreign oil prices skyrocket again, the wet corn milling industry has ethanol production tech-

nology in operation on a limited scale. Ethanol is used to make gasohol. Many new wet milling plants are being constructed to allow for production of ethanol along with corn sweeteners.

Further Reading

Economics of the Product Markets of Agriculture, Harold F. Breimyer. Iowa State University Press, 2121 South State Avenue, Ames, IA 50013. $12.95

Marketing of Agricultural Products, Fifth Edition, Richard L. Kohls and Joseph N. Uhl. 1980. Macmillan Publishing Company, Front and Brown Streets, Riverside, NJ 08370. $27.95

Agricultural Marketing: Systems Coordination, Cash and Futures Prices, 1979, Wayne D. Purcell. Reston Publishing Company, Inc., 11480 Sunset Hill Road, Reston, VA 22090. $12.95.

Marketing Alternatives for Agriculture, Is There a Better Way? "Vertical Integration Through Ownership," Leaflet No. 7, William E. Black and James E. Haskell. Cornell University, Distribution Center, 7 Research Park, Ithaca, NY 14850. $1.30.

Who Will Market Your Products? March, 1978, Texas Agricultural Extension Service, Department of Ag Economics, The Texas A&M University System, College Station, TX 77843. $1.

High Fructose Corn Sweeteners: Economic Aspects of a Sugar Substitute, Hoy F. Carman and Peter K. Thor. University of California, 2200 University Avenue, Berkeley, CA 94720. $1.20.

Rules of the Game – for Market Stability

By Bruce Gardner

tability of a market involves two quite different issues. The first is stability of the environment in which buyers and sellers of a commodity meet to attempt to consummate their trades most advantageously. Stability in this environment means that all traders can rely on their bids and offers being honored, that theft, mayhem, or fraud do not normally occur in the marketplace, and that if a trade is made there will be certain implicit guarantees concerning delivery and condition of the merchandise traded. The second aspect of stability in a market involves the stability of market outcomes, that is, a lack of unanticipated change from one day to the next, or one month to the next, or one year to the next in the prices at which goods trade.

Both these aspects of stability inevitably involve governmental action. Individual buyers and sellers would have a very difficult task guaranteeing either stability of the market environment or stability of market outcomes. If a seller could guarantee such stability, the seller would almost certainly be a monopolist or one of very few sellers in the market, which in itself raises policy problems that bring governmental intervention into the picture as a real possibility. Similarly, a buyer who could guarantee stability raises problems of monopsony, or monopoly on the buyer's side. An inde-

pendent entrepreneur, such as the owner of a flea market or the Chicago Board of Trade, could establish nongovernmental rules of trading, but there is still an inevitable governmental involvement in the legal situation in which such a market operates.

Exchange of commodities between individuals can occur in the absence of markets. This was historically the usual means of exchange before development of markets as we know them today. Exchange outside of markets still occurs in bilateral agreements between individuals or in agreements between nations such as bartering, say, grain for gold between the United States and the Soviet Union.

It is even reported that early forms of exchange took place without any contact between buyers and sellers. For example, a tribe might produce goods such as arrowheads for which it had especially suitable materials at hand, or had developed especially good skills. The tribe might exchange these goods by leaving them at some specified place after which members of another tribe would take the goods and put something else in their place. If the first tribe found what was left to be a good bargain, then trade in this form would continue.

Such nonmarket exchange is necessarily

Bruce Gardner is a Professor in the Department of Agricultural and Resource Economics, University of Maryland, College Park.

an uncertain and at times unreliable institutional arrangement. It is not an arrangement conducive to stability in exchange under conditions in which the prices of goods or the cost of materials or other factors might change. Development of markets was a notable economic advance in human history. An early European market might be a place in the territory of a prince or other ruler of the region. Buyers and sellers could meet under the prince's protection and exchange goods without fear of third parties interceding to seize the goods. Rules of the market would establish what a buyer was agreeing to undertake when a product was bought, and what a seller was agreeing to supply when a product was sold. The prince provided stability in the market environment.

In roughly the same way, governments today provide a stable market environment for much more complicated systems of exchange. Goods are exchanged whose qualities or characteristics change from batch to batch, in which technical change may even alter the nature of the commodity. Terms of sale vary from cash to check to credit of various forms. Delivery of the commodity may be deferred or may be made at a different place from the location of the agreement to buy and sell.

In these circumstances, stability in the market environment is in large part a matter of the legal system of the country where the market is located. In complex markets such as futures markets, separate institutions have the job of setting up special rules of exchange for the markets. In the United States, there is the Commodity Futures Trading Commission. In the case of livestock sales, we have the Packers and Stockyards Admin-

istration. For exported grain, we have the Federal Grain Inspection Service. For transportation of agricultural commodities there are several agencies of government that become involved. And in regulating sales to consumers the number and degree of involvement of government becomes even greater.

Government a Destabilizer

Indeed, the role of government in regulating markets for agricultural products in the United States today has become so great that one of the principal uncertainties in the market environment is the timing and extent of changes in these rules themselves. This has led some to say that government has ceased to be a provider of a stable market environment, and instead has become a destabilizing economic participant. It would, of course, be possible for the government never to change the regulations that govern market exchanges. But we would not want to go so far as to say that these regulations should never change. That would be carrying the goal of stability too far, making it an idol to which other benefits and costs of exchange are sacrificed.

For example, the Packers and Stockyards Administration has traditionally been concerned with the power of buyers of livestock products from farmers who hold down prices by monopolistic buying behavior or other activities that take advantage of information buyers may have but the farmers who are selling do not. This concern stems from the days when the marketplace most important for setting livestock prices was the central markets of Chicago, Omaha, and a few other places. But in recent years the marketing of livestock has become decentralized.

In 1923, some 89 percent of cattle and 76 percent of hogs purchased by U.S. packers were from terminal markets. By 1980 these percentages had declined to 8 and 14 percent, respectively. Also, packing plants and other firms in the marketing chain are no longer found so predominantly in a few large cities, but instead are scattered throughout the livestock producing areas. This leads to a new marketing situation where the old rules and regulations may no longer pertain. In such cases, it is by no means clear there should be stability in the regulatory environment regardless of any other changes occurring.

Iowa Beef — A good example of the policy problems that can arise is the expansion of Iowa Beef Packers (IBP) from its Midwestern base to the Northwest. This would have been viewed under the traditional regulatory scheme as a threat to competitive pricing of livestock because if Iowa beef expanded its market share, it would become nearly a monopsonist in the classical sense, that is, a single buyer in the market. But it is not clear in today's decentralized marketing system whether the overall market share means much, especially when new firms can become established more easily and transportation alternatives give farmers a wider variety of ways to market their products.

Moreover, there is some evidence that IBP was enabled to expand by certain technical and personnel management innovations which permitted it to process livestock at lower costs than its competitors. This creates the possibility that farmers could receive more, consumers pay less, and the packer make more profit all at the same time. The regulatory actions taken should certainly not be

such as to prevent something like this from occurring. Nonetheless, the potential of monopsony still does exist.

The result is a real policy dilemma for the Packers and Stockyards Administration or other regulatory agencies in this area. Its resolution depends on a complex set of facts and analysis which still has not been completed. The point is this may be a circumstance in which the regulatory environment should change. If so, it would not be appropriate to stick to "tried and true" rules under the new circumstances.

Another instance where the rules of exchange are as yet not stabilized is in the grain trade with the Soviet Union and other Communist countries. For years, there had been a relatively stable market environment, one characterized by a simple regulation: no trade shall take place. But in the mid-1960's, and more strongly in the mid-70's, the Soviet Union began to change its view about appropriate market relationships in this area. The United States, while not initiating the changes, found it beneficial to cooperate in opening up lines of trade that had not existed before.

Rules governing this international exchange were not well established. At several times there were government-enforced halts in U.S. grain exports to the Soviet Union, or at least indications such halts were being seriously considered. This seems clearly a case of an unstable market environment due to policy. However, whether that was a worse state of affairs than alternative stable market environments is open to question. For example, it possibly was preferable to the former state of affairs where no trade took place.

Policy Statement Might Help

Perhaps it would be best in characterizing policy pertaining to stability of the market environment to distinguish between uncertainty and rule-based change. Uncertainty refers to change which takes the participants in the market by surprise. Rule-based change refers to events that change the market environment, but where market participants have an opportunity to make adjustments before the changes occur.

What we would like to see in cases such as grain trade with the Soviet Union is not necessarily a perfectly unchanging set of conditions for trade, but at least a statement of what the policy is that will determine conditions for trade with the Soviet Union. That is, what are the circumstances under which the United States will invoke an export embargo on grain for the Soviet Union or other communist countries? Recent attempts by Congress to put limits on the President's powers to invoke embargoes may be seen as an attempt to spell out such a set of rule-based changes in policy.

Obviously it is difficult to establish rules for markets in conditions in which the world in general, the commodities traded, and characteristics of the traders change as rapidly as they do today. Thus we can expect in the future a good deal of political effort and contentious discussion of that effort as the United States attempts to provide an appropriate set of rules.

Less Regulation? — We are used to thinking that an increasingly complex world implies a need for increasingly complex governmental activity in order to cope with the situation. This would mean an expanding scope for government agencies that deal with areas like livestock markets, international grain markets, or futures markets. However, we ought at least to entertain the idea that the nature of recent changes in these markets is such as to make it possible for less regulation to be a workable response to the increasing complexity.

One of the key changes is that market information is becoming less costly to obtain, to distribute, and to act upon by many market participants. Also it is easier for people not directly involved in commodity markets to participate as speculators, or investors in funds which speculate or hedge in commodity markets or financial futures, or agricultural futures. And there is a tendency to have more and more types of contracts and other financial instruments traded. The expansion of options trading is an example. And there are an increasing number of markets for trading futures and other financial instruments, as for instance the recent establishment of the New York Futures Exchange.

Overall, there appears to be an extent and an intensity of competition in these areas that is greater than ever before and still expanding. In addition, providers and potential providers of market-making services compete vigorously. The self-interest of investors, buyers, and sellers in becoming informed creates strong incentives to invest in information. There is a resulting demand for the services of people who specialize in generating and distributing market information. Why not rely on competition among these economic actors to regulate the markets?

Governmental regulation can provide valuable services to the users of markets, but in today's world it is becoming ever more costly to provide these services and ever more feasible to rely on decentralized self-regulating mechanisms. This means the regulatory bodies that currently exist should be subject to continual scrutiny, even as to the need for continued existence of agencies like the Commodity Futures Trading Commission, the Packers and Stockyard Administration, and the Federal Grain Inspection Service.

Such scrutiny need not reflect inherent hostility to governmental action. But it is intensified by the recognition that today, even more than in the past, a great many unmet needs could be served by appropriate governmental responses, and these needs are increasingly in jeopardy because of limitations on the resources U.S. citizens are willing to pay in taxes. Therefore it is more essential than ever, perhaps, to not spend these resources on activities that don't yield benefits commensurate with their costs.

Stability of Market Outcomes
Agricultural markets are unstable because both the quantity produced and the demand for these products is subject to unpredictable fluctuations from year to year, even month to month. It has long been a stated goal of U.S. agricultural commodity policy to increase the stability of these market outcomes. However, this is much harder to do than you might expect.

Also, it is not the case that optimal policy would act so as to provide complete stability, that is, to eliminate all change in prices (it goes without saying that it is impossible to prevent all change in quantities produced). As long as cost of production and market demands change, prices should change. Holding prices constant when the underlying economic conditions call for a change can be just as damaging as permitting unnecessary fluctuations in prices to occur.

Suppose we had an all-powerful price stabilizing agency for the main agricultural commodities. Instead of relying on bids and offers to determine a daily market price on institutions like the Chicago Board of Trade, this agency would simply state at the close of business each day what price all the main commodities should be traded at on the following day at certain locations and for certain qualities of goods, with discounts or premiums for various other places and qualities.

The potential benefit of such an agency is that it could prevent purely transitory runups or declines in prices that served no economic function, or at least a very minor function. For example, consider the runup in soybean prices a few years back, which was supposed by some to have been a consequence of large purchases by speculators who hoped to corner the market or else take advantage of an impending shortage. When the shortage failed to materialize, the price of soybeans came back down. But meanwhile there had been, it was alleged, considerable disruption of plans and activities of the users of soybeans and soybean products.

Now imagine the stabilization board observing a sudden increase in buying by an unknown investor in soybeans. This means that we see an excess of buy orders over offers to sell at the current regulated price. The question for the stabilization board is: Should we ration sales, or allow the price to rise until enough additional sellers are attracted to meet the speculative demand?

If we ration at the going price, we will have to decide who is allowed to buy and who is shut out of the market. Presumably there will be no basis for shutting anyone out completely, so there will be some kind of pro-rata share allocation at the going price. Such an approach could work to limit purely transitory rises based on false information. But suppose that in fact a shortage is impending and people somewhere out in the world away from Washington, D.C., are able to obtain information about this more quickly, and perhaps more accurately, than can be done by the stabilization board.

Information Investing Cut
Then the correct information will become embodied in market prices less quickly and completely than it could have been done otherwise. Not only that, but incentives for people outside the government to invest in this information will be reduced. For example, suppose that once every 2 years a private citizen has occasion to find out something important that could result in substantial profits if he were allowed to buy all that market conditions justified. If such people are severely limited in what they can do in speculating, the upshot could well be less information generated and therefore less accurate and economically meaningful prices, and perhaps even larger price fluctuations.

The reason for larger price fluctuations is that in the event of impending shortage, the sooner it becomes known that the shortage will occur, the sooner users of the commodity will have an incentive to reduce their consumption. This will result in more of a commodity, if it is a storable commodity, being available later, and also will give quicker signals to producers to

attempt to offset the shortage by increasing production.

On the other hand, if the stabilization board keeps the price officially low, this will be an inaccurate signal to consumers to keep on consuming at a now economically unjustified rate and will fail to send to producers the appropriate signals to start to increase output. The result would be in some cases that the stabilizing efforts will intensify the shortage situation when it finally occurs.

In short, we can all agree that providing for a relatively stable market is an important function the government should not neglect. But there is a real question of how best to obtain this objective. A wealth of experience is available on attempts to stabilize markets by governmental activity, and on the operations of speculative markets with varying degrees of stabilizing influence imposed on them. One could compare the history of price fluctuations in different countries with different institutions, or within the United States the experience of different commodities with different institutions and degrees of instability in the underlying commodity supply and demand situation.

Unfortunately, the lesson to be learned from these experiences is not obvious. Knowledgeable observers have concluded both that there should be more intensified stabilizing efforts by government, and that these efforts have been counterproductive and we would be better off to rely on decentralized stabilization by means of laissez-faire.

Stockpiling Grain
An independent area for stabilization that has received more attention than most

others is the idea of stabilizing grain prices by governmental stockpiling. For this purpose, we need not have a governmental agency set price every day or every month or every year. We simply have an agency that will buy commodities when the price is obviously lower than normal, and sell commodities when the price is higher than normal.

This seems a very simple and straightforward approach, so much so that it has been tried in many commodities in many foreign countries. It was the basis for the Federal Farm Board in 1929, the first major intervention in large commodity markets. The experiment, as many others since, experienced great difficulties and was ended in the early 1930's. The reasons for difficulty are basically the same as the reasons why price setting is difficult. The main advantage of a buffer stock, which attempts to maintain a price range instead of a fixed official price, is that one needs greater fluctuations in order to make serious mistakes. But in the markets these programs were attempting to stabilize the fluctuations have historically been large indeed.

An approach to price stabilization that combines decentralized decisionmaking with governmental action is a subsidy for private storage of a commodity. The more the cost of storage is reduced by means of payments, the larger the quantities it will be profitable to hold off the market in low price years. And the larger the quantities in stocks, the more will be available to moderate prices in years of scarcity. Such a storage subsidy is the main element of the Farmer-Owner-Reserve Program that has been in place since 1977.

Summary — In providing a stable environment for marketing and in promoting stability in prices, there is a wide variety of possible courses of action, only some of which have been discussed. The approaches require varying degrees of governmental involvement, and their merits are a subject of longstanding dispute. This chapter has outlined some of the arguments supporting and opposing important stabilization schemes and methods of market regulation. There is evidence from the consistent failure of past price fixing and price stabilization efforts that governmental management of markets is no panacea, but current scientific knowledge of either economics or political action is not sufficient to provide a firm guide to policy choice on some of the most important issues.

Transportation Handles the Surge in Production

By William W. Gallimore

*T*he United States is a land of vast distances, with differences in climate, topography and soil, a land of crop specialization, and of heavy concentrations of people in urban areas. Many crops are grown considerable distances from consumption areas. More than 60 percent of all fresh vegetables are grown in California, Florida, and Texas. Florida and California grow about 95 percent of the oranges and grapefruit. About 58 percent of the corn comes from Iowa, Illinois, Nebraska, and Minnesota, and six States grow 48 percent of the wheat. Transportation is the physical link connecting these widely scattered producing areas with consumers.

Specialization in production, which benefits both consumers and producers, has been possible because of dependable transportation at reasonable cost. A head of lettuce growing in California one week may be in a salad in New York or Boston the next. Foreign consumers also depend on food produced in the United States. Wheat grown in Kansas may end up as bread in Egypt, corn produced in Illinois may be fed to cattle in the Soviet Union.

During the 1970's there was a rapid increase in quantities of grain exported, from 1.8 billion bushels in 1970 to 4.9 billion bushels in 1981. This grain had to be moved from interior producing points to ports. Rail and barge systems have changed significantly to meet the increased export demand.

Agricultural products move to market through a network of railroads, highways, waterways, and to a lesser extent airlanes. For domestically produced food, the estimated cost of long distance transportation was $15.7 billion in 1981. This represented 5.5 percent of the marketing cost, or around $70 for each person in the United States. Trucks and railroads are the major movers of fresh produce and processed foods, but rail and barges are the major transporters of grain and other bulk agricultural commodities.

In most cases, a combination of transportation moves the farmer's produce to the consumer. Trucks, or farm wagons pulled by tractors, move grain to elevators. Trucks or railcars then move the grain to the final destination or to barges, which move grain to domestic destinations or to ports for shipments to foreign markets. Fresh fruits and vegetables move from the farm to the final destination by truck, sometimes clear across the country. Or truck trailers can be placed on railcars for long distance moves and the trailer again pulled by truck at the destination. Specialty products move by air, such as live lobsters, fresh fish, flowers, and livestock for breeding. Although

William W. Gallimore is Section Leader, Transportation Research Section, Food Economics Branch, National Economics Division, Economic Research Service.

more expensive than other forms of transportation, shippers are willing to pay extra for the speed and service. The exact combination of transportation modes for moving products from farms to consumers will depend upon availability, quality of service, and cost.

Fuel Costs Spur Rail Innovation

The transportation industry faced rapidly increasing fuel costs during the 1970s. It was a time when new foreign markets were being developed, and rising consumer incomes increased the demand for fresh fruits and vegetables and specialty foods. Diesel fuel, the major fuel for trucks, increased 114 percent between June 1976 and February 1980. About two-thirds of this increase occurred after June 1, 1979. Diesel fuel also increased in cost for trains and barges. Although the basic transportation system did not change, there were changes in the combination of transportation modes. New technologies were developed to serve established and new markets in a period of rapidly increasing fuel costs. Many recent innovations in transportation have been aimed at reducing energy requirements and thus costs.

Railroads initially opened up sections of the United States not served by waterways to development. During the westward push across our country many of the railroads were built specifically to haul grain, livestock and other farm products to market. They still haul about 50 percent of the grain but transport less than 1 percent of the livestock and poultry to market and less than 10 percent of the fruits and vegetables. Barges now transport much of the grain and trucks most of the fruit, vegetables, and livestock.

Railroads are major transporters of grain and other bulk agricultural commodities. Here, a trainload of grain moves through the Illinois grain belt.

David F. Warren

Despite past losses of traffic to trucks and barges, railroads are attempting to increase their market share of perishable products. New equipment and procedures are aimed at increasing the share of transportation service required to move grain to ports, and to reclaim part of the perishable product traffic lost to trucks. Railroads are more energy efficient in many applications than trucks, and energy efficient transportation will be needed for agricultural producers to continue to serve present markets. A number of new technologies and innovations have been developed to help railroads maintain their viability as carriers of products from farmers to consumers.

Many of the new covered hopper cars for hauling grain are made from lightweight material such as aluminum or fiberglass. Less energy is required to move these cars and there is a significant saving in motive power.

Rail-Truck Combinations — Railroads for some years have hauled truck trailers on special flatcars (TOFC). This TOFC concept has substituted to some degree for rail shipment of perishable products in refrigerated railcars. Recently lightweight railcars have been developed to haul trailers, with a considerable reduction in fuel. One railroad estimates 1.5 million gallons of fuel saved annually with a corresponding reduction in costs.

This trailer can be pulled on the highway by a truck tractor or coupled with other trailers to form a train. The trailer is backed onto the railbed, and compressed air is used to raise one set of wheels while the other set is lowered.

Bi-Modal Corporation

Another innovation is a trailer that can be pulled by a truck tractor on the highway and also be coupled together into a train. The trailer has a set of truck wheels for road use, train wheels for rails, and the conversion is simple. The trailer is backed onto the railbed. With the turn of a valve, compressed air raises one set of wheels and lowers the other. No special equipment is required. Placing the car and changing wheels takes less than 5 minutes. Gravel or crushed stone is used to bring the ground level up close to the rail level. Although this dual purpose trailer weighs more than a conventional road trailer, a train composed of these new trailers is much lighter than a train of regular railcars. Freight can move with a saving in fuel. The equipment was tested on railroads in 1981 and 1982. It combines the truck's flexibility with the railroad's long haul advantages. It is in regular daily service on one railroad. This may help fruit and vegetable growers continue to supply long distance markets.

Cattle Pullman — A new rail cattle car has been developed that can reduce weight loss in transit and possibly lower transportation costs. Large numbers of cattle are transported to Colorado and Texas to be fed on grain in the large commercial feedlots. Many of these animals move hundreds of miles by truck from Florida and other Southeastern States. Regulations requiring a maximum time cattle can be transported without rest, feed and water have made it difficult for rail transportation to compete with trucks. The U.S. Department of Agriculture (USDA) has developed a cattle railcar for use by railroads which will contain feed and water for long trips. The car has room for the cattle to lie down and rest, and will help prevent weight loss as cattle are transported.

The car has been tested but not put in commercial service.

125-Car Unit Trains — Foreign grain sales almost tripled from 1970 to 1980. Both barge and rail grain traffic increased over this period. If the domestic transportation system had not expanded rapidly, these markets would have been lost. Railroads met the challenge with innovations such as 100-ton covered hopper cars and by adopting the unit train concept. Unit trains contain up to 125 cars that are loaded at one point and moved intact as a train, generally to a port.

These unit trains are able to move grain at reduced rates because rail yards and other congested areas are avoided, switching costs reduced, equipment used more efficiently, and loading and unloading facilitated. Since a unit train may carry 12,500 tons — equivalent to 3,720 acres of corn in major high yield States — unit trains are feasible in areas of concentrated production. Special elevators and loading facilities called subterminals have been developed in high production areas that can load a unit train in less than one day. These subterminal elevators now contract with railroads for unit train services. Some of the lowest rate contracts require that as many as 60 unit trains per year be shipped.

Trucks Cut Costs

Trucks are the major movers of fresh fruits and vegetables and some other perishable and semiperishable farm products. As diesel fuel got more expensive, truck manufacturers and others in the industry developed fuel-saving technologies that lowered costs and enabled trucks to continue hauling produce to established markets. Windscreens were added to conventional truck trailer combinations to decrease air resistance. Radial tires cut ground resistance. New fans that operate on demand cut the horsepower needed for engine cooling. More fuel-efficient engines have been developed. Diesel engines are replacing gasoline engines in medium and small trucks with a total saving in fuel. These innovations were not developed for specialized uses to open new markets but to help trucks serve present markets more efficiently. Without improvements in fuel efficiency some markets for agricultural products would be lost or there could be a shift in supply areas for the markets.

Restrictions Eased — California is our major supplier of fresh fruits and vegetables, and also supplies farm products for processing. These products, along with fruit from Washington and Oregon, move by truck to the East Coast. As late as January 1981 a tier of States stretching from the Gulf of Mexico to Lake Michigan had restrictions on maximum allowable weights that were below Federal limits, creating a "barrier" to trucks meeting Federal weight limits.

This created inefficiencies in truck movements as they had to travel at less than the Federal load limits or unload part of the farm products when reaching these States. Currently only Arkansas, Missouri, and Illinois have not raised their weight limits to Federal standards. Uniform regulations will permit trucks to operate more efficiently. In some States multiple trailers and weights which exceed Federal standards are permitted, increasing efficiency even more.

Trucks are the major movers of fresh fruits and vegetables and some other perishable and semi-perishable farm products.

William E. Carnahan

How Barges Met Challenge

Barges operating on our inland waterway system provide a low cost, energy-efficient means of transportation. Water transportation is especially suited to bulk commodities which move long distances. A 1,500-ton barge can carry the equivalent of 15 covered hopper rail cars or 63 semitrailer truckloads. One limitation on barge transportation is that ice on the Upper Mississippi and some of its tributaries stops barge traffic during severe winter weather as the rivers freeze and as ice blocks the locks. Barge service is slower and more inflexible than rail or truck since service is restricted to waterways. It is not as suitable as other modes for perishable products.

During the 1970's wheat and soybean exports about doubled and corn exports increased some fivefold. Fortunately, three of the top four major corn producing States — Iowa, Illinois, Minnesota — have access to Gulf Coast ports through the Upper Mississippi and Illinois Rivers. Grain from the upper Midwest can also move through the Great Lakes ports and out the Saint Lawrence Seaway. On the West Coast, wheat moves through the Snake and Columbia Rivers to Vancouver, Portland, and other ports from as far inland as Lewiston, Idaho.

Total grain and soybean shipments by barge increased from 844 million bushels in 1970 to 1,945 million bushels in 1980, an increase of 130 percent. Corn was slightly more than half of these barge shipments in 1980.

30 to 40 Barge Tows — How were barges able to move more than double the shipments of grain in a 10-year span while maintaining their share of other commodities? Waterways had the capacity to handle the barge movements although certain locks on the Upper Mississippi, Ohio and Columbia Rivers are reaching capacity. With the basic waterway system adequate, the unregulated and competitive barge industry was able to attract sufficient capital for needed investments. New covered barges were built by the industry and towboat horsepower increased until tows of 30 to 40 barges move on the lower Mississippi.

Although towboats are relatively fuel efficient, rising fuel costs have caused towboat owners to investigate engines which operate on heavy petroleum fuels that are less costly than higher grade diesel fuel. These engines are operational and are beginning to be installed on the inland towboat fleet. The barge industry has gradually upgraded equipment, and locking procedures have been improved to relieve congestion at locks reaching capacity. Thus far the system has been able to meet the transportation needs of an expanding foreign market for agricultural commodities. Work is underway to enlarge Lock and Dam 26 which is located just below where the Mississippi and Illinois Rivers meet. About three-fifths of all barge shipments of grain and soybeans move through this complex.

Transportation in the Future

Many who write about the future picture a world startlingly different from the present. Immediately after World War II some writers envisioned a helicopter sitting in every suburban driveway, ready to whisk the owner into the city for work. Many predicted a rapidly increasing air freighter fleet would move substantially more agricultural products than proved to be the case. Although there are rapid changes in industries such as electronics and communication, other industries such as transportation change more through evolution than revolution. Improvements are gradual rather than abrupt. This is likely to be the pattern in the future, barring some unpredictable breakthrough in fuel or other transportation technology. Changes in transportation of agricultural products will continue to be influenced by the high cost of petroleum-based fuels and by the economic regulations that affect transportation.

Increases in fuel costs will prove the incentive to develop more fuel-efficient transportation. Air transportation will supply special needs and markets but will not be a major mover of agricultural products. Trucks will continue to be the most important movers of perishable products, yet may serve increasingly as collectors for funnelling agricultural commodities to barge or rail transportation for the extremely long hauls. This does not mean trucks will carry less — they may have to pick up the slack in areas where train service no longer is available — but the role of truck transportation may change. New fuel-saving equipment will continue to be introduced. Lighter weight vehicles with less wind resistance will be developed for rail and trucks.

Go With Snow — Alternative ways of refrigerating trucks and railcars, such as carbon dioxide snow to replace mechanical refrigeration, may become more widespread. Studies by USDA have shown a savings of about 30 percent in refrigeration costs by using carbon dioxide snow instead of conventional diesel-powered mechanical refrigeration for refrigerated railcars. Additional research is planned for a high volume car with modern insulation and an improved carbon dioxide system.

Deregulation — For years, both rail and trucks have operated under a degree of economic regulation, administered by the Interstate Commerce Commission (ICC). Among regulations for trucks were controlled entry into the industry, procedures for determining rates, and route allocations to trucking firms. For railroads, ratemaking procedures, quality of service, and a number of other regulations applied. In 1980, two laws were enacted which substantially lessened economic regulation and promoted competition. One impact of increased competition may be a reorganization of the transportation system to provide more efficient service.

If railroads speed up abandonment of branch lines in major grain-producing regions, they may be replaced by large subterminal facilities on the remaining branch lines with trucks moving the grain in from the farms. There will be more incentive to develop new equipment and procedures as entry and pricing restrictions are eased. For example, exempting trailers hauled on flatcars from economic regulation in 1979 brought an increase in fruits and vegetables moving by this method on railroads. Recently the ICC approved a number of rail mergers and more are pending. In most instances these mergers greatly extend the system, and a railroad can move traffic over longer distances without interchanging with other railroads. Critics have charged that continued mergers will lessen competition among railroads, but efficiency of the merged lines should improve.

The Challenge of Foreign Marketing

By Robert J. Wicks

*T*he significance of international trade for U.S. agriculture has become increasingly important. It has grown substantially in recent years, and the vitality of our agricultural sector to a large degree depends upon exports. About a third of our coarse grains and tobacco, more than half of our cotton and soybeans, and about two-thirds of our wheat production ultimately find their way into export markets.

These exports account for about one of every four jobs in agriculture. Each $1 billion in exports generates about $2 billion in GNP (Gross National Product) which in turn generates some $400 million in tax revenue. The sheer magnitude of our agricultural production and exports illustrates the ability of U.S. farmers to produce, and the importance of foreign markets. However, there remains the question of what means are available to American farmers to enable them to develop or influence these markets that have become so important to all producers.

Unlike manufacturers, farmers operate within a system where productive resources are fragmented. For the most part, they lack control over marketing, product price and total output. Production is frequently determined to a large extent by weather rather than farmers'

management decisions. Due to all this and the fact that product differentiation is virtually impossible, an individual farmer has little incentive to devote resources to influence the market, either foreign or domestic. Benefits of such efforts would accrue primarily to others because of the individual's small share of total production. As a result of these circumstances, and the risk involved, individual producers typically are not well prepared to seek or take advantage of foreign market opportunities. As individuals they stand little chance of either influencing or gaining access to foreign markets.

Yet, there is a need to seek and develop markets for U.S. farm products. To be effective, the effort has to be concerted — one which includes producers as a group, and often the Government as well. Since many barriers to increased trade are not truly economically motivated, there is a need for other than purely commercial responses, and this is a legitimate role for the Government to assume on behalf of its producers.

Despite the complexities, U.S. farmers are not completely without ways to find and gain access to or develop foreign markets. As a group, producers can and do have an impact on foreign markets. Gaining access, however, is frequently a process which requires Government

Robert J. Wicks is Chief of Program Evaluation, Foreign Market Development, Foreign Agricultural Service.

involvement and is often carried out at the request of, and in conjunction with, groups of producers.

Ideally, production and hence exports should be based on comparative advantage. (Production advantage arising from favorable natural conditions such as soil fertility or climate.). On a global basis, this means that production and therefore exports of specific commodities would come from countries with a comparative advantage in producing those commodities. Fortunately the United States has a comparative advantage in a number of commodities traded on the world market such as corn, wheat, and rice. Were it not for the effect of politically motivated schemes such as import duties, levies, production and export subsidies, our competitive position would better reflect our comparative advantage. Unfortunately these schemes act as barriers to trade and abrogate the effect of comparative advantage. Although the most visible barriers to exports are primarily political, several other types of barriers may be just as detrimental to free trade. But because they are less obvious in some cases, they receive less attention.

"Legitimate" Barriers

Institutional barriers could be thought of as legitimate barriers to trade so long as these are situations or conditions naturally occurring and not humanly contrived or politically motivated. Such barriers are frequently the result of imperfect knowledge and include lack of consumer awareness, lack of producer or processor interest, or lack of appropriate quality or quantity in demand. To a degree, some institutional barriers can be influenced in the framework of promotional activities, a subject which will be taken up later.

Other legitimate types of barriers to exports include economic constraints of consumers, and comparative or economic advantages of competing producers. Where our competitors have either comparative or economic advantages, we would become a residual supplier, furnishing only that amount which more competitive exporters would be unable to supply. In these cases — unless we can change our comparative advantage by increasing productivity through improved technology, better management, etc. — we must rely on building relationships with importers, traders, and foreign governments in an effort to influence them to choose our products for reasons other than purely price, such as quality or continuity of supply.

Economic constraints act to reduce effective demand. In the case of serious economic constraints which result in lack of effective demand, a shortsighted approach would be simply to ignore the market. Had that been the policy in the past, today we would not have some of our most important markets. Korea is an example of a country that grew economically as the result of developmental food aid programs which fostered growth of that economy. Developmental aid essentially amounts to guiding assistance so that economic growth enables foreign consumers to earn the capital needed to purchase our commodities.

"Man-Made" Curbs —The most visible and commonly thought of barriers to trade are those in one way or another politically motivated. They may be either tariff or nontariff, but are put in place to restrict movement of commodities and products into a market or gain unfair advantage. These "man-made" barriers take many forms. They may, for example, be import quotas, levies, or duties designed to restrict imports and protect an inefficient domestic industry. Or they may be "unfair" trade practices such as export subsidies in the form of special credit terms for producers, fertilizer subsidies, or tax rebates for exporters, which all give competitors an unfair advantage and therefore negate naturally occurring comparative or economic advantages. Embargoes, the ultimate form of trade barrier, may be imposed by either importers or exporters and are the most disruptive.

Some trade barriers can be overcome more easily than others. With time and resources, many institutional barriers can be reduced or eliminated by an array of market development techniques. Even some of the humanly contrived barriers can be made less harmful or negotiated away through an effective trade policy. In combination, market development activities and an aggressive trade policy are the best means to assure maximum foreign market opportunities for producers. As noted earlier, individual producers are hardly in a position to make a significant impact on foreign markets. To be effective in foreign market development, producers need to pool resources and join forces with the State and Federal agencies that are engaged in foreign market development.

USDA Assistance

The U.S. Department of Agriculture (USDA) plays a significant role in developing foreign markets for U.S. farm products with programs for both bulk commodities and processed agricultural products. Objective of the programs is to develop, maintain, and expand long-term commercial foreign markets for U.S. farm products. The vanguard of USDA's market development program is a joint agri-industry/Government effort where the Agriculture Department underwrites part of the expense of promoting a number of U.S. agricultural commodities in foreign markets. In effect, USDA acts as a catalyst in a free market system to get producers to do what neither they nor the Government can do alone.

Under the foreign market development program which began in 1955, USDA is currently working together with some 57 nonprofit trade associations largely comprised of producer-based farm groups. This year these producer groups will carry out some 2,400 promotional activities in foreign countries with help in funding and supervision from the Department. Response by foreign markets to these efforts of U.S. farm and agribusiness groups has been so positive over the years that both the American groups and participating foreign entities have been stimulated to increase markedly their financial support for these U.S. market expansion efforts.

Last year, program expenditures for the foreign market development program were about $72.5 million, of which USDA funded $21.2 million. The remainder was provided by U.S. producer groups and foreign organizations whose contributions for the past 9 years have exceeded those of the Government by a two-to-one ratio. In the 27 years since the program started, USDA has invested about $266 million. Producers have more than matched the Government funds with some $444 million generated from both domestic and foreign sources.

Incentives — Besides programs aimed primarily at expanding markets for bulk and unbranded commodities, there also are programs aimed at assisting private firms attempting to enter foreign markets. Export Incentive Programs are those which assist private firms, by underwriting a portion of the risk, in introducing to foreign markets their branded products such as fresh produce, processed fruits, vegetables, and wines. Assistance to participating firms depends upon export performance, with higher payments tied to substantial increases in sales. Currently about 35 firms compete for funding under this program, where Government funds never exceed 50 percent of allowable promotional expenses.

USDA, together with most State departments of agriculture, also provides a forum for individuals and firms, particularly small firms not presently exporting, to gain or increase exposure to foreign markets. This forum consists of several mechanisms which are either informational or exhibitory. Exhibitory mechanisms include participation in international trade shows and special USDA-sponsored shows for specific products such as meats, health foods, or produce. Informational activities include sponsorship of sales teams, a computerized referral system providing U.S. traders with information about foreign opportunities, and a monthly bulletin to inform foreign buyers about U.S. firms and their products.

In operating these mechanisms, USDA relies heavily on the assistance of four regional State organizations. These groups — the Mid-America International Agri-Trade Council, the Eastern U.S. Agricultural and Food Export Council, the Southern U.S. Trade Association and the Western U.S. Agricultural Trade Association — have each entered into an agreement with USDA and serve as the primary link with firms and individuals in the States they represent.

Agricultural Trade Offices

Functioning as a market development focal point in key overseas locations, USDA has established a number of agricultural trade offices. They serve as a support center to coordinate market development activities sponsored by USDA, as a support center for U.S. exporters, and as an information center for potential foreign buyers. In a number of locations, overseas offices of the previously discussed producer groups have been jointly located within the trade office complex. The producer representatives work hand in hand on a daily basis with agricultural trade officers in South America, Asia, and Europe. In the Middle East and Africa, agricultural trade offices have been established, and producer representatives plan to locate soon in the new facilities.

There is little doubt that exports are beneficial for U.S. farmers. Without foreign markets, producers would have to reduce production — by two-thirds in the case of wheat — and would not be able to take full advantage of the economies of scale they presently enjoy (economies resulting from large-scale production). However, producers would like to see exports give them higher prices for their products, not just bigger markets. Consumers, of course, do not want anything to drive up prices. And to the extent that economies of scale do not offset price strength resulting from export markets, foreign sales could become a point of friction for consumers. But since the share of the consumer dollar spent for food and fiber products represented by raw commodity prices to the producer is small, even substantial changes in commodity prices generally have minimal effect on consumer prices.

U.S. agricultural trade offices help U.S. exporters to introduce their products.

Attempts to measure the impact of exports on producer and consumer prices have been made, but evidence is scarce and generalizations from one commodity to another not at all relevant. In a recent study by the research staff of one of the Nation's major banks, it was found that for the 1979-80 season exports strengthened soybean prices to producers by 9 cents per bushel with an impact on the consumer price index of 1/20th of 1 percent. On balance it is generally agreed that the economies of scale from exports more than offset any positive price impact on consumers.

U.S. A Reliable Supplier? — An extremely important factor in building and maintaining foreign markets for agricultural commodities is the need to be recognized as a reliable supplier. It is widely accepted that U.S. producers are among the most efficient in the world and able to produce abundant supplies of many of the internationally traded commodities. However, the United States (not U.S. farmers) has a credibility problem when we try to project ourselves as a reliable supplier. Why? Because of U.S.-imposed embargoes.

Since 1973, for both domestic and foreign policy reasons the United States has imposed a number of export embargoes and other export restrictions. Discussions of their effectiveness go on unending. But whether or not the embargoes achieved their stated purposes, they did give importers a clear signal. The result: foreign buyers continue to question the United States as a reliable supplier. When we talk to importers about the United States' ability to supply, they smile and say "Yes — but will you?" Clearly, actions and not words are the only means to reestablish our credibility in the market.

As a means to that end, producer groups suggested a national policy be adopted to guarantee the sanctity of export contracts. Under such a policy, countries with most favored nation status would receive a guarantee that sales registered with the U.S. Government would not be restricted except in a national emergency or war. For countries not having most favored nation status, such as the Soviet Union, a less comprehensive guarantee extending for some limited time period into the future has been suggested.

Priorities Announced — Many feel such a policy is unnecessary in view of the Government's new long-term policy for farm exports. Recognizing that previous embargoes and restrictions on exports have damaged our reputation as a reliable supplier, President Reagan in the spring of 1982 announced two policy priorities designed to strengthen our image as a reliable supplier. Briefly, the new policy insures that: 1) Restrictions will not be placed on exports of farm products because of rising domestic prices. 2) Exports of farm products will not be used as an instrument of foreign policy except in extreme situations, and only as part of a complete boycott.

Understandably, the impact of this proexport policy will not be immediate, but the long-term effect will without question be positive. The fact remains, however, that as a result of past U.S. export embargoes and export restrictions, importers will continue to remind us of our past record. Some traders and even foreign governments have adopted policies to diversify their sources of supply. To the extent those policies are effective, U.S. producers stand to lose market share and are forced to find alternative markets.

Section III.
Food Buying—Making Decisions

Food Patterns – Where Are We Headed?

By Betty B. Peterkin and Richard L. Kerr

onstancy best describes overall food-buying patterns in the United States over the past decade or more. The part of disposable income allotted to food has remained at about 16 to 17 percent. The way food dollars are spent has also remained fairly stable. However, some changes of interest have occurred.

Changes in food purchases might be expected to reflect changing eating and working patterns. Surveys tell us that the U.S. population tends toward less structured meal patterns, more meals away from home, smaller households, and increased preferences for convenience, and is concerned about nutrition. Purchases also might be expected to show the effect of the ever-growing variety of both processed and unprocessed foods available to Americans. Also affecting purchases are economic factors such as food prices, household incomes, and Federal and local food assistance programs.

Several sources of data have been used to identify areas of stability and change in the way Americans budget their food dollars. Change in allocation of food dollars is one way to appraise shifts in food preferences, given the food supply and price situation at the time. More foods have gone on the market and prices for most foods have increased, but not evenly over the past 10 to 15 years. Although we know that changes, or lack of them, are influenced by these factors, as well as the preferences of consumers, we do not attempt to measure the effect of any given factor.

Primary data sources were the Annual Consumer Expenditure Studies (CES) from which the shares of total food consumption accounted for by various foods and food groups were computed for 1970 and 1980. Shares are in terms of retail store value. Also, the shares of the value of food that U.S. households used in 1977 were compared with 1965 data, as reported in USDA's Nationwide Food Consumption Surveys (NFCS). Comparisons of meal patterns are also from USDA's 1965 and 1977 surveys and from the National Household Menu Census for 1977-78 and 1980-81.

Food Groups: The Daily Food Guide

In the first comparison all food, whether fresh, processed, or ready to eat, was sorted into the food groups in USDA's Daily Food Guide. Foods with the basic

Betty B. Peterkin is Deputy Center Director, Consumer Nutrition Center, Human Nutrition Information Service (HNIS).

Richard L. Kerr is an Economist, Consumer Nutrition Center, HNIS.

Food dollar shares by food group, 1970 and 1980

Food Group	Share of each $100		Percentage Change
	1970	1980	
Vegetable-fruit	$ 17.95	$ 19.21	+ 7.0
Bread-cereal	6.81	7.27	+ 6.8
Milk-cheese	12.96	12.41	− 4.2
Meat-poultry-fish-bean	38.95	36.74	− 5.7
Fats-sweets	7.79	7.74	− .6
Mixtures from 2 or more groups[1]	7.77	7.81	+ .5
Nonalcoholic beverages, condiments, leavenings, and seasonings	7.77	8.82	+ 13.5
	$100.00	$100.00	

[1]Includes bakery products other than bread and rolls.

ingredients from more than one of the food groups and nonalcoholic beverages (coffee, tea, cocoa, and soft drinks) are shown separately. Alcoholic beverages are not included in this study. The share of each $100 worth of food accounted for by each of the food groups in 1970 and 1980 and the percentage of change in the shares are shown in the table.

In 1970 and 1980, Americans allocated the largest share of their food money for the meat-poultry-fish-bean group. Over one-third of food dollars went for meat, poultry, and fish alone. Vegetables and fruits commanded the next largest share, with milk and cheese accounting for slightly less. The other four groups— bread-cereal, fats-sweets, mixtures from two or more groups and nonalcoholic beverages — accounted for much smaller, but similar shares. The small shifts between 1970 and 1980 in shares is primarily in the direction of more even distribution of food dollars among the food groups. A slightly lower share was allocated to the meat group and slightly higher shares to the vegetable-fruit and bread-cereal groups. The share for the milk group declined while the share for

nonalcoholic beverages and accessories increased.

A 10-percent increase in shares allotted to fresh vegetables and fruits offset decreases for canned and frozen ones. Frozen juice was one exception; its share increased by almost 60 percent. Also, fresh fruit juices have come into the market prominently since 1970. The dried fruit share also increased by 17 percent over the decade.

In the bread-cereal group, cold breakfast cereals, rice, crackers, and cookies were responsible for the group increase in shares while shares for flour and corn-meal decreased. Bread and rolls accounted for $5 of every $100 in food consumption value in 1980 — about the same as 10 years earlier. CES does not report white bread separately from other breads; therefore the shifts in shares for whole grain bread could not be compared for 1970 and 1980. NFCS data, however, show a 65-percent increase in the proportion of household food dollars allotted for nonwhite bread accompanied by a 35 percent decrease for white bread between 1965 and 1977.

In the milk-cheese group, dollar shares declined for all major dairy products except cheese, which increased about 50 percent. Shifts in the use of fluid whole, lowfat, and skim milks cannot be measured from CES data because fluid milk is reported as a single item. NFCS data showed major changes between 1965 and 1977 — a threefold increase in shares of household food dollars for lowfat and skim milks and a 40-percent decrease for whole milk.

Shares for most of the primary components of the meat and meat alternates food group declined slightly between 1970 and 1980. Fresh fish and shellfish was the main exception with a 40 percent increase. Frozen and canned fish also showed a substantial gain. Nuts increased by 7 percent. Eggs showed the greatest decline over the decade, almost 40 percent.

In the fats-sweets group, substantial increases in shares of food dollars for salad dressings and margarine were offset by decreases for candies and butter. Dollar shares for mixtures showed little change, while those for soft drinks and coffee each increased over the decade. However, the increase in the dollar share for coffee probably resulted from price increases rather than increases in consumption. NFCS data substantiate this. Indeed, coffee consumption (pounds) by survey households decreased by over 40 percent between 1965 and 1977, although the value of coffee used as a percent of total food dollars increased by 30 percent.

No Surge in Processed Foods

Everyone is aware that the variety of processsed and "convenience" foods displayed in supermarkets has increased

markedly over the decade. Because of this we sometimes assume that the U.S. diet is fast approaching one of highly processed foods. This assumption is not upheld by comparisons for 1970 and 1980 in the share of food dollars allocated to four degree-of-processing categories plus a beverage-accessories group.

Category I, fresh, unprocessed foods (fluid milk and cream; fresh meat, poultry, and seafood; eggs; nuts; and fresh vegetables and fruits) accounted for $45 of every $100 worth of food consumption in 1980 — only a 4.5 percent decline from the dollar share a decade earlier. Increases in shares for fresh produce (+10 percent), seafood (+40 percent) and nuts (+7 percent) failed to offset substantial declines for milk (−17 percent), cream (−46 percent), and eggs (−38 percent) and lesser declines for meat and poultry (−4 and −5 percent).

Category II consists of frozen, canned, dried and cured foods and refined foods that have undergone little change. Dollar shares for Category II increased due to a threefold increase for fresh and frozen juices and substantial increases for natural cheese (+50 percent), canned and frozen unbreaded seafood (+18 percent), margarine (+14 percent), and sugar (+39 percent). Major decreases occurred for bacon (−25 percent), frozen and canned vegetables (−11 percent), flour and cornmeal (−16 percent), and butter (−19 percent).

Category III contains food to which some minor ingredients have been added. Dollar share increases for the category reflect the increased popularity of processed cheese (+94 percent) and cold breakfast cereals (+59 percent). Decreases occurred for canned fruits (−19

Dollar shares by degree of processing, 1970 and 1980

Category	Share of each $100 1970	Share of each $100 1980	Percentage Change
I. Fresh, unprocessed	$ 47.49	$ 45.35	− 4.5
II. Frozen, canned, dried, cured, or refined with little change	16.50	16.74	+ 1.5
III. Minor ingredient such as sugar added	8.51	9.09	+ 6.8
IV. Mixes and mixtures, ready-to-heat or ready-to-eat	19.73	20.00	+ 1.4
V. Nonalcoholic beverages, condiments, leavenings and seasonings	7.77	8.82	+ 13.5
	$100.00	$100.00	

Dollar shares for selected mixtures, 1980 vs. 1970

Food	1980 share of each $100	Percentage change from 1970
Yogurt (mostly with fruit)	$ .50	[1]
Salad dressing	.63	+40
Crackers, biscuits, cookies, tidbits	1.79	+16
Potato chips	1.09	+ 5
Frozen prepared dinners and entrees	1.55	+ 3
Bread, rolls	4.86	+ 2
Canned soups	.59	− 5
Sweet baked goods, ready to eat and frozen	2.17	− 8
Ice cream	1.51	−12
Candy, gum	3.19	−13

[1]Not reported separately in 1970.

percent) and olives, pickles, and relish (−23 percent).

Category IV includes a wide range of commercially prepared mixtures. Some — such as canned soups, bread, ice cream, mayonnaise, jams, jellies, and candies — have been staples of U.S. diets for decades. Others — such as yogurt, fresh fruit juices, and some "Nationality" foods — were not widely available in 1970. Foods in Category IV that accounted for $.50 or more per $100 of food consumption in 1980 are shown with the percentage change in dollar shares from 1970 to 1980 in a table.

This listing suggests a trend toward greater popularity of salads and ready-to-eat nonsweet snack items and a decline in sweet snack items and desserts. The increase in dollar shares for prepared food expected because of increased varieties available and increases in working women did not occur. The relatively small 3 percent increase for frozen prepared dinners and entrees was offset by the decrease for canned soups.

Home Food Paramount

Despite the proliferation of fast food and other types of restaurants, Americans continue to get most of their meals from home food supplies. NFCS 1977-78 found that 85 percent of all meals reported were eaten at home or carried from home as packed lunches, picnics, and the like. The National Household Menu Census by the Market Research Corporation of America (MRCA) cites continued growth in away-from-home eating through June 1981 despite inflation and high unemployment. Even so, it reported that only 15 percent of all main meals (17 percent when skipped meals are excluded) were eaten out in 1981.

The predominant pattern of eating occasions is three or four per day. NFCS found that 67 percent of all individuals surveyed in 1977 ate three or four times daily. The hypothesis that we are fast becoming a population of snackers was not borne out when 1965 and 1977 data were compared: In 1965, 64 percent ate four or more times a day while in 1977 only 53 percent ate that often. However, the more recent MRCA data showed that the declining pattern of in-home snacking over the past 5 years was reversed in their latest census. Snacking gains appear to be occurring now throughout all age groups and across all periods of the day — morning, afternoon, evening, and bedtime. Snacking gains were complemented by slight increases in skipped meals.

Past and Present — To summarize, considerable stability is evident over the 1970 to 1980 decade and since for: 1) The share of disposable income allotted to food, 2) The shares of food dollars allotted to major food groups, 3) The share of food dollars allotted to fresh, unprocessed foods (almost one-half), and 4) The share of food dollars allotted to mixes and mixtures, ready-to-heat and ready-to-eat (about one-fifth).

Shifts in allocations of food dollars show shifts toward food purchasing patterns

Despite the proliferation of fast food and other types of restaurants, Americans continue to get most of their meals from home food supplies, as this homemaker is doing in Mississippi.

that may be perceived to be more "nutritious": Continued use of a variety of foods. More vegetables and fruits, especially fresh ones. More salads. More fruit juices. More cereals and bread, especially nonwhite bread. More fish and shellfish. Less whole milk, cream and ice cream; more lowfat milk (somewhat counteracted by increases for cheese). Fewer eggs. Less butter, more margarine and salad dressings. Less candy and gum. Less coffee.

On the other hand, some shifts appear to ignore nutrition messages: 1) Increases in snacking, 2) More food dollars for crackers, cookies, potato chips, and tidbits, and 3) More food dollars for soft drinks, punches, and ades.

Some shifts in food dollar shares may have been for economy reasons: Less meat, poultry, and fish. Less ready-to-eat sweet baked goods. More bread and cereals. The lack of increase in "convenience" foods. The continued tendency to have meals at home or carry them from home.

George A. Robinson

The Future — We have no indication that the interest of the population in diet, health, and fitness will subside. Therefore, shifts toward diets perceived to promote health can be expected to continue.

The need to economize also persists. For example, nationwide interviews conducted by the Roper Organization Inc. in March 1982 found 68 percent "being more careful in expenditures for food" — up from 55 percent in September 1980. The means of economizing reported most often are: Buying more of things on sale, or "specials." Buying less expensive cuts of meat. Using more coupons. Buying the store's own brand. Making more use of leftovers. Cutting down on nonessentials (snacks, soft drinks, desserts, etc.). Shopping around at different stores. Eating out less. Substituting another dish for meat at some meals. If large numbers of Americans continue to believe they must be more careful about food purchases for economic reasons, trends such as these might be expected in the future.

Shoppers are "being more careful in expenditures for food," according to a survey by the Roper Organization Inc. Among the means of economizing reported, most shoppers were buying more things on sale and buying the store's own brands as this homemaker is doing in a large supermarket.

Where to Eat – At Home or Away

By Robert B. Reese and Sharon J. Mickle

*H*ave the folks at your house decided where they will be eating today — tomorrow — or the next day? Will they be eating at home, carrying food from home, buying and eating meals and snacks away from home, or perhaps doing all of these things? Will other household members eat with you or will they be doing their own thing?

When most of us eat away from home, our choices of eating places are restricted by location, time, and money. Often, mealtimes are scheduled between work, school, shopping, meetings, or recreation. When eating is a social occasion, the food, service, surroundings, and price will influence where we eat. If we have wheels and "bread," our options may be numerous and varied. The eating places available to us now are the results of earlier decisions by entrepreneurs based on past food wants, preferences, and ability to satisfy them. This is a continuing process. Our wants today in food services are different from what they were in 1970.

Our interest here is in consumers who are able to eat either at home or away — who is eating, when, where, what foods and nutrients are consumed. Information is derived primarily from 3-day reportings of food and beverage intakes at home and away in the Individual Food Intake phase of USDA's Nationwide Food Consumption Survey 1977-78 (NFCS 77-78). Food expenditures at home and away were obtained from two sources — the household phase of NFCS 77-78 and the Department of Commerce's Personal Consumption Expenditures data (PCE). Consumer food expenditures exclude payments made by others, as hosts or through expense accounts.

Food away from home accounts for an increasing share of consumers' food dollars. In 1980, nearly $96 billion was spent on food and alcoholic beverages away from home, or almost 28 cents from the consumer's food dollar. This increased from $35 billion in 1970, or 25 cents out of the food dollar. During the 1970's, consumer expenditures for foods and beverages away from home increased faster than food prices (which more than doubled) in combination with population growth (up 11 percent). Also, expenditures more than kept pace with growth in spendable income.

Robert B. Reese is Group Leader, Food Consumption Research Group, Consumer Nutrition Center, Human Nutrition Information Service.

Sharon J. Mickle is Home Economist with the same Food Consumption Research Group.

Percentage of disposable personal income allocated to food and alcoholic beverages at home and away

Item	1960	1965	1970	1975	1980
Away from home					
Food	4.0	3.9	4.0	4.2	4.4
Alcoholic beverages	1.2	1.1	1.0	.9	.9
At home					
Food	16.0	14.0	13.2	12.7	12.2
Alcoholic beverages	1.8	1.7	1.8	1.7	1.5

Average money value of home foods and expenditures for meals and snacks per household member in a week, by income

Household income before taxes (1976)	Money value per household member	
	Food at home dollars	Bought away from home dollars
Less than $5,000	14.99	2.52
$5,000-$9,999	14.20	3.06
$10,000-$14,999	14.15	4.35
$15,000-$19,999	14.99	4.99
$20,000 and over	16.36	6.83

Commercial food service establishments may use 45 to 65 percent of prices paid by consumers for costs other than food and for profits. Actual food costs account for about 40 cents from the average consumer dollar spent for food away from home.

Meal Out Costs 2½ Times More

In the household food consumption phase of NFCS 77-78, information was obtained over a 1-week period on meals eaten, the money value of household foods used, and expenditures for meals and snacks away from home. The equivalent of an average meal from home food supplies was estimated to contain foods worth $0.81. An average away-from-home meal costs $2.06, or about 2½-times the value of food in the home meal. As incomes rise, we tend to spend more for food (including beverages) away from home. Although we may live a little "higher on the hog," the money we spend for food at home may change relatively little. This is shown in NFCS 77-78 data.

During the 1960's and 1970's, a combination of consumer-related elements led to increased food consumption away from home. A partial list includes: Many households moved up the income scale into levels where people eat away from home more frequently. Women entered the labor force in large numbers, leaving less time to prepare meals at home. Average household size decreased; numbers of people living alone (who usually eat away more frequently) increased dramatically. Average age increased, while birth rates dropped (young and middle-aged adults eat out more than the elderly or preschoolers do). Suburbia expanded, and greater consumer mobility increased possibilities for food service specialization. Child nutrition programs expanded, more schools offered lunches, and the school breakfast program was initiated.

Food-service Shifts — During the past 20 years, major changes have occurred in away-from-home foods and services, mostly in the restaurant and public eating place sectors. In the 1950's, most restaurateurs were independent operators who usually prepared a variety of foods on the premises. However, restaurant chains increased their outlets, food service organizations became more active in institutional feeding services, and fast food outlets were opening in many localities, offering items such as hamburgers, frozen desserts, chicken, and hotdogs.

Subsequently, major changes occurred in the structure of the industry: Fast food places have proliferated. Characteristics include limited menu selections, standardized operations, rapid service, and moderate prices. Specialty food places have increased in importance. Menus feature specific types of foods such as steaks, seafoods, or nationality dishes. Often, unified merchandising concepts are used in planning menus, facilities, and food service systems. Food service chains and management contractors have increased shares of the "commercial" and "captive" markets. Large corporations have taken over food service firms, providing access to additional capital and services.

During the 1960's, growth segments in the "commercial" food service market included beef, seafood, pizza, and doughnuts. In the 1970's, new interest focused on specialties, breakfasts, and nationality foods. Menus were expanded and more attention was given to dining concepts when developing new outlets. Trends for the 1980's indicate that industry expansion has slowed. Operators are now competing with a variety of foods and services, some of which have been with us for a long time and others that are new.

In the future, new elements will enter into decisions by consumers to eat at home or away. Innovations in household recreation, such as television services and computer games, may encourage people to stay at home. Supermarkets, convenience stores, and delicatessens are providing increasing varieties of take-out foods. Spendable income, employment, women in the work force, household size, and other factors will continue to affect food consumption at home and away.

Eating Away — Facts and Figures
In the 1977-78 study, 62 percent of all people obtained and ate food away from home at least once during a 3-day period. (A lunch taken from home and eaten away does not count, since foods were from home food supplies.) Consumers most likely to eat out were men 23 to 34 years (79 percent), with incomes $16,000 and over (72 percent), from the West (66 percent), from suburban areas (65 percent), and were white (64 percent). People least likely to eat out were women 74 years and older (27 percent), with incomes less than $6,000 (43 per-

cent), were black (49 percent), from the South (57 percent), and from central cities (58 percent).

Most people eat and/or drink three to five times in a day, at home or away, although some eat more or less frequently. These occasions vary from a beverage break to a banquet. In the NFCS 77-78, the number of eating/drinking occasions ranged from 1 to more than 13 (averaging 4). Of these, 16 percent occurred away from home.

More men ate away from home than women, and more teenagers and young adults ate away than elderly persons. Among adults, further differences were related to income. Among highest income males, 19 to 50 years of age, 27 percent of all eating/drinking occasions occurred away from home. Among lowest income females, 51 years and over, less than 6 percent of all such occasions were away from home. Adult males, 19-50 years, ate 13 percent of their breakfasts, 35 percent of their lunches, and 20 percent of their dinners away from home during a 3-day period.

Survey participants told us what they called their eating/drinking occasions. Information was also obtained as to where each away-from-home eating occasion took place. Most occasions were readily defined as at a restaurant, fast food place, work, school, or someone else's home. Eating at a store included delicatessens and foodstores when food was eaten on premises or taken out and eaten away from home. "Other" eating places included churches, clubrooms, taverns, child-care centers, airplanes, and sports arenas.

Sex, age, and income of the consumer were associated with where people chose to eat as well as their decision to eat at home or away. Eating at school, work, or at someone else's home comprised a major portion of all eating occasions. Among the lower income, very young, and older groups, eating at someone else's home accounted for a relatively large share of eating occasions away from home. Higher income adults were most likely to eat at commercial eating places.

When and With Whom

NFCS data indicated differences about when people ate away from home. Adult men were more likely than women to eat away from home before 11 a.m., and less likely to eat away after 4 p.m. Women 51 years and older ate away from home the least in the morning (15 percent) and the most in the late afternoon or evening (37 percent). During eating occasions away from home, adult men were more likely to eat alone than were women, regardless of age. When others were present, they were most likely not members of the same household.

If we select foods differently at home than we do away from home, we are not alone. Indicators of differences in foods consumed at home and away were derived from the NFCS 77-78. Percentages of respondents reporting consumption of major foods and food groups during a 3-day period provided a basis for comparison. In the meat, poultry, and fish group, beef was the most popular item both at home and away. In the higher income group, 63 percent ate beef at home and 22 percent away. Other people ate beef in mixtures such as stew, potpie, or soup. Among lower income people, beef also was the item most frequently reported. Among the other food groups, the items eaten away from home most

Total Nutrient Percentage from Foods Obtained and Eaten Away from Home

Age (years)	Energy and energy nutrients			Minerals and vitamins		
	Children	Males	Females	Children	Males	Females
1-5	8-12			7-11		
6-8	20-21			17-23		
9-18		21-23	21-24		17-24	17-24
19-22		24-25	22		21-24	18-22
23-34		24-26	18-19		21-25	15-18
35-50		19-20	15-16		16-20	12-15
51-64		15-16	12-13		11-15	9-12
65-74		8-10	9-11		7- 9	7-10
75 and over		6- 8	6- 7		5- 7	5- 7

frequently were: fluid milk (23 percent); breads, rolls, and biscuits (35 percent); other baked goods including cakes, cookies, crackers, and pastries (27 percent); white potatoes (30 percent); coffee (20 percent); and soft drinks — carbonated and noncarbonated (26 percent).

School age children get about a fifth of their energy nutrients from food eaten away from home.

Nutrient Content — What proportion of individuals' intakes of energy and nutrients per day come from food eaten at home and away? For all individuals surveyed, food obtained and eaten away from home contributed 17 to 18 percent of the total amount of food energy and energy-yielding nutrients (protein, fat, and carbohydrate) and 14 to 17 percent of the minerals (calcium, iron, magnesium, and phosphorus) and vitamins (thiamin, riboflavin, preformed niacin, and vitamins A, B6, B12, and C) studied. Among consumers, by sex, age, and income group, the contribution of foods obtained and eaten away from home to nutrient intake generally reflected the proportions of individuals eating out. Foods eaten away from home made the smallest contribution to elderly people's intakes and the largest contribution to young men's intakes.

Where Consumers Buy Their Food

By Edgar P. Watkins

*T*hose buying food for the home now have a greater choice of food sources than at any time in the recent past. In addition, the selection of food products has expanded to provide customers year-round availability of most items of fresh produce, meats, dairy and poultry products, table-ready foods, and a tremendous variety of processed food. Customers interested in quickly prepared meals have a wide array of foods ready to heat and serve either by conventional cooking methods or with microwave ovens. Those interested in preparing food from basic ingredients can find the makings in their favorite foodstores.

Although supermarkets continue to dominate the grocery business, their share of this business has decreased from 79 percent in 1973 to 71 percent in 1981. Convenience stores, specialty and health food stores, nontraditional food outlets such as department and discount store food sections, direct marketing from farmers to consumers, and home gardens have grown to nibble away at the share of the market sold by supermarkets.

This greater diversity of foodstores and food products is widely available to most of the Nation's population with perhaps two major exceptions. 1) Supermarkets in some metropolitan areas have experienced major problems operating in low income central city locations. Customers in these areas may depend on older small-sized stores with a limited choice of foods, often at higher prices. 2) In very rural areas, customers have little choice of places to shop because such areas may support only one or two stores. These stores serve a relatively small population living in a large geographical area.

Each of the types of stores selling food has some advantages. Most have some disadvantages. Small stores in general have higher costs, higher margins and less choice. Some larger stores may be impersonal, offer less service, be located farther from the home, take more time to shop but offer a greater choice. Stores with high sales volume (both large and small) may offer lower prices, be crowded, and require more checkout time. In 1981, the 165,000 stores classified as grocery stores had sales totaling over $240 billion.

During the 1920's and 1930's many service grocery stores converted to self-service where customers picked their selections off shelves rather than being waited on by clerks. This change greatly reduced store operating costs. Self-service stores offered lower prices.

Edgar P. Watkins is retired from the Agricultural Economics Department, Ohio State University, Columbus.

During the 1940's the grocery industry largely converted to self-service and larger stores, and the name supermarket evolved. Each decade since that time the newer supermarkets have about doubled in size as retailers and food manufacturers offered customers more choice and customers responded favorably. During the 1940's and 1950's perishable departments (produce, meat and dairy) were also converted to self-service.

The grocery industry defines a supermarket as a foodstore having sales of over $2 million a year. In 1981 about 28,600 supermarkets had sales totaling $171 billion. Seventy-five to 80 percent of this total was for food. In recent years several types of supermarkets evolved as retailers competed for additional business. Today in many areas customers may choose to shop superstores, conventional supermarkets, warehouse supers and limited assortment stores.

Superstores — These supermarkets, developed in the 1970's, generally have over 30,000 square feet of shopping area, offer customers a choice of 15,000 items, and have annual sales of over $8 million. The stores offer extensive service departments to augment the self-service departments.

Most of these stores have service meat (and self-service meat), delicatessen, bakery, lunch counters or restaurants and cheese shops. The service departments are labor intensive and have high labor costs. This may increase total operating costs and require higher store margins than in conventional supermarkets. Store margins are the difference between what a store pays for a product and what it sells for. For example, if an item costs the store $.81 and sells for

$1.00, the margin is $.19 or 19 percent of sales. Store margins in superstores range from 21 to 23 percent of sales.

Dry grocery prices in these stores tend to be very competitive with standard supermarkets. A variation of the superstore is a combination store where more nonfoods are sold (clothes, small and large appliances, pharmacy, hardware, auto supplies, etc.). These combination stores may have sales areas as large as 100,000 square feet (about 2½ acres).

Superstores and combination stores account for about 25 percent of all supermarket sales. This share will probably grow during the years ahead. The attractions of these larger stores for customers are one-stop shopping, more items, the opportunity to buy custom cuts of meat, fresh deli and bakery products, and cheese from many countries. Retail prices tend to be competitive with conventional supermarkets and with bakery and deli specialty stores for their products. These larger stores also tend to offer more private label (store brand) and generic label products.

Conventional Supermarkets

These stores are familiar to most food shoppers. They have dominated the food business for the past 30 years. The stores average about 17,000 square feet of selling space ranging from 6,000 to 20,000 square feet, and have $2 to $8 million annual sales. These markets usually have self-service meat, produce, and dairy. Some stores (newer and recently remodeled) may also have small deli's, bakery and service meat counters.

Conventional supermarkets account for about two-thirds of all supermarkets sales. They offer a smaller selection of items (8,000 to 12,000) than super-stores, and fewer nonfoods. Margins, averaging about 20 percent, tend to be about 2 percent lower than in super-stores largely because most conventional stores do not have service departments and offer fewer higher margin nonfoods. The conventional supermarkets are still where most of America shops for food, but they will increasingly be replaced by superstores in areas where there is enough population to support them.

The warehouse supermarket or economy format store was nurtured by high inflation during the 1970's. About 1,500 of these stores nationwide account for about 6 percent of supermarket sales. Many were conversions from conventional supermarkets, although some were built expressly for warehouse type operations. The stores average about $6.5 million sales annually. Margins in these stores are about 16 percent, some 3 to 4 percent less than in conventional supermarkets.

Most merchandise is displayed in cartons, which are sometimes located on pipe rack fixtures. Hence, the name "warehouse stores." The stores feature slightly lower prices but carry a limited selection of items. Perishables (meat and produce) are limited, and in some stores not carried at all. The number of items displayed ranges from 1,500 to over 7,500. Customers usually shop these stores because of price, and fill in their food needs by purchasing items in other stores. Other customers do not care to shop the stores because of the "ware-house atmosphere." Not all market areas in the country have warehouse stores available, although the warehouse format has been tried in most major markets.

Limited Assortment and Box Stores

These markets operate on the lowest margin of all supermarkets, averaging about 12 percent. They account for a rather minor 1 percent share of super-market sales. Most of the stores were converted from older, unprofitable conventional supermarkets.

Limited assortment stores average about 9,000 square feet, may have three

Warehouse supermarkets were nurtured by high inflation in the 1970's. Most merchandise is displayed in cartons, as at this food store in Silver Spring, Md.

checkouts, and carry under 1,500 items — some as few as 500. They stock only the items which have the fastest turnover, in hopes of building sales on the basis of the fast moving items, and stock few or no perishables. There now are between 600 and 700 of these stores in the U.S. Grocery industry people forecast stores with this format will survive only in specialized market situations.

Box stores carry as few as 500 items and usually offer few or no perishables. Customers may provide their own bags. The idea for the these stores was im-ported from Europe where they have been very successful. Customers in this country continue to indicate their preference for one-stop shopping, which works against limited assortment and box stores. The fast-moving items stocked by these stores are also items commonly used for low-priced specials in other supermarkets, so the price appeal is somewhat blunted.

Convenience Stores —These small stores first appeared in substantial numbers in the late 1950's. The stores average about 2,500 square feet in size, stock about 3,000 items, offer few nonfoods,

William E. Carnahan

have one or two checkouts. Some feature a limited number of fast foods. About half sell gasoline. Convenience stores average about 30 percent margin, which is some 10 percent higher than conventional supermarkets. Their appeal to customers is quick service, convenient location, and having fill-in items readily available. Products that have the largest sales are tobacco, grocery, soft drinks, beer, dairy, candy and gum, bread and pastry, health and beauty aids, chips, and snack foods.

For the last 20 years convenience stores have been the growth phenomenon of the grocery industry. From a few stores in the 1950's, their number has grown to over 38,000. This exceeds the present number of supermarkets by almost 10,000. Convenience stores now account for almost 6 percent of all grocery store sales. Paradoxically, convenience stores have grown in numbers as supermarkets have grown in size. For customers who need a fast fill-in of items on which they run short, convenience stores provide the location, product, and quick service needed. Hence the name "convenience stores."

Non-Conventional Food Stores

Three types of business may serve as examples of nonconventional sources of food for use at home. Food sections found in department stores make up one of these. The food operation may feature higher priced, hard-to-find food specialty items. The operation may be limited to one counter or may be a featured department in the store. A second type may be

found in discount stores. These sections often feature foods commonly used for picnics and other informal meals. Also featured are snack foods. Casual observations lead to the conclusion that prices are very similar to nearby supermarkets.

A third type is represented by fast food outlets with a drive-in window. Chicken, hamburgers, roast beef, pizza, and other entrees are featured with side dishes and beverages which the shopper picks up at the drive-in window for a meal ready to eat at home. In some fast food operations the value of food sold at the drive-in window approaches that sold for consumption on the premises.

Small Stores —There are 98,000 small-sized neighborhood foodstores. This is almost 60 percent of the 165,000 grocery stores. These small stores account for some 23 percent of grocery sales totaling

Convenience stores offer customers quick service, convenient location, and have fill-in items readily available. Many convenience stores, such as these, stay open late at night.

about $55 billion annually. Most small stores are operated by independents who own and manage their own business. The stores may be a small version of a supermarket offering a limited choice of products, may be similar to the old style corner grocery store, may be a specialty store featuring meats or bakery, or a health food store.

"Supermarket" neighborhood stores are small-scale versions of the larger supermarkets. They often are located in mature sections of a metropolitan area, or in a rural area with a population base too small to justify a large-scale supermarket. In fact, they may well be an early supermarket still in business some 40 years later. The stores range in size from 4,000 square feet to 8,000 square feet.

Most such small foodstores have high operating costs as measured by a percentage of sales. Prices are typically higher than in conventional supermarkets but lower than in convenience stores. They may also be at a competitive price disadvantage in buying groceries. There are about 8,000 of these stores which account for about 5 percent of the grocery business. They stock from 5,000 to 7,000 items and have sales of $1 to $2 million per year per store.

Corner Groceries — These are remnants of stores which were replaced by supermarkets. They can typically be found in older sections of cities. A sizable portion of customers walk to the store rather than drive. Choice and selection of products are limited. Parking may be limited to the street. These neighborhood stores may offer credit to regular customers. Cost of operations as a percentage of sales is high. Prices are higher than in small neighborhood supermarkets. The stores are small, ranging in size from 500 to 3,000 square feet.

William E. Carnahan

247

Specialty stores compete by offering a quality product and customer service. Meat markets and bakeries may be found in mature sections of cities and towns. Some small meat processors in the country also retail meats. The meat markets usually feature service meats where the customer deals directly with the meat cutter. Margins and prices are usually slightly higher than in large supermarkets. Selection of products available to customers is reasonably good within the specialty area.

Health food stores are rather recent additions to the foodstore lineup. Often located in shopping centers, they specialize in food supplements, whole grain products, foods with no additives, spices and herbs. They may be featured as natural food specialists, although the term in most States has no legal meaning and is difficult to define. The stores may be franchised by an organization which assists the owner with buying, advertising, and supervision. Prices are difficult to compare, as identical products may not be carried in supermarkets.

Food Cooperatives

Interest in food cooperatives reached a peak during the mid-seventies as inflation rates soared. Not all groups were formally organized as co-ops. Typically, several families got together and decided to pool their purchases of food. Some individuals volunteered to take orders one week to be made available at a given time the following week, others totaled the order and made purchases from cooperating wholesalers, still others hauled the groceries and divided the total order into individual family purchases. Some groups were successful in saving their members money. These groups seem to survive as long as enough members are willing to

spend volunteer time ordering, purchasing, hauling, collecting money, and dividing the total purchase into individual customer orders.

Some groups organized co-ops to operate out of church buildings or small stores. The latter operations were called store front co-ops. A few of these are successful. Many store front co-ops ran into trouble early as they hired people to work in and manage the store and meet their overhead costs. As these groups began to hire employees and pay rent, they found it difficult to price competitively with supermarkets. They seem to persist best in areas where there is a renewable supply of volunteer labor, such as near college campuses.

Direct Sales — Three methods of selling dominate where food is sold directly by farmers to consumers. Sales at a roadside stand or market is one method. Some roadside markets are very seasonal, others have grown to feature sizable buildings and year-round operations. Many markets have a specialty, such as sweet corn or apples or peaches. As these markets grow, they supplement farm-grown products with purchased items. Most of the markets feature fresh produce. Prices tend to be competitive with supermarkets. Customers patronize the markets for country atmosphere, quality, freshness, and availability of varieties not found in supermarkets.

The second method of selling direct is pick-your-own, where the customer goes to the farm and harvests the product. In some areas of the country most of the strawberries, blackberries, and other small fruits grown locally are sold this way. Other crops sold are tomatoes, beans, apples, peaches, cherries, sweet corn and other specialty crops. Of all the direct sales methods, this one is growing most rapidly and may present the best opportunity to both increase the farmer's income and save consumers money.

The third method of direct selling is an old one, farmers markets. These markets are community based where several farmers bring their products to a location in or near town. The markets may operate one or more days each week. Some are open-air seasonal markets where farmers sell off their truck. Others may operate most of the year in a market building. The number of these markets may be decreasing, as some were established recently in towns too small to support them. Consumers find the markets appeal to them because of personal contact with farmers, quality products, freshness, and the social atmosphere.

Other Sources — Home gardens can supply much of a family's fresh produce during the growing season. A garden may also provide enough for canning and freezing for use during the rest of the year. Those who garden successfully know that no purchased produce tastes quite as good as that harvested from the garden just before it is prepared for the table. Hunting and fishing may provide some families who have the talent, training, motivation, and location to seek out small and large game, fish, waterfowl and other game birds during the legal season. The number of hunters and fishermen with licenses probably exceeds by far the number of those who put a substantial quantity of meat on the table for the family.

Using Computers — Computer-assisted shopping may become a part of the home of the future. This prospect has been predicted to be just around the corner for the past 15 years. Several trials involving telephone-computer hookups between the home and a distribution center have not been successful. With the recent availability of low price computers and interactive terminals for the home, the possibility of computer-assisted shopping may have moved closer. In theory one could order any time of the day or night.

Questions still remain about whether shoppers would sit at a terminal when putting in a grocery order rather than see and feel the quality of perishables in the store. And what happens after the order is placed? Is the order delivered to the home? Does the customer pick it up? When? Where? Also unanswered are questions about cost. Will it save consumers money? Will the ultimate system simplify or complicate shoppers' lives? Large-scale, computer-assisted shopping appears to be still in the future, but yet a distinct possibility.

Further Reading

National Food Review, Fall 1981, ERS/ USDA. For sale, Domestic $7, Foreign $8, from Superintendent of Documents, Washington, DC 20204.

Farmers Markets, Grantham and Bell. Agricultural Economics Department, Dr. James Bell, 307 Hutchenson Hall, Blacksburg, VA 24061. Free.

Farmer to Consumer Direct Marketing, Statistical Bulletin 681, February 1981. ERS/USDA, Washington, DC 20250. Free.

Food Co-ops for Small Groups, Vellala, 1975. Workman Publishing Co., 1 West 39th Street, New York, NY 10018. $4.95.

Motivating Factors in the Marketplace

By Effie Hacklander

Human behavior, of which our marketplace behavior is only a part, begins with needs. Needs are as consumers perceive them. Products or services that the consumer sees as satisfying the need are known as satisfiers. Any given need can be satisfied in a variety of ways.

When a need, a lack of something, is perceived, a chain reaction is set up and a psychological state of tension or imbalance occurs in which activities are begun to fulfill that need. This process becomes the motivation for action to fill the need. For example, noon generally is considered as lunchtime in our society. Thus as the clock approaches the hour, a need develops (hunger) creating anticipation of a break and satisfying the basic need for food and also possibly the need for socializing. One could say that "time," as well as "hunger," are motivating factors. This example also illustrates that needs can be either internal or external in source.

Needs and motives provide the foundation for explaining consumer behavior in the marketplace. Obviously, marketers have a high interest in identifying and providing satisfiers for consumer needs. By understanding the types of information held by marketers, consumers can adjust their behavior in a coping manner. For example, consumer research has indicated that such variables as store layout, placement of goods on shelves, and colors used in packaging all influence whether or not a purchase is made. Additional information, such as specific demands for item pricing, low-sodium foods, or other label information, are consumer input actions which have caused changes in marketplace alternatives.

Numerous classification schemes have been derived to organize the seemingly limitless number of needs and motives. Various research efforts have come to one generalization: the consumer behaves in a consistent and purposeful manner in the marketplace. This implies that we incorporate motivational factors into a meaningful component — in short, consumer behavior is motivated behavior. To cope with the marketplace, you the consumer need to discover what it is you do, decide if this is what you want to do, and maintain or consciously change your behavior.

It must be recognized that consumers are multimotivated, not single or limited motivated. For example, when entering a supermarket you notice such general factors as cleanliness of the store, number

Effie Hacklander is Assistant Dean, College of Human Ecology, University of Maryland, College Park.

of shoppers, and the number of open checkout lanes. Then as you progress through the store, you notice specific factors such as price specials, new products, and the quality of fresh produce.

Many of the factors affecting consumer behavior in the marketplace can be described as general or specific economic factors, general or specific behavioral factors, and general or specific personal factors. In each category some of the motivating factors will be internal (physiological) and some of the factors will be external, or initiated by others or the environment (psycho-social).

Economic Behavioral Factors

All consumers care about *economic factors*. Price of a product is often used as a motivating factor. Research indicates there is a range of prices consumers are willing to pay, as well as a reference price or "right" price that influences our decisions. An acceptable price may be based on prices paid in the past, attitude about what is a fair price, and anticipation of prices in the future. Consumers are thought to use price as an indicator of quality. Thus, statements such as "You always get what you pay for," or "The middle-priced product is the best quality for the money" become general motivating factors. Specific economic factors are illustrated by item pricing, or price specials and coupons promoting sales of certain products. Use of price as a criterion of quality varies from product to product, and may be overrated. If a large number of alternatives are available — for example, with snack crackers — price may not be the most important consideration, but rather taste, texture, or specific ingredients.

Behavioral factors deal with our overt ac-

tions and responses to situations. In a consumption society, consumers must learn to be consumers, meaning that they have acquired needs through socialization for approval, status, security, affiliation, and achievement. The appropriate consumer goods for fulfilling these needs must also be learned. These learned needs account for the wide diversity of brands within product categories. Thus, we have name brands, house brands, and generic brands of various products — for example, frozen peas. Generic brands may fulfill the need for frozen peas to include in a casserole for the family, but may not satisfy the need for frozen peas as a vegetable to serve to company, where our acquired needs have programmed us for a perceived higher quality product.

Not all needs are fulfilled immediately. Many times the motivation to buy is there, but the dollars aren't and thus the purchase is postponed until some future date. Recent economic developments (inflation, high interest rates, unemployment) have put many large ticket items such as houses and cars beyond reach for many consumers. Consumer behavior is adjusted by delaying a purchase or simply deciding not to make one. The success of "box stores" and generic brands are other indications of consumers altering their behavior as a way of coping with increased prices.

Marketers structure advertising to appeal to learned needs, and often multiple needs. Thus, not only does toothpaste clean your teeth, it makes you socially acceptable, and adds sex appeal. Much has been said about the persuasive effect of advertising on consumers. However, given the complexity of the marketplace and the multimotive orientation of consumers, it seems likely that advertising serves as a reminder, or raises our awareness of the availability of products, but does not force us to buy an item.

Personal Factors — Consumers are not a homogeneous group, but are persons who may be quite different from one another. Personal factors refer to the unique qualities that every individual possesses, such as the ability to see or hear messages, and the individual's needs, moods, memory experiences, and values, all of which modify behavior.

In addition, demographic factors such as age, sex, and education mean that any given product may not satisfy the needs of all consumers. For example, geographic differences in food preferences have been well documented. Barbecued ribs means one particular type to Midwesterners, another type to Texans, and still a third type to Chinese-Americans. Differences in lifestyles, goals, aspirations, and interests as well as social group and individual influences may change our preferences for food over time. Although preschoolers may prefer macaroni and cheese, hotdogs, and applesauce for dinner, as one matures and learns more of the world, other food preferences are cultivated.

Implications for Consumers

Marketing practices include consideration of many personal factors as identified by segmenting the market by social class. Market segmentation, the process of defining homogeneous groups, defines the purchase and use patterns of a variety of products and services of each of the major social class groupings. When combined with other variables (income, life cycle, etc.) the marketer can develop advertising campaigns based on consistency with social class characteristics.

A recent study investigated differences in women's food shopping and preparation attitudes and behavior. The researchers found that whether a woman was employed, or was not employed, made little difference in food shopping behavior. Instead, food preparation styles of the individual women were more important. Those individuals who enjoyed cooking had a concern for quality, while those with a negative attitude about food preparation illustrated a concern for time.

Concern for price was not group specific. In other words, it appears that regardless of social class, there are individuals in each group who are price-sensitive when shopping for food. It is not clear, however, whether this sensitivity is due to the necessity (lower income) of attaining the lowest possible cost for food, or whether it is a sensitivity to get the best value for the money spent.

By using a multidimensional view of the consumer, and considering economic, behavioral, and personal factors, marketers can influence consumption decisions. Wise consumers analyze their behavior with the same scrutiny and reasoned approach.

Family Economics and Food Purchases

By Carolyn G. Carter and Frances Cogle Lawrence

Changes in the age groups in the population and changes in lifestyles have influenced where and what foods are purchased. Factors such as rising household income, more women in the labor force, and smaller households have altered food purchasing patterns.

Even after inflation most families continue to have increased purchasing power. A recent U.S. Department of Agriculture study shows that although food prices have risen, their growth has not matched the increase in consumers' discretionary income. In reality, shoppers are spending a smaller percentage of their income on food than ever before. Nevertheless, food is still a major part of the typical household budget, with more than 25 percent devoted to feeding the average family. Food dollars as a percent of disposable personal income has continued a long-term decline. In 1981 it averaged a little more than 16 percent of disposable personal income.

As incomes of families increase, more money is spent for food, but the percent of income spent on food declines. Lower income families spend fewer dollars than higher income families, but the amount represents a larger percentage of their income than the higher income families.

Over 35 percent of the food dollar is now spent on food away from home. This figure may rise to 50 percent as more and more women join the paid labor force, and food outlets respond to changes in family eating habits. Geographic location also affects the amount a household member spends on food away from home. The average money value for eating out was higher in the Northeast and the West than in the North Central area and the South. Typical household members spent more outside the home if they lived in a suburban area rather than in the central city or a nonmetropolitan area.

Eating outside the home may not always save time, but it does reduce time spent in meal preparation and cleanup, and provides recreation for the family. The increase in convenience usually costs more than the same food prepared and eaten at home since the consumer pays not only for the basic food, but also for preparation, service, cleanup, supplies, and entertainment. Despite the higher costs involved, the trend toward more away-

Carolyn G. Carter is Associate Specialist, Family Resource Management, Louisiana Cooperative Extension Service, Baton Rouge.

Frances Cogle Lawrence is Associate Professor, School of Home Economics, Louisiana State University, Baton Rouge.

from-home meals continues. Retailers, in general, believe consumer acceptance of microwave ovens, convenience foods, and other appliances and innovations will stimulate eating at home, slowing the growth of eating out, with a substantial impact in the early 1980's.

Spending for Food at Home

As mentioned earlier, a household's income has less effect on food purchased to be prepared at home than on food purchased in restaurants. In spring 1977 the average money value of food per household member was only 20 percent more for the highest than for the lowest income group. A 10-percent increase in income is associated with a 1.5-percent increase in food purchased for preparation at home.

Differences in the types of food purchased have been found among the various income groups. As income increases, the amount spent on such products as pork, eggs, and cereal declines. But households with higher incomes spend more on such items as beef, beverages, bakery products, and vegetables. Place of residence also seems to influence spending for food at home. Suburban households were found to spend more for food than households in either the central city or nonmetropolitan areas.

Spending for food prepared at home increases significantly as household size increases, while spending for food away from home increases modestly. Given the same income, larger households spend more per household but less per person for both at-home food and food away from home than smaller households. They also spend a smaller share of their food dollar on food away from home.

Working Wives — In the United States today, there are more working wives than full-time homemakers. More than half of all married women work for pay. Of married women ages 16 to 44 years, three-fourths are working outside the home. By March 1980, 62 percent of all married women whose youngest child was 6 to 17 years old and 45 percent of those whose youngest child was under 6 worked in paid employment.

Families with two wage earners enjoy incomes 40 percent higher than incomes produced by a single family worker. Even though some costs are associated with working, including more meals eaten away from home, the family income is still greatly enhanced by having the second wage earner.

This longer-on-money but shorter-on-time group regularly purchases ready-to-serve products, such as packaged mixes, ready-to-eat entrees, and canned meats. In comparing cooking habits of one- and two-income households, dual-earner families are more inclined to purchase cookout foods and go the simple route to meal preparation. Bulk purchases are made in order to prepare big batch meals.

The working woman is making fewer shopping trips to purchase food. One-stop shopping is a trend for working customers. Nearly half the dual-income earners said they are now more likely to buy everything they need at a well-diversified supermarket.

Family eating styles have changed, as well. Foods purchased for the traditional breakfast are alive and well in the one-income household, but two-income households seldom cook the typical morning meal of juice or fruit, eggs, bacon, and toast. Dual-incomers most often grab a bite on the way out the door.

Men Participate in Shopping

The profile of today's food shopper is also changing. Although women continue to be the primary shoppers in both single-income and dual-income families, more men are joining them for the shopping chores. About one-third of single-income families and 40 percent of dual-income families report husbands helping with food purchasing.

One-third of those participating in major food shopping are male. Males most likely to participate are those 55 years of age and older. The under 35 male is less likely to participate in family food shopping. Men who do participate in family shopping are less likely than women to prepare conscientiously by reading store ads, clipping coupons, or making shopping lists.

Almost 38 percent of male shoppers live alone, Both men and women are living alone more due to later marriage, divorce, or death of a spouse. Single people are a special type of food consumer with particular needs and wants. The young, single shopper may not be very skilled in shopping and in choosing foods wisely. He or she may lack skill in managing a total budget.

Shopping Trips Rise — For the first time in several years, shopping frequency edged upward. The number of shopping trips per week was 2.53. As gas lines become an event of the past, consumers seem more willing to get in the car and make that extra trip to the supermarket.

More and more men are participating in grocery shopping.

A decline in the number of weekly shopping trips in the past was primarily due to the impact of working women and high gasoline prices. Less frequent shopping called for larger containers of such foods as milk, eggs, and chilled juices. Back in the 70s quarts were the biggest sellers but as trips to the store declined, consumers found a need for larger quantities of foods to last between shopping trips.

One-stop shopping for food and other household and grooming items is becoming the rule for many customers. Half the dual-income earners (as noted earlier) and just under half the single income consumers agreed they now are more likely to buy everything they need at a well-stocked supermarket. Types of food packaging needed by consumers have also been influenced by lifestyle changes. Working women, two-income households, and more male shoppers all mean an increased demand for ready-to-serve food items. At the same time, smaller families indicate a need for small size or serving size packages where freshness can be maintained until the next serving.

Generics and Income Levels

As consumers change their food shopping habits, they continue to rely on coupons, private label brands, newspaper ads, and most recently generic (nonbranded) products to reduce their food expenses. Consumer acceptance of generics has been rather high. The lower price and no-frills items should appeal more to lower income shoppers looking for a bargain buy. It has been found, however, that those with low incomes were no more likely to buy generic items than those with high incomes. Those in the lower income range were even less likely to have tried a no-frills product than their higher income neighbors. Younger, better educated consumers are the ones most likely to buy generic items. Of the generic food items, canned vegetables and fruits are most often purchased. Consumers are less likely to purchase soft drinks, soup, or canned tuna in generic packages.

The age-group makeup of the population continues to change as the last of the postwar "baby boom" children moved into their 20's and the first of this group moved into their mid-30's. These relatively well-educated and affluent young consumers have changed food purchase behavior as they have new and different lifestyles which in turn shape their purchasing decisions. Those in the population under age 15 now account for a lower percentage of the population, and the over 55 age group continues to be a larger part of the total population. These factors affect food purchasing as teens favor hamburgers, pizza, and other fast foods while older people most often prefer a more traditional menu.

Over-65 Patterns — About 25 million Americans belong to the over 65 age group, and by 1990 it is projected their numbers will increase by 20 percent. Elderly shoppers have shopping behaviors different from other segments of the population. Rapidly rising food prices can have an even more devastating impact on the lifestyles of elderly shoppers on fixed incomes than they do on the average supermarket customer. Surveys indicate that one-quarter of their fixed income goes for food items. One way the elderly have found to cope with inflation is by purchasing less nutritious and less expensive foods. Older shoppers show little interest in shopping fast or in shopping late. They like to take their time to shop around and compare prices.

Personal Beliefs, Preferences and Food

By Merry Jo Davis and Joyce R. Garrick

There is a wide gap between the science of nutrition and its application in food buying, preparation, and consumption. Knowledge of what foods are nutritionally required for good physical sustenance does not dictate individual choice of what we consume. Habits have a predominant effect on our food intake and health. We must recognize some of the factors which influence behavior before we can effectively alter them.

Some important determinants which mold existing individual and family food behavior patterns are one's culture, ethnicity, and social and psychological perceptions toward food. These factors influence where, how, what and sometimes why we eat or purchase the foods we do. Food availability, costs, and one's economic status are factors which are interwoven into food selection. Each of these facets will be examined individually in this chapter and related to food consumption and purchasing trends.

A people's culture develops over a long period of time. Anthropologists study mankind's culture to provide us with clues to our ancestral beginnings. Culture incorporates the historical events which participate in the development of our current way of life. It is the conglomeration of everyday living. Such things as birth, death, pregnancy, sex, illness, disease, the process of food acquisition and preparation, caring for family members, and hierarchical structure are included in "culture." Culture evolves as language, religion, politics and technology change. Culture has a value system and is a learned phenomenon.

Food habits are an effective means to communicate many aspects of one's culture. Habits can determine what foods are eaten as well as when, why or how. Culture determines what foods we should eat. It may determine what combination of foods comprise a meal. For example, what would be appropriate for lunch may be unsuitable for dinner. Generally bacon and eggs are more acceptable for breakfast fare than for dinner fare. There are regional variants to meal patterns too. Southerners prefer grits while Northerners choose fried potatoes. Specific foods become symbolic with various life events. At Thanksgiving, Americans expect turkey and dressing feasts; a birthday needs its cake; New Years Eve parties require champagne; for some,

Merry Jo Davis is Nutrition Education Consultant, Milk Foundation, Inc., Chicago, IL.

Joyce R. Garrick is a Nutrition Consultant in Chicago.

herring wishes in the New Year with good health.

How Customs Develop

Changing food availability can affect customs. During the Middle Ages, inadequate meat supplies motivated a papal ruling requiring fish on Fridays. Food taboos often developed when eating a food was linked to subsequent illness or death. The development of Orthodox Kosher dietary laws was motivated by high rates of diseases such as trichinosis and hepatitis following impure pork and shellfish consumption, respectively. Although the association of pork and shellfish with those diseases has been virtually eliminated, the taboo of these foods for many prevails.

Food use has had political significance in history. The interrelationship between food, economics and a new nation's political views escalated to war and the birth of a new nation's independence with the Boston Tea Party. Today food is still a weapon in foreign policies and diplomacy. The price of food in the United States today is still affected by worldwide supply and demand. It is anticipated that by 1990 America could be supplying 15 percent of the rest of the world's food.

Social Influences — Through the study of sociology, human behavior is understood in terms of social phenomena. It is the study of man's group behavior. Social class influences value systems, social symbols and behavior patterns. In the United States, social classes are less rigid and distinct than in some countries. Class lines blur as movement from class to class occurs.

Food is symbolic of motherhood. Breast feeding is often the first bonding between mother and child. Much conscious and unconscious learning occurs between parent and child during the early feeding regimen. Long after childhood certain foods will provide memories and will be valued for reasons other than nutritional density.

People tend to eat foods that are readily available. Affordability is contingent to their choices. The breaking of bread together, the second helping, and the party with the most abundant food supply are ways people have expressed — through food symbols — sociability, warmth, and friendliness. Eating together as a family unit tends to build stability and closeness.

Foods may be accepted or rejected because of their status. . . . Lobster and steak, generally considered high prestige foods, are served at dinners with honored guests. Beans and frankfurters would not be considered guest fare and may be ranked low in prestige.

Ethnicity — Our Nation is a melting pot of people from many lands. We have the unique opportunity to learn and share our diverse ethnic backgrounds with each other. For the most part, however, people resist change. Yet the mobility of the American way of life affords us the opportunity to experience many ethnic cuisines and cultures.

People share a tendency to be culture bound. Familiarity with one's culture — that is, the values, customs, and traditions — tends to make it difficult to change. With different cultures we almost automatically become judgmental. Ours is "the best." We are resistant to experience new foods and cultures. Many Americans are overcoming these bonds of ethnocentric prejudices. These people are lucky individuals as they are experiencing and learning new tastes and customs, and, as a result, new eating habits may materialize. Still, the ethnic base of our food consumption patterns provides homogeneity within a group, diversity between groups, and persistence in chosen patterns.

Psychological Influences

Individual behavior patterns are the result of many interrelated psychosocial influences. Perception and motivation shape food habits. Perception is the process of adding meaning to what is absorbed through the senses. Perception limits understanding but enables people to organize the multitude of sensory input. Subjective stimuli like hunger, thirst, fear, self-interest and values influence responses to the outer world. Responses are identified as behavior. Motivations, however, differ among people. Foods accepted by one individual may be rejected by another in different circumstances. Hunger and thirst are our primary physiologic needs. Yet our need for safety, affection, self-esteem and self-fulfillment may supersede priority.

Emotional responses to food originate in early feeding experiences. Food nourishes the psyche as well as one's body. Foods carry symbolic meaning. To many, milk symbolizes security and comfort. Meat is symbolically the only food that can make men strong. Eggs never quite substitute for meat despite their nutritional equivalence. Fruits and vegetables symbolize love, beauty, sexuality, and luxury. Sweets, often used to bribe children, are perceived as reward foods.

Foods used in early feeding patterns can carry the same reward/punishment concepts throughout adulthood. Some foods are age related. Strained foods can be considered as infant food by pubescents and adults and thus rejected. Adults are privileged to consume coffee, tea, and alcohol. Peanut butter is labeled as children's food. As can be seen, food perceptions can motivate food choice for a lifetime.

Consumption Trends — Food habits have altered significantly since the beginning of the century. Changes reflect such factors as shifting population stratification, new technologies, changing affluence, the development of government food programs, and growing concerns with health. Food consumption surveys provide a means of evaluating trends of food disappearance. However, specific values exaggerate actual intakes of food by up to 25 to 30 percent.

Trends are a tool which indicate what an "average American" consumes. When evaluated in terms of prior surveys, they offer a general idea of what we are consuming as a people and some changes in our eating habits over time. For example, Americans today are consuming more meat, fish, poultry and dairy products (except butter) than we did in 1900. We are also consuming more sweets, fats, and processed products. Since food consumption patterns are one of many aspects of culture, the forces which produce cultural change generate changes in food practices and purchases.

Food Buying and Economics

Food-buying patterns in the 1970's and 1980's are rapidly changing. Americans are eating out more frequently at primarily fast food restaurants. At home there is an increased demand for convenience products, labor-saving devices, and small-portion packaging. The fast food industry has expanded enormously over the last 25 years. Between 1970 and 1980 fast food sales have increased over 300 percent. These establishments provide the assets of convenience and reasonable cost. They serve the busy American lifestyle well. Young middle and upper middle income families are patronizing fast food restaurants most frequently. Convenience foods such as frozen prepared meals, and processed foods such as luncheon meats, additionally serve as time-saving devices for people on the move.

In urban areas there has emerged an "occupational" meal pattern. Adults not employed outside the home generally consume leftovers from the previous day's dinner, some time between breakfast and dinner. Light breakfasts of coffee and doughnuts and quick lunches of sandwiches and fruit drinks or soda are more common for people employed outside the home. The traditional heavy breakfast pattern of milk, eggs, biscuits, and bacon or sausage are reserved for weekends, holidays, and "off days."

Technological advances such as freezing, dehydration, canning and food additives have made it possible to purchase a wide variety of products. Foods like orange juice are now available year-round. Extended shelf life of grain products, such as breads and cereals, have enabled the American consumer freedom of choice between store-bought bread and home-made bread. Microwave technology enabled development of a much faster cooking procedure. With increased accessibility to microwave cookery, a new market of convenience foods was created.

Convenience products are taking a larger portion of our food dollar. They require more shelf space in the supermarket. This ultimately will affect food cost. There are increased costs due to processing, packaging, distributing, and transportation. Often there is greater waste. Yet Americans are demanding convenience products.

Traditional family structure is changing. Today there is a shift toward more households comprised of either two working parents, single-parent families, or self-sufficient singles. Family size is shrinking. There is growth in the teenage-parent and older citizen populations. As individuals and families adapt to the requisites of new lifestyles, concurrent changes are realized in chosen meal patterns. For example, more households have both wife and husband employed. Men are seen partaking more in household chores which include the purchase of foods and preparation of meals.

Teen Parents Have Minor Impact

In recent decades changes in the sexual behavior of teenagers involve all segments of the population. There is a growing number of teenage parents today. Teenage parents appear to have minor impact on food purchases in the marketplace. Most teenage parents remain dependent on their immediate family for advice and support. While they remain in their parents' home, their parents generally are the gatekeepers to their food choices. Some teenagers manage to establish independent households. Due to limited resources — including income, education, and job opportunities — their shopping habits remain those established and learned from their parents or those of low-income populations.

Teenagers have unique eating habits. They frequently skip meals and replace them with low-nutrient density snacks. Many meals are eaten out at fast food restaurants. Food variety may be minimal. Snacking is an integral part of their eating pattern and may provide up to one-fourth of their caloric intake.

Older citizens are increasing in absolute numbers as well as proportionate contribution to the population. If the current trend toward small families continues, it is estimated the elderly may comprise one-fourth of the population by the year 2000. Food selections of older Americans are determined primarily by economic,

The fast food industry has expanded enormously over the last 25 years. Such establishments provide the assets of convenience and reasonable cost. At some fast food restaurants, such as this one, you don't have to leave your car.

social, and health factors. Many seniors are on restrictive budgets and may be unable to purchase or physically prepare many foods. They tend to follow simple, monotonous diets which are compatible to available limitations. Unfortunately, their diets are incompatible with their nutritional needs. The older population group frequently purchases convenience and economical foods. Small quantity purchases and smaller portion purchases are more common among this group of people.

Income, food availability, and market atmosphere influence purchasing behaviors and consumption choices. As income diminishes, people begin setting priorities for their available funds between housing, transportation, food, clothing, health care, and entertainment. Some of these are fixed costs and cannot be altered. The food budget, however, is a variable cost and thus becomes a primary target for constraint. Either a larger proportion of the income is spent on food, or less luxury food items are purchased. More attention is given to planning, preparing, and purchasing foods of comparable nutrient value and high nutrient density during inflationary times.

Problems Among the Poor

Tremendous problems exist among the poverty stricken. The "culture of poverty" permeates not only income but all aspects of their lives. Generally they reside in inadequate or overcrowded housing. Problems related to cooking, refrigeration, storage, and sanitation exist. These problems affect food selection. Often limited education serves as a barrier to job opportunities. Poverty, unlike inflation, is a chronic problem.

For the poverty-bound person, food purchasing provides limited freedom of choice and ability to meet food needs. Limited transportation restricts the ability to shop at a variety of stores for the best prices, selections, and quality. Limited funds restrict purchasing of nonessential sale items. Quantity purchasing of items when available at special prices for future use is often held to a minimum. Small neighborhood grocery stores and supermarkets in low-income neighborhoods often charge more than comparable stores in higher income neighborhoods. Some of these consumers are entrapped to purchase foods in these stores because of outstanding credit indebtedness and other limitations. All of these problems among poverty stricken individuals demonstrate how both physical and financial availability can affect their food-purchasing patterns, habits, and choices.

Government food programs offer opportunities to increase the food purchasing power and, to some extent, nutrition awareness of this sector of the population. There are several government programs such as school lunch programs; supplemental food programs for women, infants and children; and the food stamp program. While each program has different goals, they guide the recipients' purchases and/or consumed food choices.

In Summary — Many factors influence our eating patterns and purchasing power. Our cultural, social, and ethnic backgrounds are unique. These factors seem most influential in the American diet on holidays and/or special occasions. At the present time, economics is the major determinant in food purchasing choices. Therefore food consumption trends are changing as economics vary.

Nutritional Needs: Eat for Good Health All Your Life

By Chung Ja Lee

Nutrition has an impact at every stage of the life cycle. Frequently we are told "We are what we eat," implying that what we eat influences how we feel, physically and psychologically. We Americans have the potential to be the best fed people in history. But today's consumer faces difficulty in selecting foods that make up a good diet. Scientific knowledge in nutrition and health is advancing rapidly. Development of new food products and an outpouring of food fad literature is appearing in popular magazines and newspapers. Our lifestyle has changed from those "good ole days," but we have not yet fully adjusted eating habits to suit the new lifestyle.

All essential nutrients are needed by everyone. However, each stage in life poses its own demands and problems. Hence, needs for nutritionally vulnerable groups including infants, toddlers, teenagers and the elderly are among the things discussed in this chapter. Nutritional needs in relation to health conditions and physical activity will also be considered.

The Infant — Infancy represents the highest growth rate as most full-term infants triple their birth weight by the end of the first year. The rapid growth and high metabolic rate of the infant require ample supplies of nutrients for growth and development.

Milk is the baby's first food — from the mother's breast or from a bottle. If all other things are equal, breast milk is recommended. Human milk is custom-made for the baby, and provides increased resistance to infection, reduces allergies, is convenient, and allows no chance of error in mixing. Most commercially prepared infant formulas are based on cow's milk. If a baby is allergic to cow's milk, alternatives such as goat's milk, soybean or meat based formula are available at higher costs. If the baby is breast-fed, supplementation of nutrients other than vitamin D and iron (for example, fluoride, folic acid, and — if vegetarian — vitamin B_{12}) is usually recommended. For the formula-fed baby, vitamin C and iron should be supplemented unless the formula is iron-fortified.

Unless a definite need is indicated, it is recommended that addition of solid foods be delayed until the infant is about 6 months old. Addition of solid foods too early may lead to overfeeding, poor digestion, and allergic reactions. If the parent wants the baby to have family foods in place of commercially prepared

Chung Ja Lee is Professor of Nutrition, and Program Director of Community Research Service — Home Economics Research, at Kentucky State University, Frankfort.

baby foods, the baby's food should be pureed before adding seasonings for adults. This way the baby will not develop a preference toward salty food.

Caloric requirements vary from baby to baby. Some infants sleep and are mostly inactive; others are awake, crying and kicking, so have greater energy needs. Infant obesity should be avoided, because it generally remains in childhood and often throughout adulthood. Introduction of vegetables before fruits is encouraged to reduce the baby's preference for sweets and also because vegetables are more nutrient-dense.

The Toddler and Food Habits

Toddlers between 1 and 3 years undergo certain physical and mental changes. The rate of growth slows after the first birthday, while the physical activity increases and a spirit of independence develops. This is a formative period in development of food habits. There is continuing need for a well-balanced diet that supplies nutrients required for growth and maintenance, with adequate amounts of proteins, minerals, and vitamins. Appetites of young children fluctuate frequently, and their needs are so great that there is very little room for foods of low nutritional quality. By 12 months of age, most

babies can handle junior food or properly prepared table foods, and begin to eat with the family.

The usual three meals and two snacks a day can be planned around the Daily Food Guide, a basic pattern which can be used as the foundation for a good diet *by all age groups:* Four or more servings of fruits and vegetables. Four or more servings of breads and cereals. Two to three 8-ounce servings of milk (more for teenagers and nursing mothers and less for adults). Two servings of meat, poultry, fish, and beans. (Note that amounts served under the Daily Food Guide may differ — small servings for young children, extra large ones or seconds for active teenagers and adults.)

Parental and sibling influences are important in molding food eating habits of the toddler. Today's children are exposed to continual messages on "sugar coated" and "chocolate covered" foods, as almost all homes in our country have at least one television set. However, parents should not give in to pressure to buy every food or snack advertised.

Teenagers — In the teenage period, nutritional requirements for the body are at a maximum. The growth spurt reaches its peak at 12 in girls and at 14 in boys. Just as growth and appetites peak, psychological and social pressures dramatically alter the teenager's response to food. The rising desire for independence, peer acceptance, and socializing may conflict with greater physiological needs for more food and more sleep. To support growth, increased quantities of all nutrients are needed. Iron requirements increase because of the onset of menstruation in girls and the increasing lean body mass in boys. Caloric requirements vary widely depending on growth rates and wide disparities in physical activity level.

Teenagers may have nutritional problems such as anemia (which results from a deficiency of dietary iron or folic acid especially among girls), obesity, and low intakes of calcium and vitamins A and C by both boys and girls. At least three

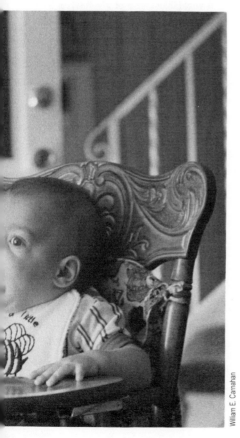

William E. Carnahan

Infancy represents the highest growth rate as most full-term infants triple their birth weight by the end of the first year. Their rapid growth requires ample supplies of nutrients. This 8-month-old baby is well on the way to tripling his birth weight by the end of his first year.

glasses or an equivalent amount of milk and four or more servings of fruits and vegetables daily are recommended to provide adequate amounts of these nutrients. In general, boys have better diets than girls as their food intakes are higher.

A special case of nutritional need is that of the pregnant teenage girl. Demands of pregnancy at a time of unfinished growth and increased nutrient requirements for the mother create serious competition between her needs and those of her growing baby. Nutritional guidance, medical supervision, and counseling should be available for the pregnant teenager.

The Retirement Years

Nutrition for people in the retirement years is a subject of growing interest in the United States, for this subgroup of the population is increasing disproportionately to the population as a whole. The National Academy of Sciences — National Research Council's daily dietary recommendations for older men and women are slightly lower in calories, riboflavin and niacin than for young adults. Recommended amounts of iron for women are markedly lower after menstruation stops. However, requirements for a majority of other nutrients remain fairly constant during adulthood. Since absorption of nutrients diminishes in some people, quality of the diet is very important as more nutrients may have to be derived from less food.

The Daily Food Guide is a suitable pattern also for diets of the elderly. Including at least two glasses of milk or the equivalent daily is recommended. Use of nonfat or low-fat rather than whole milk would lower intakes of calories, saturated fat, and cholesterol. A major problem encountered by the elderly is bone loss that often results in fractures. Recent evidence suggests that increased dietary calcium counteracts this condition for some people. Two servings of meat or meat substitutes daily are needed as in earlier years. Use of ground meats, fish, and cheese and modification of cooking methods may be necessary for people with poor dental structures.

A recent survey showed that many elderly persons, especially men, had inadequate intakes of vitamins A and C and fiber because they did not regularly eat four or more daily servings of fruit and vegetables. Use of a variety of fruits and vegetables and of cooking methods is recommended to make these foods more acceptable to this group. Use of wholegrain breads and cereals is recommended also to provide a variety of nutrients as well as fiber to alleviate constipation. At least the equivalent of six to eight glasses of liquid as beverages, soups, fruits, and vegetables is recommended daily. Frequent small meals rather than three regular meals may be better suited to some.

Older adults are more likely to use multiple medications on a routine basis than younger people, and thus the possibility of creating an adverse biologically significant interaction is increased. Professionals should provide information about when to take drugs in relation to mealtimes and about food items to be restricted to maximize the effectiveness of medication without affecting the nutritional status.

Good nutrition aids older people to be active and productive. Adequate diet is an effective means to help maintain good health and minimize chronic degenerative changes in old age. Poor eating habits increase the incidence of physical and emotional disability and need for medical attention.

Nutrition in Relation to Health

A growing body of scientific evidence indicates that diet is one of several factors contributing to the risk of hypertension, and diabetes. Becoming overweight increases your risk of developing these chronic degenerative diseases later in life. Other contributing factors include heredity, smoking, physical inactivity, and alcohol consumption. Let's briefly review current knowledge on the role of diet in relation to prevalent disorders such as obesity, hypertension, diabetes, and cancer.

Obesity — Overweight and obesity are the condition of excessive body fatness. Abundance of a wide variety of foods and lack of physical activity are two contributing factors. Emphasis must be on maintenance of desirable weight, beginning early in life, because it is difficult to achieve and maintain desirable weight once obesity is established.

A safe and successful way to accomplish weight change and maintain desired weight is to reduce calorie intake and increase activity. A diet based on the Daily Food Guide made up of lower calorie foods that the individual likes to eat is the best approach. No particular diet is magical. Persons seeking to lose weight need to reduce serving sizes and rely on foods with high nutrient density (foods low in calories but rich in other nutrients), such as tasty vegetables, fruits, whole-grain cereals, lean protein-rich foods and skim milk.

The plan for a reducing diet should be realistic and provide adequate amounts of nutrients. One pound of body fat is equivalent to about 3,500 dietary calories. A gradual reduction in weight such as an average of one pound per week is recommended. This would mean consuming 500 fewer calories per day than the body uses. A permanent change in food practices is needed to maintain the appropriate weight when it is reached. Crash diets or fad diets, starvation, and liquid protein diets are health hazards due to nutritional imbalance. Use of diuretics (water pills) and diet pills may pose potentially serious side effects without sustained weight loss.

Hypertension — Hypertension (high blood pressure) is a physiological abnormality that can result from a variety of causes. Lowering blood pressure reduces the burden on the heart and lessens the chances of stroke and heart attack. In the United States, about 17 percent of adults have hypertension. Sodium intake is but one of the factors known to affect blood pressure. Obesity, in particular, seems to play a major role. Mortality rates for obese hypertensives are higher than for those with either obesity or hypertension alone. Therefore, total caloric intake also should be restricted in the overweight hypertensive.

In populations with low sodium intakes, hypertension is rare. In contrast, in populations with high sodium intakes, high blood pressure is common. If people with hypertension severely restrict their sodium intakes, their blood pressures will usually fall — although not always to normal levels. At present there is no good way to predict who will develop hypertension. Low-sodium diets may help some people avoid high blood pressure.

Because most Americans eat more sodium than is needed, consider reducing your sodium intake. Since many foods naturally contain sodium, indiscriminate use of salt at the table should be discouraged. Instead an increase in potassium with reduction in sodium intake is suggested in preventing or retarding hypertension. Many unprocessed foods are high in potassium and low in sodium.

Physical work helps to use energy and prevent obesity. An exercise program should involve continuous use of large muscle groups and should be rhythmic in nature, such as walking, jogging, or swimming.

William E. Carnahan

Diabetes — The most common of the diseases known as diabetes is *Diabetes mellitus*. It is associated with abnormal handling of glucose and insulin. *Diabetes mellitus* occurs in two forms — the insulin-dependent (juvenile-onset) and the noninsulin dependent (maturity-onset) types. Maturity-onset type is the condition referred to in this chapter as diabetes. Obesity and a genetic predisposition are the major risk factors in maturity-onset diabetes. About 80 percent of maturity-onset diabetics are obese. In many cases, weight reduction alone will reduce the risk of developing diabetes and its complications.

Dietary control is an integral part of management for the diabetic. Recognizing the need for a flexible and realistic approach to dietary management, a joint national committee with representatives from the American Diabetes Association and the American Dietetic Association formulated a system of dietary control based on the concept of equivalents. In this system, commonly used foods are grouped according to similar nutrient composition and are designated Food Exchange Groups. These six food groups are: milk, vegetables A and B, fruits, bread, meat, and fat. Food items within any one group can be freely exchanged, since all foods in that group, in the portion indicated, are of about the same food value. The key to satisfactory management of diabetes is sound, realistic patient education with a flexible plan that allows a variety of food choices.

Nutritional Needs and Activity

Both sound nutrition and physical fitness are required for health. Many Americans choose to be inactive, preferring to let machines do their work and professionals play their games. However, more Americans are becoming interested in exercise and physical activities as their lifestyle becomes more sedentary.

Physical work helps to utilize energy and so prevents obesity. Contrary to popular opinion, moderate exercise does not increase appetite. The exercise program should involve continuous use of large muscle groups and should be rhythmic in nature, such as walking, jogging, or swimming. The more muscle movement involved, the more calories consumed. There are many ways to practice physical fitness within one's normal routine — using stairs instead of an elevator, walking to stores, and participating in active sports. Moderate exercise on a consistent daily basis is an important aid in weight reduction and physical fitness.

The benefits of physical activity are many, including improved work capacity, muscular strength, and reduced blood pressure and pulse rate. Physical fitness helps lower the risk of heart disease. Inactivity also is associated with osteoporosis, and the epidemiology of hip fracture suggests that hard physical work throughout life may protect against it. Promotion of a regular exercise program starting in the early stages of life is recommended.

For assistance with your food and nutrition questions, contact the dietitian, home economist or nutritionist in the following groups: Public Health Department. Local Dietetic Association office. Local Heart Association office. Local Diabetes Association office. County Extension office. State or local medical society. Hospital outpatient clinic. Local Dairy Council.

Appliances and Their Effect on Food Buying

By Fern E. Hunt

sk any cook, "What effect do your kitchen appliances have on your food-buying decisions?" The answer you get will likely be, "well, none." If you asked further, "Without a refrigerator, how would you manage?" the answer would show that availability of at least one common appliance greatly affects food buying practices. Virtually all U.S. households (99.9 percent) have and use a refrigerator. Ninety percent of refrigerators sold in 1981 were combination refrigerator-freezers. About 45 percent of households in the Nation have a separate food freezer. And commercial processing and freezing of foods has burgeoned into a thriving segment of the food industry within the past 25 years.

Perishable foods may be purchased almost the year round — strawberries, lettuce, oysters, and eggs, to name a few — because refrigerated equipment is available to transport the food over long distances, store it in warehouses and display it in retail stores. Further, after purchase the food may be held safely in the home refrigerator or freezer for a reasonable time with little if any spoilage and with little or no fear of foodborne illnesses. So shoppers in the United States may buy supplies for a week or more at a time and take advantage of special sales to stock up on foods. In many other countries chilled storage space for foods is not available in the marketplace or home, and food shopping is a daily chore.

Affordable refrigerators and freezers for homes have had more to do with changes in quality, availability of out-of-season items, forms of food eaten, and shopping practices than with total amounts of foods consumed. However, with availability of food freezers and commercially frozen foods, civilian consumption of commercially frozen fruit — exclusive of citrus juices — doubled from 1940 to 1979 (from 1.28 to 2.57 lb. per person). The increase was due primarily to increased consumption of commercially frozen strawberries. In the same period, use of citrus juices on a single strength basis increased from 5.12 to 33.37 lb. per person per year — an increase of 650 percent.

Consumption of commercially frozen vegetables increased from 2.2 lb. per person in 1940 to 23.4 lb. in 1979. At the same time total consumption of commercially produced vegetables (fresh, canned and frozen) increased from 186.9 to 233.6 lb. per person. There was a gradual change from home-produced to commercially produced items rather than consumption of greater quantities of

Fern E. Hunt is Professor of Home Equipment, School of Home Economics and Ohio Agricultural Research and Development Center. The Ohio State University, Columbus.

Shoppers with home freezers can take advantage of store specials and hold foods for a
reasonable time with little if any spoilage or fear of foodborne illnesses.

vegetables per person. With modern specialized agriculture, even many farm households buy commercially produced foods for much of their food needs.

A further change in food choices coming with availability of frozen food storage space in households is the whole array of frozen desserts and of ready-to-cook or heat-and-eat specialty items and dinners. Such foods are a boon particularly to people who must prepare meals in a hurry, people who do not like to cook or who lack cooking skills, and to elderly and handicapped people living independently.

Capacity of household refrigerators and refrigerator-freezer combinations on today's market varies from 10.0 to 27.8 cubic feet. Freezer space is as small as 1.2 cubic feet in the smaller refrigerators and as large as 10.8 cubic feet in the largest refrigerator-freezer combinations.

Refrigerator, Freezer Needs

Recommendations for refrigerator sizes are based on number of people in the household. A minimum of 6 (and preferably 8) cubic feet has been suggested for 2 people plus one cubic foot for each additional person in the household. Thus for a household of 2 adults and 2 children, minimum recommended capacity would be 8 cubic feet; the preferred space would be at least 10 cubic feet. If a separate food freezer is not available, 2 cubic feet of freezer space in the refrigerator has been suggested per person. Separate freezers can be purchased with capacities from 5.2 to 28.0 cubic feet. Some experts suggest that where very large amounts of freezer space may be required, a household would be wise to have two smaller freezers and disconnect one as frozen food stocks dwindle during the year.

Determinants of needs for refrigerator-freezer and separate freezer space include marketing habits of the household, age and health of family members, amount of entertaining, and home food storage practices. Families that freeze much of their own fruit, vegetables, and meat may need 5 to 6 cubic feet of freezer space per person in separate food freezers, while 3 to 4 cubic feet per person will provide ample storage space for most families.

Cooking Appliances — Currently available cooking appliances might be classified into two groups: 1) Those that promise to affect use of time and/or energy — permitting quick meal preparation either by rapid cooking or by long, slow, unattended cooking with conservation of energy, and 2) Those that satisfy special interests such as gourmet, outdoors, nostalgia, and natural food enthusiasts. Such appliances as microwave ovens, convection ovens, pressure saucepans, and slow cookers might be listed in the first group. Food smokers and dehydrators might fall into the second.

Portables — Some small or portable cooking appliances have the potential to be a factor in consumer decisions in the food marketplace. For example, appliances that cook foods by moist heat methods — such as a pressure saucepan or a slow cooker — cook less tender cuts of meat satisfactorily with minimum energy inputs compared to cooking them in a covered pan in the range oven. But intended use, consumer knowledge of meats, financial resources, and tastes will be the major determinants of the choice of type or cut of meat rather than availability of a particular cooking appliance.

One of the least energy intensive and quickest ways of cooking food by moist heat is in a pressure saucepan. The heat penetrates food quickly at the high temperature and pressure, and the cooker is effective for foods that ordinarily require a long time to tenderize. It works well in softening tough connective tissue found in less tender cuts of meat. With the pressure saucepan, some foods cook in as little as a fourth of the time required in a regular saucepan and as quickly as in a microwave oven. A microwave oven will do more kinds of cooking than the pressure saucepan, but the pressure cooker currently has the advantage in both purchase price and cost of operation. Pressure saucepans come in 2½-, 4-, and 6-quart capacities.

Types of Ovens on Market

Changes in recent years in oven design and types of ovens available on the appliance market have largely reflected changes in uses of time by family members (particularly women), convenience and desired lifestyle factors, energy concerns, and advances in the food industry. Table model (or counter-top) ovens have flourished in the 1970's because of needs to heat or cook small quantities of food and concern about amounts of energy used in small ovens versus full-size range ovens. Development of frozen precooked, brown-and-serve and heat-and-serve food items has gone hand-in-glove with innovations in cooking appliances and vice versa. Many of these foods are purposely marketed with containers in which the food may be cooked or heated and which fit well into small ovens.

Use of conventional types of ovens — range and table model or portable types — is an inefficient way to cook food. Only 6 to 14 percent of the energy used in a range oven goes into the food. Microwave ovens offer a more energy efficient way to cook foods normally cooked in an oven, and with skill excellent meals can be produced in the appliance. Generally about 50 percent of the energy used goes into the food. In presently available appliances, cakes, pies, and other baked products are generally less acceptable in a microwave oven than in a conventional oven, even with combinations of microwave and conventional oven cooking. Microwave ovens are now owned by about one-fourth of U.S. households. According to a recent nationwide *Merchandising* study (1982), microwave oven owners surveyed used the appliance 44 percent of the time for cooking regular meals; 39 percent of the usage was for reheating foods; and 16 percent, for simple defrosting.

Convection Ovens — Forced convection ovens are theoretically more efficient than traditional types of ovens. Foods should heat faster in forced movement of hot air than with the natural convection in ovens. Countertop convection ovens have not achieved the market success of microwave ovens, but they do offer an alternative to heating up a full-size range oven for oven-cooking jobs. Sales in one year have never surpassed the half-million mark. Price differences depend primarily on types of controls and automatic features.

Recommended temperature settings for baking in a forced convection oven are 25° to 50° F lower and cooking times are shorter than for an oven with natural heat distribution; therefore energy usage should be lower with the convection oven. In a study of four different brands and styles of countertop forced convection ovens, a countertop regular oven of a corresponding size, and a 30-inch range oven, the average energy use in countertop forced convection ovens was significantly less than in the electric range oven. But the table model regular oven (without forced convection) required the least energy of all for cooking jobs. Further, one of the table model forced convection ovens used as much energy as the large oven in the electric range for baking jobs. Baked products from all ovens were similar in eating quality characteristics, but top browning was more uneven in the forced convection ovens than in ovens with natural circulation of heat.

Dehydrators and Smokers

Sales of commercially manufactured food dehydrators and smokers for home use have not reached levels high enough to be noted in 1982 annual statistical marketing reports for the appliance industry. Impact on the food market caused by use of such equipment is likely to be minor, if perceptible. People who must buy the foods they dehydrate or preserve by smoking will not usually find it cost effective. Further, relatively few people will want to take the time and trouble necessary to cure meat before smoking or to sulfur fruits and blanch vegetables before drying in order to preserve them.

There are several reasons for interest in home dehydration of foods — for example, convenience for hikers and other sports people in transporting and storing dried products, nutritious natural snacks, relatively low energy use in processing, and storage without use of energy resources. Dehydrating foods is less costly than some other means of food preservation, because intense heat is not required

in processing and refrigerated storage is unnecessary afterward. Also, storage space requirements and shipping weight are low.

Several models of dehydrators with temperature controls and forced air circulation to hasten drying have appeared on the market. In addition, some forced convection ovens are designed with controls to provide temperatures of 150° F or below (suitably low for satisfactory drying of food), and some manufacturers offer accessory kits and instructions for dehydrating foods in their ovens. Good dehydrators may be homemade as well. Construction of homemade dryers requires some carpentry skills and an investment for materials and parts. In commercially made drying equipment for home use, only relatively small quantities of food — usually less than 10 pounds — can be dehydrated at one time. That could be a disadvantage for a household wanting to preserve large quantities of food.

Smoking — As it is currently done, smoking is more a way of enhancing flavor of foods and a method of cooking than a method of food preservation. In smoker-cookers the material deposited on surfaces of food during smoking contains formaldehyde and phenols among many other chemical components. Formaldehyde and phenols are bacteriostatic, and creosols produce smoked flavor.

Foods smoked without a high salt cure generally will keep for only a short time unless refrigerated. How long they keep depends upon degree of curing, amount of dehydration and smoking, and the storage temperature. Signs of spoilage include development of surface molds, sour taste or smell of ammonia, and rancid flavor. Commercially made smoke ovens may be designed to smoke only or to smoke-cook and roast, barbecue, steam and/or shish kebab. Various styles are available, some with gas heat and some with electric. An advantage of the commercial smoke oven is portability. A disadvantage is the small usable capacity.

Shelf Life of Foods

Commercially canned food is sterilized during canning, so problems with microbial spoilage are extremely rare if the can remains undamaged. Metal containers for commercially canned foods are designed with inside coatings to resist chemical reactions between the can and its contents and to have an unlimited shelf life. Two years is considered the norm for storage. Some foods are more corrosive than others, and the rate of the reaction between can and food is affected by temperature — the higher the temperature, the faster the deterioration. Corrosiveness of the foods depends upon their acidity. Acidic foods such as fruits, juices, and pickles are the most corrosive and have the shortest shelf life. Low acid foods — such as vegetables, meats, and fish — generally keep well. Ideal storage conditions for canned foods include cool, but not freezing, temperatures and a dry environment to prevent rust from the outside.

A new type of package for processed food is the retortable pouch, a flexible package made of two layers of film with a layer of foil sandwiched between. The package is flatter than cans and the food is sterilized in a shorter time than is required for heat to reach the center of a cylindrical can. Shelf life of the food is 1 to 2 years at room temperature. A drawback to the use of pouches is the relatively high cost in comparison to cans.

Dehydrated Foods — Shelf life of dehydrated foods depends to a large extent upon storage conditions. Since moisture content is very low — 2 percent to 10 percent of the original product weight — the foods absorb moisture in a humid atmosphere. In a moisture-tight container which excludes light and at room temperature or cooler, many dehydrated foods have a shelf life of up to 2 years. The lower the moisture content, the longer will be the shelf life at any temperature. Oxidative deterioration can occur in dried foods. Since plastic bags may not completely exclude oxygen, glass or metal containers are better for dried food storage.

Frozen Foods — When temperatures in freezer storage space are maintained at 0° F or below and packaging materials are moisture-vapor proof, many foods could be stored indefinitely with little or no deterioration in eating quality. But storage of frozen fruits and vegetables beyond the next growing season is poor management of expensive storage space. Also, ground meats and foods containing fats tend to develop rancid flavors if stored longer than 3 to 6 months. The freezer manual and the local county home economics extension agent are good sources of information on recommended storage times for frozen foods.

How to Be a First-Rate Food Manager

By Mary E. Mennes

*I*f you could conveniently package the skills of a dietitian, psychologist, consumer expert, engineer, short order cook and gourmet chef, you'd probably have the perfect food manager — able to produce exciting, nutritious, delicious, low-cost meals quickly and without leaving the kitchen in a mess. Most of us don't have all of those talents, but the basic skills needed to manage the family food supply can be picked up by anyone willing to learn and apply several basic strategies.

Effective food management is decision-making that makes the best use of the money, skills, equipment, and time that a family can spend on food-related activities. The result should be a satisfying and healthful food supply for household members. Changing lifestyles with demands of work, school, economic pressures, and leisure activities have changed the way that food management activities are carried out in most families. And the modern "family" encompasses many kinds of living arrangements that include the traditional family, one or two persons young or old living together, married or not, and single parent families. Each of these presents special problems and challenges in food management.

Good food management is possible in each unique family if family members are willing to discover, discuss, and work out their food-related goals to guide decisions and to share in the food managing tasks. Goals need to be flexible enough to accommodate changing situations, but specific enough to act upon. For example, is saving time important? More important than saving money? If it is, decisions to purchase highly convenient forms of food are likely to result. If both are important goals, the food manager can consider made-at-home mixes and convenience foods that will save money and cooking time. As a family, review the Food Goal Inventory chart with this chapter to help you identify and arrive at goals you can accept and live with. Management requires planning that enables you to match your family's resources and activities with the goals you want to reach.

Plan Before Shopping

Plan menus for meals and snacks before you shop. Fully planned meals and snacks will give you the greatest control over nutrition, budget, food appeal, and time required for meal preparation. If all family members help in planning, varying activities can be accommodated, favorite

Mary E. Mennes is Extension Foodservice Administration Specialist and Professor, Department of Food Science, University of Wisconsin-Madison.

Food Goal Inventory

Nutritional Goals:
Meet basic nutritional needs of each person
Provide enough food to avoid hunger
Build acceptable food habits
Change undesirable food habits
Meet special needs of overweight or underweight family members
Provide modifications needed for those on a prescribed special diet

Social Goals:
Encourage family communication and interaction at mealtime
Provide foods that are interesting and acceptable to family members
Entertain guests
Serve foods that are socially popular

Economic Goals:
Control the amount of money spent for food
Eat out less (or more)
Reduce food waste and spoilage
Become more self-sufficient by gardening and home food preservation
Save fuel and energy in storage and cooking
Take advantage of various food sources (co-ops, supermarkets, farm
   markets, specialty shops)

Cultural Goals:
Strengthen or build family food traditions
Enhance holiday celebrations or special occasions
Maintain ethnic traditions of family members
Learn about cultures and communities through foods

Educational Goals:
Help children lean how to make appropriate food choices
Help family members learn food shopping and cooking skills
Learn about nutritional values of foods
Develop time management skills

Time and Energy Goals:
Reduce (or increase) shopping time and trips
Improve time use in food preparation
Involve all family members in food managing activities
Prepare meals with less physical effort
Provide food at times that fit schedules of family members

foods included, and workload sharing determined. Complete planning makes it much easier to shop for several days' food supply at one time and to be sure you have a sufficient quantity and variety of food on hand.

Plan meals that will be attractive and acceptable. If you plan menus when you're hungry, it's easy to visualize the colors and shapes of foods as they will look when you serve them and to mentally "taste" the flavors. Check over planned meals for pleasing contrasts and complements in foods and make changes to improve the attractiveness of menus.

Plan meals that save time and energy for busy days. Casseroles and one-dish meals can usually be assembled ahead of time and refrigerated or frozen to help reduce meal preparation time. Partially prepared meal or recipe components such as biscuit mixes, dry or canned sauces, condensed soups cost less than ready-to-use complete dinners yet can save a lot of time and effort. When you have ample time, plan to cook extra amounts of food that can be frozen or stored for use on busy days.

Use Specials, Plentiful Foods

Plan to use advertised specials. Use the newspaper food ads to locate foods which may be offered at lower-than-usual prices. If you have a choice of several stores, plan to shop in the one which has attractive prices on more of the foods you need. Plan to use seasonally plentiful foods frequently. Fresh fruit and vegetables supplies and variety vary from month to month, with prices lowest in peak supply periods. Farmers' markets, roadside stands, and home gardens can usually provide excellent quality produce at lower than supermarket prices. Other

foods show less dramatic seasonal differences, particularly if they are processed before retailing.

If you have coupons for items you need, use them. Most cents-off coupons offered by manufacturers or stores are for the more highly processed foods or for foods in abundant supply. Using coupons for coffee, prepared foods, breakfast cereals, flour and flour mix products can save about 10 percent in most food budgets. However, don't let a coupon tempt you into buying a food that your family doesn't like or need or which costs more than a store brand even if you use the coupon. Put coupons you plan to use with your shopping list.

Use Food on Hand — Plan to use foods on hand. Check your refrigerator, freezer and cupboards as you plan menus and use perishable items before they spoil. Frozen foods should be used regularly since they slowly lose quality if stored for extended periods of time. Check open dates on food packages so you can plan their use while the food is still at peak quality.

Decide how much of each food you need to purchase. Use recipes for foods on the menu and your knowledge of family eating habits to estimate needed quantities of food. The Daily Food Guide can provide information on quantities of foods needed to meet nutritional needs at various cost levels. Purchase amounts of perishable foods that can be used before they spoil. But if there is an especially good price on foods you regularly use and which can be stored, stock up. Runouts on food can cost you money and cost you time. Each extra shopping trip can lead you into impulse buys as well as cost you time and travel.

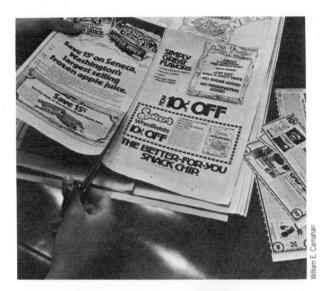

Coupons may save you about 10 percent in your food budget. But don't let a coupon tempt you into buying a food that your family doesn't like or need or which costs more than a store brand even with the coupon.

It's a good idea to plan menus before shopping. Complete planning makes it much easier to shop for several days' food supply at one time. Use the newspaper food ads to find the best buys.

William E. Carnahan

William E. Carnahan

279

Compile a complete shopping list. Planned menus make this much easier. If you don't plan complete menus, at least list the major categories of foods you will need, such as seven dinner meats, seven green or yellow vegetables, fresh salad ingredients, and so forth. Then wait to decide the specifics when you can compare price and quality at the store. During the week, keep a running list of staple foods you need to buy on the next shopping trip. Note the price of advertised specials on the shopping list so you have a ready reference for price comparisons with unadvertised alternatives. Organize the list by categories or according to layout of the store where you plan to shop.

Compare Stores, Brands, Prices

With the planning steps completed, you are ready to carry out the shopping activities of food management. It is usually most efficient to shop in one store only on each shopping trip, unless another store is nearby or on the same general route. If possible, try to shop when the store is not too crowded and when you have time to shop carefully. Eat something before you go to the store so that you'll be less tempted by appetizing odors and attractive displays.

Compare brands as you shop. Most supermarkets carry several brands of most food products. Compare prices of national brands with private label (store) brands and generics. In many cases the quality of top-level store brands is comparable to nationally advertised brands but the store brands cost less. The quality of most generics is lower than these brands and varies more over time, but the cost savings may be significant. If you don't need top quality appearance or size uniformity, generic foods will provide

nutritional products suitable for many uses. To compare quality, purchase one can of several different brands, open them up side-by-side when you get home, and make your own quality judgments.

Price Per Serving — Compare prices per serving rather than price per pound on foods. This is particularly important on meat and poultry and on fresh fruits or vegetables which require considerable trimming during preparation. Boneless cuts of meat which have little or no waste often cost less per serving than a lower priced cut with a great deal of bone, fat, or gristle.

Compare unit prices. When a food product is available in several different-sized containers, the price per ounce — or "unit price" — will help you select the most economical package size. Some stores post unit prices on the shelf below foods, or mark them on the package. If the store doesn't provide this service, divide the price of the container by the number of ounces it contains. For some foods, there may be little or no difference between the cost per ounce from large or small containers, but an ounce of ready-to-eat cereal from an individual pack may cost twice as much as an ounce from an 18-ounce package.

Read labels carefully. Ingredients are listed in descending order by predominance, so you can see, for example, which vegetables in a frozen vegetable mixture are going to be present in the greatest quantity. Nutrition labels can help you make better choices from that standpoint. Look for dates on perishable foods. Most open dates state the period of time you can expect peak quality from the product. However, products can remain wholesome and safe to eat for a few days past the peak of quality period if stored properly.

How to Buy Convenience

Buy only as much convenience as you need and can afford. Partially or fully prepared foods often but not always cost more than their home-prepared counterparts, but may be worth the extra cost if the quality is good and if it saves you considerable time and work. Most baked products — cakes, biscuits, pies, and pancakes — made from a mix cost about the same as if you made them from the basic ingredients. But frozen and chilled bakery products, combination dinners and entrees, and vegetables in sauces cost much more than home-prepared ones. At times a convenience item can add needed variety to menus or compensate for lack of skill or equipment for home preparation. If you live alone, they may be a more practical alternative to recipes that require a wide variety of ingredients that you don't use frequently. Many convenience foods such as canned or frozen vegetables cost less than the fresh product and save preparation time.

Check marked-down items. Day-old bakery items are usually a good value if you can use them up in another day or two or if you plan to freeze them. If canned foods are marked down because of damage to the can, select with care. Check seams for rust or evidence of leakage. Don't buy badly dented or bulging cans. Marked-down fresh produce with cuts, bruises, or signs of spoilage is not a very good buy at any price.

Be sure you locate advertised specials. This is where your priced shopping list can help. Stores often use end-of-aisle or jumble displays to attract you to new

When food is available in several different-sized containers, the price per ounce or pound, or "unit price", will help you select the most economical package size. Look for posted unit prices like the one shown here.

William E. Carnahan

products or items which may not be on special. Don't let an alluring display or tasty food sample lure you into an impulsive buy that you can't afford. And select frozen foods last. Quality of frozen foods can be damaged by thawing and refreezing, so pick them up on the way to checkout.

Be a responsible shopper. If you change your mind about buying a food already in your cart, take it back to where you found it. Careless shoppers add to the cost of food retailing by damaging products, disrupting displays, and tasting food as they shop. If you shop with small children, help them learn to be good customers rather than giving in to their pleas for samples or products you don't need. And, be ready for the checkout counter. If produce has to be weighed before checkout, take care of that in the produce section. Don't wait till you get in the checkout line to rummage around for cents-off coupons. Be prepared with identification for cashing a personal check or have it authorized in advance.

Frills Add Up — If you are on a really limited budget, cut out the frills. Soft drinks, snack foods, fancy nuts, olives, specialty pickles, candy, and other tempting treats can add several dollars at the cash register but aren't essential for good nutrition. Unsweetened drink mixes, popcorn to pop at home, and simple condiments can be money-saving choices. Fats, sweets, and alcoholic beverages

are a good place for the dollar and calorie-conscious food manager to start cutting.

Check over the cash register receipt as you put away the foods. Separate the costs of nonfoods from foods to get an accurate cost for family food. Most consumers spend a great deal for nonfood

Be ready when you get to the checkout counter. Have "cents-off" coupons ready, and be prepared with identification if you plan to pay for your groceries with a check.

supplies at the supermarket, yet tend to include money spent for these items as part of family food costs. If you haven't been doing this, you may be surprised to find your food bill is a lot less than you thought.

Store foods immediately. Put away frozen and chilled foods first. If you bought fresh meat, poultry, or fish for freezing, rewrap in a freezer wrap. Plastic films used for fresh meat overwraps are designed to allow oxygen passage to keep meat surfaces red and are not suitable for freezer storage.

Food Preparation Strategies
Once you have the food supply on hand,

William E. Carnahan

the remaining management challenges are in food preparation. Control time and personal energy in preparing food. If you find it difficult to get all the foods for a meal ready to serve at the same time, a written preparation schedule can help. Consider how long it will take to prepare foods for cooking, actual cooking times, and last-minute details before serving. Start with the menu item requiring the greatest amount of cooking time and after it's cooking, work on other items. When you do a plan like this, you may find that some changes in planned menu items may be needed to make preparation go smoothly. Delegating tasks to other family members makes meal preparation easier. Whenever you can mix, cook, and even serve in the same container, you will save cleanup time.

Conserve energy in cooking. Plan ahead before you open the refrigerator, so you can get the items you need in one trip. If you need the oven for one food, cook the other foods for that meal in the oven or cook foods that can be eaten at future meals. For example, an oven pot roast can include the potato and other vegetables for the meal and you'll still have room in the oven for baking cookies, a couple of loaves of quick bread, or a dessert for the same meal or for the next day. Preheating the oven isn't necessary except for leavened foods. Glass and ceramic baking utensils allow you to set the thermostat 25 degrees lower. Set a timer and don't open the door frequently to peek. A pressure cooker can save energy for less tender meat cuts, soups, legumes, and stews. If you have a microwave oven, use it whenever you can instead of surface burners for items that cook quickly and for reheating foods. Many portable electrical appliances use less energy than surface burners or regular ovens, but select those which have more than one use. For example, an energy-efficient electric frypan can be used for frying, baking, or stewing.

Control Food Waste — This is an obvious way to save money. Buy food in usable amounts, store it properly, and use it before it spoils. Cook smaller quantities of food to avoid leftovers, or deliberately plan the use of leftovers for packed lunches, reheating or in a new form for a future meal. Refrigerate leftovers immediately after cooking or freeze them. Freeze small amounts of leftover vegetables and the nutrient-rich cooking liquid to use in a soup. To cut down on plate waste, serve smaller portions and offer seconds for those who want them or let each family member determine their own serving size.

Prepare some of your own baby or toddler foods. If you have small children, you can save money and provide good nutrition by making baby foods from items used in family meals. Using strict sanitation measures, grind or puree meats, poultry and vegetables. Freeze in ice cube trays for easy single-serving portions later on. If you add a considerable amount of salt in cooking vegetables, you may want to remove the portion used for baby food before adding salt.

How do you measure up on the management scale? Were meals nutritionally balanced, good to look at, and to eat? Did the costs stay within your budget? Did you use time and energy efficiently? Did you cut down on waste? If family meals meet the goals that your family has decided are important, you've conquered the food management challenge.

Buying Food for the Nutrients It Provides

By Linda E. Cleveland

Spending a reasonable amount on food does not automatically lead to nutritious diets. A variety of foods is needed to supply the energy and nutrients for normal growth and good health. U.S. Department of Agriculture (USDA) food and nutrition scientists have translated what is known about the nutrient needs of people and the nutritive value of foods into a flexible, easy-to-use guide. This guide — *The Daily Food Guide* — can help you select the foods your family needs. It tells you the kinds and amounts of foods that make up a nutritious diet. But it also lets you make choices to fit your eating style, nutritional needs, and budget.

In the guide, foods are sorted into five groups according to the nutritional contribution they make. They are as follows: 1) Fruits and Vegetables. 2) Breads and Cereals. 3) Milk and Cheeses. 4) Meat, Poultry, Fish, and Beans. 5) Fats, Sweets, and Alcohol. You can be reasonably sure you are feeding family members wisely if you give them the number of servings suggested from each of the first four groups each day. Additional foods can be chosen to round out meals and satisfy appetites.

The guide will help you get the nutrients (vitamins, minerals, and protein) you need, and consider calories too. Calories are a measure of energy that food provides. Almost all foods provide calories; most provide nutrients too. Everyone needs calories as well as nutrients, but too many calories result in obesity — a common nutritional problem in our country. There is enough variety within each food group in the guide to allow choices of food that fit the family budget. Each group includes some foods that are low in price and some that are high.

Fruits and Vegetables Group

How many basic servings daily? Choose four or more. Include one good vitamin C source each day. Also frequently include deep-yellow or dark-green vegetables for vitamin A. Count as a serving ½ cup or a typical portion of any fruit or vegetable, such as: one orange or banana; half a medium grapefruit or cantaloupe; a wedge of lettuce; a bowl of salad; or one medium potato. This group is important for its contribution of vitamins A and C, folacin, and fiber, although individual foods in the group may vary widely in how much of these nutrients they provide.

Dark-green and deep-yellow vegetables provide vitamin A. *Vitamin A* helps keep

Linda E. Cleveland is a Home Economist, Consumer Nutrition Center, Human Nutrition Information Service.

the skin and inner linings of the body healthy and resistant to infection. It protects against night blindness and promotes growth. Citrus fruits (oranges, grapefruit, tangerines, lemons), melons, berries, tomatoes, and dark-green vegetables are good sources of vitamin C. *Vitamin C* helps build the material that connects the body cells. The body needs it to assist normal teeth and bone formation and to aid in healing wounds. Some of the important sources of vitamins A and C such as leafy green vegetables and oranges also provide folacin in substantial amounts. *Folacin* helps build body proteins and make sure cells grow and function normally.

Unpeeled vegetables and fruits, especially those with edible seeds, such as berries, okra, and cucumbers, are important for the fiber they provide. *Dietary fiber* is plant material which is not digested in the human gastrointestinal tract. There are some indications that eating fibrous foods may prevent constipation and help to prevent some chronic diseases of the large intestine. In addition, fiber is a plus in weight reduction because bulky foods fill you up. Note that nearly all fruits and vegetables are low in calories and fat.

Buying on a Budget? — U.S. households spend about 20 cents of every food dollar for fruits and vegetables. But costs vary widely so careful selection can have a large effect on your food budget. Cost studies done in the winter of 1981 show you can spend as little as 12 cents or more than 25 cents for a serving, depending on the fruits and vegetables you select. Many factors such as container or package size, brand name, grade, and seasonal abundance affect cost. Foods in season will be at their

peak in quality and often are low in cost. Keep in mind, however, that some fruits and vegetables, even in season, may not be within your budget.

Bread and Cereal Group

Choose four or more basic servings daily. Count as a serving: one slice of bread; ½ cup to ¾ cup cooked cereal or pasta; 1 oz ready-to-eat cereal. Any product made with whole grains or enriched flour or meal can be served such as: bread, biscuits, muffins, waffles, pancakes, cooked and ready-to-eat cereals, cornmeal, grits, macaroni, spaghetti, noodles, rice, rolled oats, barley, and bulgur.

What's in It for You? — You get B vitamins and iron from most whole-grain and enriched breads and cereals. *Thiamin, niacin,* and *riboflavin* – three of the B vitamins — help you grow at a normal rate. They play a central role in releasing energy from food, and they help with proper functioning of nerves, normal appetite, good digestion, and healthy skin. *Vitamin B_6* helps the body use protein. *Iron* is an important part of hemoglobin, the substance in blood that carries oxygen from the lungs to muscle, brain, and other parts of the body. The bread and cereal group provides about one-third of the iron in U.S. diets. But the body can make better use of this iron if it is eaten at the same time as a good source of vitamin C or along with meat — an important fact to remember.

Bread and cereal also provide *protein,* and they are a major source of this nutrient in vegetarian diets. Whole-grain products contribute *zinc, magnesium, folacin,* and *fiber.* Most breakfast cereals are fortified with some nutrients at levels higher than found in natural whole grain.

If refined, cereals may be low in other nutrients the whole grain contains. It's a good idea to have some whole-grain products in your diet. The lower calorie items are those with little or no fats and sweets used in their preparation.

Buying on a budget? Whole-grain and enriched products are among the most inexpensive sources of many nutrients. Many cost only pennies per serving. A recent national food consumption survey showed that only 12 cents of every food dollar went for flour, cereals, and bakery products. At the same time, however, these foods supplied 41 percent of the thiamin, 33 percent of the iron, 28 percent of the riboflavin, 23 percent of the calcium, and 19 percent of the protein in diets.

Milk and Cheese Group

How many basic servings daily? Children need two to three servings; teenagers need four. Adults need two servings except for women who are pregnant or lactating. They need more — three for the pregnant woman and four for the lactating woman. Count as a serving an 8-oz cup of milk or yogurt. Milk can be served in any form: whole, skim, lowfat, buttermilk, evaporated, or nonfat dry. Ice cream, ice milk, and cheese can replace some milk in diets, but they do contain additional calories from fat and/or sugar.

Examples of tradeoffs you can make with other dairy products based on their calcium content and, in addition, their calories, fat, and total carbohydrate content are: 1½ oz natural cheese = 1 cup whole milk + 1 teaspoon fat. 1 oz process cheese food or spread = ½ cup 2 percent milk + 1 teaspoon fat. ½ cup ice cream = ⅓ cup skim milk + 2 tea-

spoons fat + 3 teaspoons sugar. 8 oz plain lowfat yogurt = 1 cup 2 percent milk.

Because whole milk, cheese, and ice cream can contribute substantial amounts of fat, you may choose to buy lowfat or skim milk and milk products. When you use whole milk in one meal, you might be more moderate in your use of other fats. The sugar in ice cream, ice milk, and flavored yogurts raises the calorie count.

What's in It for You? — This group is the major source of *calcium* in U.S. diets. It is important for *protein, riboflavin, vitamins B_6, B_{12}, and A,* and for *vitamin D,* when milk is fortified with this vitamin. *Calcium* is needed for building strong teeth and bones. It also aids in proper functioning of the heart, muscles, and nerves, and helps the blood coagulate during bleeding. *Vitamin D* helps the body absorb and use the calcium it needs. Lowfat or skim milk products have *fewer calories,* but similar amounts of nutrients (when fortified with vitamins A and D) as whole milk products.

Buying on a budget? Today you can buy milk for your family in many forms — some costing considerably more than others. Price depends on whether milk is fresh, cultured, canned, or dried; whether part of the fat has been removed; and whether vitamins and minerals and milk solids have been added. The size of the container, where you buy milk, and whether it is home delivered make a difference in the price of milk too. Check the prices for different forms of milk in your area. Then decide which kinds of milk, what size of containers, and what services are best for your family and budget. When cheese, yogurt, ice cream, and ice milk replace milk in diets, they do so at added cost.

Meat, Poultry, Fish, and Bean Group

Choose two or more basic servings daily. Count as a serving 2 to 3 oz of lean cooked meat, poultry, or fish without bone. Foods in this group are: beef, lamb, pork, veal, poultry, fish, shellfish, organ meats, eggs, dry beans, dry peas, soybeans, lentils, seeds, nuts, and peanut butter. Meat alternates that equal 1 oz of meat are: one egg; ½ to ¾ cup cooked dry beans, dry peas, soybeans, or lentils; 2 tablespoons peanut butter; and ¼ to ½ cup nuts and seeds.

What's in it for you? This group is valued for *protein, iron, zinc, vitamins B_6 and B_{12}, magnesium,* and other minerals and vitamins these foods provide. *Protein* helps build and repair all body tissues and form antibodies to fight infection. *Zinc* is also important for tissue growth and repair, and functions in many body processes including digestion and reproduction. *Magnesium* helps the body produce and use energy, and aids in the normal function of nerve and muscle.

It's a good idea to vary your choices of foods from this group. Only foods of animal origin have vitamin B_{12}. Red meats and oysters are the better sources of zinc. Red meats are also important for the iron they provide. Dry beans and dry peas are too. But like grain products, the iron in them is used best when eaten along with meat or a good source of vitamin C. Dry beans and nuts are worthwhile sources of magnesium. Flesh of fish and poultry is relatively low in calories and saturated fat. To reduce the calorie and fat content of meat and poultry, select lean cuts of meat, trim away the fat parts, and remove skin and fat from poultry.

Buying on a Budget? — The meat, poultry, and fish items in meals usually cost the most. In fact, a recent national food consumption survey shows that more than one-third of the money U.S. families spend for food goes for this group of foods. But the range in costs of different types and cuts of meats is great, so careful selection can result in worthwhile savings.

Sample costs of a 3-ounce serving of cooked lean from some cuts of meat and of cooked poultry and fish based on average prices in the winter of 1981 are: 25 to 50 cents . . . ground beef, beef liver; whole ham — cured and ready-to-cook, picnic shoulder; whole frying chicken, turkey; canned tuna. 51 to 75 cents . . . beef chuck roast; canned ham; chicken breasts; frozen haddock and ocean perch fillet; canned sardines. 76 to 100 cents . . . beef rump roast, round steak; pork loin roast, pork chops. 101 cents or more . . . beef rib roast, porterhouse and sirloin steak; lamb chops; veal cutlets. These cost comparisons show, in general, which types and cuts of meat are expensive and inexpensive choices. But to make sure, you need to compare costs using prices at your store.

Fats, Sweets, and Alcohol Group

How many basic servings daily? Little or none is required unless for extra calories. What's included in this group? Fats and oils such as butter, margarine, mayonnaise, and other salad dressings; sweets such as sugar, candy, jams, jellies, sirups; soft drinks and other highly sugared beverages; and alcoholic beverages such as wine, beer, and liquor. Unenriched refined bakery products are included here also because most of them provide little vitamins, minerals, and protein in relation to calories.

What's in it for you? These foods provide mainly *calories* and little in terms of nutrients. An exception is vegetable oils which supply *vitamin E* and *essential fatty acids*. Butter and margarine provide *vitamin A*. Some foods in the group are especially concentrated sources of calories. Fats, oils, and pure alcohol have about twice the calories, ounce for ounce, as protein, starches, and sugars.

If you're like many Americans today, you're concerned about good nutrition. Since a large portion of income is spent on food, you want to be sure to spend this money wisely. In short, you want to plan enjoyable, nutritious meals at a price you can afford. *The Daily Food Guide* is a research-based tool that can help.

The fruits and vegetables group including orange juice as in the pitcher contains low calory sources of Vitamins A and C, folacin and fiber.

Food Safety From Farm to Market

By Patricia F. Stolfa

When Americans go to markets to buy food, they can do so without fears about its safety. They may be confused by differing scientific opinions on the long-term effects of some ingredients, or they may want to avoid certain food additives. But basically, consumers do not need to know about animal diseases or how to run laboratory tests in order to be confident that the food they buy is wholesome and accurately labeled.

American consumers enjoy this confidence because of a complex and comprehensive relationship between the government and those who bring the food to market — producers and processors. Federal, State, and local government agencies cooperate in assuring food safety. Of course, no amount of government urging could replace the basic commitment to food safety which is shared by food producers and processors. Pride in their work and the products which are the result of it is the underlying reason why the system works.

Concern about food safety begins on the farm. For example, in the special case of milk, the health of the producing animals is of more than routine interest; herds must be free of diseases like tuberculosis and brucellosis which can be transmitted to humans. Dairy farmers take special precautions to assure that milk remains clean and wholesome. Milk parlors are built with materials that are easy to clean. They are separated from other farm operations which may be dusty. Water supplies on dairy farms must meet high quality standards; bulk storage tanks must be made of approved materials and equipped for proper cooling. State officials visit dairy farms regularly to make sure that these and other safety features are being used.

Producers of livestock and poultry are also concerned about safety of their products. Modern animal husbandry practices include the use of animal drugs to prevent disease and promote growth. For instance, on contemporary farms swine no longer have to forage in pastures but may be produced in large structures. In this setting, animals are more apt to transmit disease to each other, and the use of antibiotics and sulfa drugs to prevent these diseases has become widespread. These animal drugs, which can make a big difference in the efficiency of a modern farm, are made available only after the Food and Drug Administration (FDA) has approved them as safe. Every label must have clear di-

Patricia F. Stolfa is Acting Assistant Deputy Administrator, International Programs, Food Safety and Inspection Service.

rections about how the drug is to be used.

Modern farmers also use chemicals such as pesticides to reduce crop losses caused by destructive insects and to keep food costs at a minimum. The Environmental Protection Agency (EPA) protects the consumer from unnecessary exposure to these chemicals. EPA licenses the use of pesticides, and it sets limits on the small amounts of such chemicals which can be allowed on food crops.

Sometimes, however, mixups or accidents may occur on the farm, and animals brought to slaughter may have small but unacceptable amounts of drugs or chemicals in their bodies. Because these drug or chemical residues cannot be seen, smelled, or tasted, they are difficult to detect. As part of its regular inspection, the U.S. Department of Agriculture (USDA) tests meat and poultry products for these residues.

In the past year, USDA has begun the Total Residue Avoidance Program (TRAP) to help farmers eliminate drug and chemical residue problems on the farm before livestock and poultry are sold for slaughter. TRAP is a cooperative effort between USDA and producer associations. Educational materials developed for TRAP will alert farmers to points in their production systems where residue problems can originate and be detected in a practical and economical manner.

Safety During Processing

Once the producer has raised a healthy animal or harvested a pest-free crop, the safety of the resulting food product is the responsibility of the processors who handle it. The number of processors and the nature of their work has changed dramatically in the last several decades. In general, processing operations have become more numerous, more diversified, and more advanced. This revolution in food processing has meant that protecting food safety is a job that is many times more complex and difficult — and sometimes controversial — than it was in the past.

To a large extent, the profit motives of processors help meet the food safety demands of the consuming public. Whether a company is making TV dinners or tomato juice, it cannot afford to lose its considerable investment in animal and plant raw materials through practices which let these perishables spoil during handling. Food processors are well aware also of the severe economic consequences which can result from food contamination incidents.

In recent years many processors have set up production controls which aid in assuring food safety. Under these quality control (QC) systems, the product undergoes a series of online checks as it is being made. A company using QC does not wait until the pizza is in the package or the sausage is on the truck to check and see if it meets the standards and specifications it was supposed to have. Measurements and tests are run throughout production. As a result, corrections can be made before the product is finished, a strategy which is generally easier and less costly than waiting until after a product is finished. In the past few years, both USDA's Food Safety and Inspection Service (FSIS) and FDA have recognized the value of these QC systems in providing evidence that products comply with food safety requirements.

Government Roles — In addition to the actions of processors to assure a safe food supply, there is an array of government activities to protect food safety. For example, the Federal Meat and Poultry Inspection Program, administered by FSIS, assures consumers that meat and poultry products are safe to eat and truthfully labeled.

Inspection begins with review of a slaughtering or processing plant's plan for facilities, equipment, and procedures. When the plant is operating, inspectors check the facilities and equipment for sanitation. If at any time an unsanitary condition is discovered, the operations are stopped until the problem is corrected. Animals are inspected both before and after slaughter. Before slaughter, USDA inspectors look for signs of disease. After slaughter, each carcass and the internal organs are further examined for disease or signs of contamination that would make all or part of the carcass unfit as human food.

Much of the meat and poultry slaughtered today finds its way into processed products like ham, soup, frankfurters, and potpies. FSIS reviews procedures, labels, and recipes used by manufacturers to assure that processed meat and poultry products will be safe and accurately labeled.

Meat, Poultry Product Imports

FSIS also is responsible for the wholesomeness of imported meat and poultry products, which must meet the same requirements as those produced in the United States. FSIS veterinarians regularly review the inspection programs operated by foreign countries to ensure they are enforcing requirements at least equal to those in the United States. All imported meat and poultry products are inspected at the port-of-entry or at inland inspection points before they are allowed to be distributed in this country.

USDA's Federal Meat and Poultry Inspection Program assures consumers that meat and poultry products are safe to eat. This USDA poultry inspector in Easton, Md., checks broilers for wholesomeness as they make their way through a cutting and packaging plant.

Monitoring meat and poultry products for wholesomeness and label accuracy continues even after they leave the slaughtering or processing plant. FSIS compliance officers visit businesses such as warehouses, brokers, transportation companies, and retail stores to look for labeling violations and spoiled or contaminated products. Products not in compliance are removed from the marketing chain through detention, seizure, or similar actions. Products unsafe for human consumption must be properly disposed of by the owner.

Egg Products — The Federal Egg Products Inspection Program assures the wholesomeness of dried, liquid, and frozen egg products in the marketplace. It operates in a manner similar to the Federal Meat and Poultry Inspection Program, but is administered by USDA's Agricultural Marketing Service (AMS). Egg products are important ingredients in a host of foods prepared by commercial food manufacturers, including cake and pudding mixes, macaroni, ice cream, and baked goods. Institutional food buyers also use a lot of egg products as they

Murray Lemmon

serve the morning's scrambled eggs, the luncheon omelet, or dessert crepe.

The National Shellfish Sanitation Program is a voluntary program for shellfish safety. States adopt laws and regulations for sanitation, inspect shellfish operations, conduct sanitary and bacteriological surveys of growing areas, and determine what areas should be restricted. The U.S. Public Health Service makes an annual review of the State control programs, including inspection of sample shellfish-processing plants. The industry cooperates by obtaining shellfish from safe areas, by providing and maintaining plants which meet sanitary standards, and by keeping records showing the origin and distribution of all shellfish. The National Marine Fisheries Service in the U.S. Department of Commerce provides a voluntary inspection and grading program for fisheries.

The Food and Drug Administration (FDA) carries out activities which assure the safety of most other food products. Certain substances, like food and color additives, must be approved for safety before they can be used. Manufacturers submit scientific data on these substances for review by FDA scientists before approvals can be granted. In addition, FDA has a factory inspection program through which it oversees food processing. FDA inspectors review the operations in selected plants and decide if products produced there will be wholesome and truthfully labeled as required.

Responsibility for the safety of food after it reaches retail establishments falls mainly on the business owner. Businesses have a strong economic incentive to maintain food in a wholesome condition for consumers. Local and State public health officials have oversight responsibilities. FDA, FSIS, and AMS receive and investigate complaints about food products which may have been improperly handled during production. At the point of purchase, the safety of these products becomes the direct concern of the consumer.

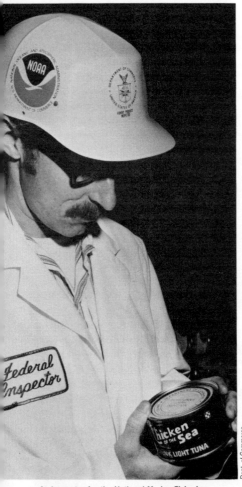

Dept. of Commerce

An inspector for the National Marine Fisheries Service in the U.S. Department of Commerce checks a can of tuna fish. This inspection program is voluntary.

Consumer Guidelines for Food Safety

By Carole A. Davis

S afe food handling practices in the home are necessary to assure safe, wholesome food. For the consumer, food safety begins with buying food. Following are some food safety guidelines to consider in buying, storing, handling, and cooking food.

Make grocery shopping your last stop before returning home. Buy only amounts of foods that you can store properly and use before they lose their optimum quality. The chances of maintaining good quality in foods during storage at home are improved if the initial food quality is high. Look for: *Fresh fruits and vegetables* that are brightly colored, free of defects and bruises, and not overripe. *Meats* that are USDA inspected. *Containers of foods* that are intact — packages not torn or crushed, cans not dented, rusted, leaking, or bulging. *Frozen foods* that feel firm — not thawed or coated with ice to indicate previous thawing.

Choose frozen foods and meat, poultry, and dairy items last before going to the checkout counter. Make sure frozen juices and ice cream are placed in insulated or plastic bags at checkout. Have all cold foods bagged together to provide a cooler environment for them. At home, refrigerate or freeze perishable items promptly.

Refrigerator temperatures of 40° F or below are required for storing many perishable foods to retard quality losses and delay spoilage. The amount of moisture and temperature needed to retain quality during storage varies with different foods. Here are guidelines for some foods:

Refrigerate most fresh, perishable fruits and vegetables. Store green leafy vegetables in the hydrator or in plastic bags to keep them crisp. Refrigerate berries and cherries covered, unwashed, and unstemmed to prevent loss of moisture. Cover and refrigerate canned fruits or juices that have been opened. Store apples and some vegetables such as potatoes, onions, and hard rind squashes in a cool, dark place. Allow bananas to ripen at room temperature, then refrigerate. Store citrus fruits at a cool room temperature or uncovered in the refrigerator.

Place meat, poultry, and fish in the coldest part of the refrigerator. Loosely cover fresh meats. Use roasts, steaks, and chops within three to five days for best eating quality. Use ground meat within one or two days; it is more likely to spoil

Carole A. Davis is a Supervisory Home Economist, Consumer Nutrition Center, Human Nutrition Information Service.

than roasts, etc., because more surface area has been exposed to the air and mechanical equipment. Store poultry and fish in their transparent wrap in the refrigerator and use within one or two days. Refrigerate eggs, milk, and dairy products. Keep milk tightly closed so it will not absorb odors or flavors from other foods; for best eating quality, use within 6 to 7 days. Refrigerate hard cheeses tightly wrapped — they should keep satisfactorily for several months.

Using Date Indicators

Many perishable products carry a "pull or sell-by date" on the label to indicate the end of the time they may be sold. Others may carry a "freshness or best-if-used-by date" that indicates the last date the product can be expected to be at its most acceptable quality. A third type of dating commonly used is the "expiration or use-by date." Packages of food that are stamped with this date, such as dry yeast, should be eaten or used before that time. A "pack date" indicates when the food was processed or packaged for retail sale. This is used primarily for foods that have a long shelf life, such as canned foods. Become familiar with the meaning of dates used on foods in your store. These dates can help you plan to avoid food quality loss and spoilage.

Frozen foods require storage temperatures of 0° F or lower to maintain the best quality. Unfavorable changes in eating quality — such as loss of color, flavor, and characteristic texture — and nutritive value take place more rapidly in foods stored above 0° F.

Hold frozen foods in the freezing compartments of single-door home refrigerators only a few days, as most of these compartments are not designed to pro-

vide temperatures of 0° F. In refrigerator-freezers where temperatures can be maintained at 0° F or lower in the freezer section, food may be kept for the same storage periods as in a freezer. Keep food in the freezer rotated by placing the most recently purchased foods behind or under foods that are already being stored. Tightly wrap meat and poultry items to be frozen in moisture-vapor-proof material such as freezer wrap, aluminum foil, plastic bags, etc., rather than store wrap.

The length of time commercially frozen food will retain good quality when stored at 0° F or below at home depends on the kind of food and how it was handled before purchase. A chart with this chapter lists some suggested maximum home storage periods to maintain good quality at 0° F in purchased frozen foods that have been subject to good commercial freezing, handling, and storage practices before you purchased them. Recommended periods are approximate.

Occasionally, frozen foods partially or completely thaw before you discover that your freezer is not operating or that the door has been left open for a time. You may safely refreeze frozen foods that have thawed if they still contain ice crystals or if they are still cold (40° F or below) and have been held no longer than 1 or 2 days at refrigerator temperatures.

Safe Preparation Practices

Foods that are handled improperly can cause illness even though they were safe to eat when purchased or initially prepared. Strict cleanliness of person and surroundings is the best way to prevent the contamination of foods and the spread of foodborne illness in the home. Make sure hands, all dishes, utensils, kitchen equip-

Maximum Home Storage Periods at 0°F to Maintain Good Quality in Purchased Frozen Foods

Fruits	Months
Berries, cherries, peaches	12
Fruit juice concentrates	12

Vegetables

Beans, cauliflower, corn, peas, spinach	8

Baked Goods

Bread and yeast rolls	3
Cake	2-6
Fruit pies (unbaked)	8

Meat

Beef, ground; pork, fresh chops	4
Beef roasts and steaks	12
Lamb roasts, veal chops	9
Pork, cured	2
Pork, fresh roasts	8
Cooked meat	3

Poultry

Chicken or turkey parts	6-9
Chicken or turkey, whole	12
Cooked chicken and turkey	4-6

Fish

Cod, flounder, haddock, halibut, pollock fillets	6
Clams, shucked; oysters, shucked; and Dungeness crabmeat	3-4
Shrimp	12
Cooked fish and shellfish	3

Frozen Desserts

Ice cream or sherbet	1

ment, and work surfaces are clean. It is especially important to thoroughly clean equipment, chopping boards, and work surfaces that have been used for raw food before using them for cooked food. This prevents the cooked food from becoming contaminated with bacteria that could have been present in the raw food. For example, bacteria on a cutting board used for cutting raw chicken could contaminate potato salad if cooked potatoes were diced on the unclean board.

Temperature and time influence the growth of bacteria. Cold temperatures inhibit bacterial growth. Thus, if foods are cooled promptly and are properly refrigerated, the number of bacteria in foods can be held to a safe level and no ill effects will follow. Food safety problems occur if foods are held for any length of time above refrigerator temperatures and below serving temperatures of hot food. The best guideline is to keep hot foods such as casseroles and meats hot (about 140° F) and cold foods such as meat or vegetable salads and custard pies cold (below 40° F). Food may not be safe to eat if held for more than 2 to 3 hours at temperatures between 60° and 125° F, the range between which bacteria grow rapidly. This includes all time during preparation, storage, and serving.

Special Handling — Certain foods need special handling. Examples are meat, poultry, and fish items, and eggs and egg-rich foods. If eggs are cracked, be sure to use them only in foods that are thoroughly cooked. Refrigerate cream, custard, or meringue pies and foods with custard fillings, including cakes, cream puffs, or eclairs.

You can cook frozen meat or poultry without thawing, but you must allow more cooking time. Allow about one and a half times as long to cook from the frozen state as required for fresh or thawed products of the same weight and shape. If thawing is desired, thaw meat and poultry in the refrigerator until pliable. For quicker results, large whole poultry can be thawed in a cool room in a double-wall paper bag.

To be certain meat and poultry products are adequately cooked, use a meat thermometer. For meat roasts and boneless poultry roasts, insert the thermometer into the center of the thickest portion. For whole poultry, insert the thermometer into the center of the inner thigh muscle. Beef roasts and steaks may be eaten rare, 140° F internal temperature, but pork should be cooked to 170° F and poultry to 180° to 185 ° F. Poultry stuffing should reach 165° F. Never partially cook poultry and finish cooking it later as bacteria can survive in partially cooked poultry.

Microwave Cooking — Microwave cooking is a convenient and fast method of cooking many foods. However, precautions must be taken in cooking some foods, such as meat roasts, due to the unevenness of cooking larger volumes of food. In cooking meat, especially pork, be sure all parts of the meat reach the desired internal temperature.

Care of Leftovers — Chill leftover cooked foods as rapidly as possible to prevent growth of micro-organisms during the cooling process. Remove stuffing from leftover cooked meat, poultry, or fish and refrigerate separately. Refrigerate broth or gravy promptly after the meal. Because leftovers have been subjected to additional handling, they have added opportunity for bacterial contamination;

thus, it is important to heat leftovers thoroughly before serving. Boil broth and gravies several minutes when reheating. It is best to freeze leftovers if you are uncertain as to when they will be served again. Most casseroles and roasted meats and poultry freeze well, as do stews without potatoes.

Home Canning Precautions

Home canning is not a difficult technique. But it must be done properly to avoid spoilage and food poisoning, such as botulism — which is often fatal. It is extremely important to use only tested reliable instructions such as those found in U.S. Department of Agriculture publications. Be sure to follow instructions *exactly*, using processing times and temperatures recommended for the food, jar sizes, and type of pack you are using.

Home-canned food will be no better than the raw foods with which you start. Therefore, select food of good quality with no bruises or soft spots. Be sure to use fresh, firm fruits and young, tender vegetables and can them as soon after purchase or harvest as possible. Do not use overripe foods because some, such as tomatoes, lose acidity as they mature, and the recommended processing time may then not be adequate. It is important to use only good quality meat and poultry when you can them at home.

To prepare fruits and vegetables for canning, wash them thoroughly but gently to remove dirt, which contains bacteria. Small quantities of product should be washed at a time under running water or through several changes of water. Peel and cut or slice fruit or vegetable as indicated in specific instructions for its canning.

Items must be packed into jars before processing in the canner. Food may be packed raw into jars and covered with boiling hot liquid such as sirup, juice, water, or broth, or it may be packed hot. Hot packed foods have been heated in sirup, water or steam, juice, or broth before packing into jars. Most raw fruits and vegetables should be packed fairly tightly because they cook down during processing. Exceptions are raw corn, lima beans, and peas. These vegetables and all hot foods should be packed fairly loosely. Overpacked containers may result in under processing. Follow directions for each fruit, vegetable, meat, or poultry as to the amount of headspace between the lid and the food or liquid in the jar.

Selecting, Caring for Equipment

The boiling-water-bath canner and steam-pressure canner are essential to home canning. Water-bath canners are readily available on the market, but any large metal container may be used if it is deep enough so the water is well over the tops of the jars and has space to boil freely. The container must have a tight-fitting lid and a rack to keep jars from resting directly on the bottom.

The steam-pressure canner is made of heavy metal and has a cover which fastens to make the pan steam-tight. The cover is fitted with a safety valve, a vent, and a weighted or dial gage. All parts of the canner must be clean and in good working order. Before the canning season, check the weighted gage to determine if it is thoroughly clean, and have the dial gage tested for accuracy by a county Extension agent or an equipment manufacturer.

Use jars made especially for home canning. These jars are the correct size for the recommended processing time and temperature, are properly heat-tempered, and are resistant to mechanical shock. Always check jars before using to be sure they do not have nicks or cracks. Wash jars in hot, soapy water, and rinse well.

Use standard jar closures — two-piece lids with metal screw bands and new flat metal lids or disks with sealing compound or porcelain-lined zinc caps with new rubber rings. Flat metal lids can be used only once since they may not seal properly if reused. Wash and rinse lids and bands. Follow manufacturer's directions for preparing flat metal lids in boiling or hot water before using.

After jars of home-canned foods have cooled and before storing the jars, examine them to be sure they are sealed. Press the center of the metal lid. If it is down and will not move, the jar is sealed.

Fred Faurot

Proper Canning Technique

Acidity of the food is the chief factor in determining the temperatures and times required for heat processing. The more acid the products, the easier spoilage organisms are destroyed by heat. Foods can be grouped into two categories, acid and low-acid. Acid foods — such as fruits, pickled vegetables, and tomatoes — can be processed safely at the temperature of boiling water (212° F) in a boiling-water-bath canner. Low-acid foods — meats, poultry, and all vegetables except tomatoes — require higher temperatures than acid foods to kill the organisms. The only safe way to can low-acid foods is with a steam-pressure canner to obtain temperatures higher than that of boiling water (240° F or 10 pounds of pressure).

In canning both acid and low-acid foods, carefully follow reliable step-by-step instructions on preparing food, packing food into jars, adjusting jar lids, and processing in the canner for the particular item you are canning. Procedures and processing times and temperatures are specific for each food.

Storing, Using Home Canned Food

After jars of home-canned foods have cooled and before storing the jars, examine them to be sure a seal has been obtained. Check two-piece lids by pressing the center of the flat metal lid; if the lid is down and will not move, the jar is sealed. Turn jars with porcelain-lined zinc caps partly over in your hands; if they do not leak, they are sealed. When jars with two-piece lids are thoroughly cooled, carefully remove metal screw bands before storing. Label jars to show date and contents. Properly canned foods stored in a cool, dry place will retain optimum eating quality for at least a year.

Be sure to use food that has the earliest processing date. Before opening any jar, check for spoilage signs. If it has a bulging lid, leaks, spurts liquid when opened, or has an off-odor or mold, do not use it. *Do not even taste it.* Destroy it out of reach of children and pets.

It is possible for canned vegetables, meats, and poultry to contain the toxin that causes botulism without showing any visible signs of spoilage. Therefore, for added safety, boil all home-canned vegetables in a covered pan for at least 10 minutes and all meats for 20 minutes, before tasting or serving. If the food looks spoiled, foams, or has an off-odor during heating, destroy it.

Further Reading

Home Canning of Fruits and Vegetables, G 8, for sale by Superintendent of Documents, U.S. Government Printing Office, Washington, DC 20402.

How to Make Jellies, Jams, and Preserves at Home, G 56, for sale by Superintendent of Documents, U.S. Government Printing Office, Washington, DC 20402.

Making Pickles and Relishes at Home, G 92, for sale by Superintendent of Documents, U.S. Government Printing Office, Washington, DC 20402.

Home Canning of Meat and Poultry, G 106, for sale by Superintendent of Documents, U.S. Government Printing Office, Washington, DC 20402.

Let the Grade Be Your Guide in Buying Food

By Sara Beck, Elizabeth Crosby, and Martha Parris

Food quality is . . . taste? price? appearance? tenderness? color? texture? nutritional value? freshness? wholesomeness? It can be all of these, none of these, or something else, depending upon your point of view — what you expect or want or need. However you define food quality, you can often judge it just by looking at a particular product.

You can also look for the grade name on the label — such as USDA Prime, U.S. Grade A, or U.S. Fancy. These grade names represent levels of quality which have been defined by the U.S. Department of Agriculture (USDA) and are based on characteristics unique to each food. For example, quality in beef is determined by evaluating maturity, color, firmness, texture, and marbling (flecks of fat within the lean). Quality in butter is measured by flavor, body, color, and salt. These and other factors can determine a food's relative value — its usefulness, desirability, marketability — and hence its price. The process of sorting foods according to quality levels, or grades, is called grading.

Meat, poultry, eggs, fresh and processed fruits and vegetables, dairy products, and fish may be graded for quality. The special considerations for each food group are described in this chapter. In addition a reference chart lists foods that are graded, and summarizes what the grades mean.

Certain things are common to the grading of all foods. Grading is performed by Federal employees or federally licensed graders on the basis of U.S. standards. Food packers and processors voluntarily request grading and must pay for it. Costs generally average only a fraction of a cent per unit of food purchased by the shopper. The place where food is graded is usually inspected and meets certain standards.

In most cases, all grades for any one food have virtually the same nutritive value. All grades are useful and there is a grade for every use. Grade standards are revised as needed to reflect changes in production, use, and marketing practices. Foods which have been graded are not required by Federal law to be grade labeled at retail, although some States and local areas may require it.

Sara Beck is Consumer Meat Specialist, Agricultural Marketing Service (AMS).

Elizabeth Crosby is Home Economist, AMS.

Martha Parris is Writer-Editor, AMS.

How Food Grades Started

In the early 1900s more and more people were relocating in cities and towns farther and farther away from agricultural areas. Wholesale food buyers were less able to examine products before agreeing to buy them. The telephone and telegraph were no help as sellers and buyers could not adequately describe their products or their expectations with such subjective terms as "good," "best," "choice," etc.

USDA established definitions — or standards — for the different quality levels of various foods and set up a food grading system to provide a universal language for producers, processors, packers, distributors and others marketing food. The first U.S. food grade standards were for potatoes in 1917, followed by butter in 1919, beef in 1926, and poultry in 1930, among others. In 1924 butter manufacturers asked USDA for permission to grade label their prod-

Grading is performed by federal employees or federally licensed graders on the basis of U.S. standards. This meat grader is measuring the ribeye muscle of a beef carcass to determine the yield grade or amount of usable red meat in the carcass.

Murray Lemmon

ucts for consumers. By the 1930s the USDA grade mark could also be found on beef, lamb, turkeys, eggs, chickens, and canned fruits and vegetables.

Meats — Only meat which has first passed a strict mandatory inspection for wholesomeness may be voluntarily graded for quality. The shield-shaped quality grade mark should not be confused with the round inspection mark which means the animals were healthy, the products truthfully labeled and not adulterated. Because *beef* can vary so much in quality, it takes eight grades to span the range. The top three are generally the only ones you see at the retail store. They are USDA Prime, Choice, and Good. The lower grades of beef usually go into processed products. Processed products themselves are not graded, only the carcasses.

Prime means the ultimate in tenderness, juiciness, and flavor. It has abundant marbling — flecks of fat within the lean meat — which enhances both flavor and juiciness. Choice grade beef will be very tender, juicy, and flavorful. It has slightly less marbling than Prime, but still is very high quality. Good grade beef is very uniform in quality and somewhat leaner than the higher grades. This grade is relatively tender, but because it has less marbling it lacks some of the juiciness and flavor of the higher grades. Many times a retail store will carry meat labeled with a store brand. Store brand meat would probably qualify for the Good grade or the lower end of the Choice grade if it were graded by USDA.

The yield of usable meat from a beef carcass can vary greatly regardless of quality grade. This variation is caused, primarily, by differences in the amount of fat on the outside of the carcass. Beef carcasses must be graded for yield at the same time they are graded for quality. Yield Grade 1 denotes the highest yield, and Yield Grade 5 the lowest. If you're buying large cuts, quarters, or sides for your home freezer, the yield grade can make a big difference.

Grades for Lamb, Veal, Pork

The grades for lamb are Prime, Choice, Good, Utility and Cull. Grade depends on the proportion of meat to bone, the color and texture of the lean meat, the firmness of meat and marbling. Most of the federally graded lamb on the retail market is USDA Prime or Choice.

There are five grades for veal and calf. USDA Prime veal is light grayish-pink to light pink and fairly firm and velvety; the bones are small, soft, and quite red. The carcass is given a lower grade as the lean meat becomes less firm, more moist, coarser in grain, and darker in color, and as size of bones increases. When calf is available in retail stores, it is generally graded USDA Choice or Good.

Unlike beef, lamb and veal, pork is not graded with quality grades. However, the appearance of pork serves as an important guide to quality. It should have a high proportion of lean meat to fat and bone. The flesh should be firm, fine textured and grayish-pink or slightly darker.

Meat Cuts — Regardless of grade, some beef cuts are more tender than others. Those that lie along the center part of the animal's body next to the backbone are the most tender. They usually command a higher price in the retail store. They include the rib, the short loin, and the loin end. Cuts of meat from these areas — rib steak, porterhouse,

T-bone — can be cooked by the dry heat method: broiling, grilling, roasting, pan-broiling, and pan-frying.

The less tender cuts — chuck, round, flank, brisket, plate and shank — are usually slightly less expensive and should be cooked with moist heat for best results. Moist heat methods include braising, stewing, boiling, and simmering. Sometimes a less tender cut such as blade chuck steak or top round steak can be tenderized first (marinated, pounded) and then broiled.

Because of the young age of the animals, most lamb, veal and pork cuts can be cooked by the dry heat method. One of the most important things to keep in mind is to plan menus in advance and select cuts appropriate for the recipe you're using.

Beef and lamb can be cooked to the degree of doneness of your liking — rare, medium, or well-done. Veal should be cooked well-done to make it tender and palatable. It needs longer cooking because it has more connective tissue than other meats. Fresh pork should be cooked to an internal temperature of 170° F (or until the juices run clear). Fully cooked, cured pork can be eaten without further heating, but reheating to an internal temperature of 140° F enhances the flavor. To eliminate guesswork and to make sure you don't overcook, use a meat thermometer. Cooking with low temperatures and cooking to just the right degree of doneness causes less shrinkage and a more palatable product.

Precepts for Poultry

U.S. Grade A is the highest quality grade for poultry and the one commonly found in stores. Grade A poultry has good con-

formation, fleshing, and fat covering, and is free of pinfeathers and various defects. U.S. Grade B or U.S. Grade C poultry is usually sold without the grade mark, or the meat is cut from the bone and used in further processed foods such as potpies, soup, and hotdogs. When poultry grades below U.S. Grade A, often it is due to improper handling during transportation and processing which causes cuts or tears in the skin, exposed flesh, broken bones, bruises, or discoloration.

Conformation, Fleshing. Shape or structure of the bird determines to a considerable degree the distribution and amount of meat. Certain defects in structure affect this and detract from the appearance. The drumsticks, thighs, and breast carry most of the meat.

Fat, Pinfeathers. The natural layer of fat in the skin should be of sufficient quantity to prevent the appearance of the flesh through the skin, especially on the breast and legs. Fat contributes moisture and flavor. Processing techniques should all but eliminate pinfeathers.

Defects. Exposed flesh, cuts and tears in the skin, broken bones, missing parts, bruises, and discolorations detract from the overall appearance and sales value of poultry. If severe, they can also affect eating quality. Air reaching the skin and meat will cause them to dry out and discolor. When this occurs during long periods of storage, it is called "freezer burn."

Poultry grading has to do with appearance and eating quality, not wholesomeness. All poultry and poultry products must be inspected for wholesomeness before being graded. Inspected poultry must not be adulterated and must be truthfully labeled. Tenderness is determined by the age of the bird and dictates the cooking method to use.

Young birds are tender and suitable for roasting, broiling, frying, rotisserie cooking, barbecuing, and ovenbaking. Young chickens may be labeled: rock cornish game hen, broiler, fryer, roaster, or capon. Other classes of young poultry may be labeled: fryer-roaster turkey, young turkey, young hen, young tom, young broiler duckling, fryer duckling, roaster duckling, young goose, young guinea, and squab (pigeon).

Older, mature birds are less tender and need long, slow cooking — simmering, steaming, braising, pressure cooking — to make them tender and develop their fuller flavor. Mature chickens may be labeled: hen, fowl, baking and stewing chicken. Other mature poultry is rarely available in retail stores.

Egg Quality and Sizes
Fresh, high quality eggs are readily available today. Eggs are the freshest and at

their peak of quality the moment they are laid. Totally automated systems can gather, wash, sort, size, package, label, and cool them — all in the same day. Eggs often move from farm to store in 1 or 2 days. If handled properly, they will retain their high quality for several weeks after being put in the refrigerator at home.

Understanding egg quality grades, which are based on factors directly related to freshness and quality, and egg sizes will help you be a better egg buyer and user.

It is important to remember that quality and size are not related — they are entirely different.

Quality — The shield-shaped mark found on egg cartons indicates the eggs have been graded under the Federal-State egg grading program. A grade designation without this mark means the eggs were graded according to State egg laws which have standards and grades based on Federal regulations. U.S. Grade AA is the top grade, while U.S. Grade A is the quality most often sold in stores. The grades are determined by the condition of the white and yolk, freedom from defects, and the shape, soundness, and cleanliness of the shell. Keep eggs cool to maintain quality. Purchase eggs from refrigerated cases in the store and put them into the refrigerator at home as quickly as possible.

Fresh, high quality eggs cover only a small area when broken out of the shell. They have a large amount of thick white that stands high and firm around the yolk, which also stands high. Over time the white becomes thinner, losing water into the yolk and carbon dioxide through the pores of the shell. The older egg spreads out and covers more area when broken out of the shell, thus looking larger. The yolk, having absorbed water from the white, increases in size, becomes somewhat flattened on top, and appears "out-of-round."

The thickness of the white of a fresh egg

All poultry and poultry products must be inspected for wholesomeness before being graded. This poultry is being graded at a poultry plant in Eldorado, Ark.

307

Fresh, high quality eggs are readily available today. The eggs shown are going through an automated system that includes candling, which is used to detect defects inside eggs.

David F. Warren

can cause it to stick to the shell when the egg is hard-cooked and peeled. Older eggs are usually easier to peel, so plan to buy eggs ahead of time for hard-cooking. Eggs usually are washed before being cartoned. This process removes the natural coating which covers the pores of the shell, so the washed eggs are often coated with a harmless, tasteless, odorless oil. It covers the pores and retards loss of water and carbon dioxide from the eggs, thus helping preserve quality. Small blood spots, though unattractive, can easily be removed with a spoon and the egg is perfectly good to eat. The spots occur occasionally because of a slight malfunction in the hen's reproductive system.

Cracked Eggs — Do not buy cracked or dirty eggs. They may contain bacteria in or on the shell that might cause food poisoning. If you do find cracked or dirty eggs in a carton, use them only in thoroughly cooked dishes. Wash soiled eggs in warm water immediately before using.

Cracked eggs found in cartons are often caused by mishandling in the store or en route to the store. Processors try to remove all the cracked and leaking eggs they can detect before the eggs are put into cartons. Sometimes, however, slight cracks cannot be detected at the plant and may become visible later. The shells must be virtually free from major stains and foreign material. Slight stains or specks on the shell, often caused by the cage housing the laying hen, are quite harmless.

Egg Sizes — Sizes are based on weight, not on how large the eggs look. Eggs are weighed on automatic scales in egg packing plants and cartoned according to the

Egg sizes based on weight.

Official U.S. Weight Classes (Sizes)	Minimum Weight Per Dozen Eggs
	Ounces
Jumbo	30
Extra Large	27
Large	24
Medium	21
Small	18
Peewee	15

minimum weight per dozen. Extra Large, Large, and Medium are the most common sizes. Most recipes have been developed on the basis of Large eggs.

Grades for Dairy Products

Butter, cheddar cheese, and instant nonfat dry milk are the dairy products most commonly found in stores with the grade shield. *Butter* grades are assigned on the basis of flavor, body, color, and salt. Quality of the milk from which the butter is made directly affects the final grade. Most butter sold in consumer packages is identified with the USDA grade shield, and is either U.S. Grade AA or A.

Cheddar cheese is graded on factors such as flavor, body, texture, finish, appearance, and color. U.S. Grade AA cheddar cheese has a fine, pleasing flavor; a smooth, compact texture; and uniform color. In addition, there are grades for Swiss (Emmentaler) cheese, Colby, and Monterey (Monterey Jack) cheese. *Instant nonfat dry milk* is evaluated for flavor, appearance, bacterial estimate, milkfat, moisture, scorched particles, acidity, and ability of the product to dissolve when mixed with water. U.S. Extra Grade is the only grade for instant nonfat dry milk.

Regular nonfat dry milk, dry whole milk, dry buttermilk, and dry whey are generally sold to producers of ice cream, bakery products, meat products, and manufacturers of blended food products. Characteristics evaluated to determine grades of these products are similar to those used for instant nonfat dry milk. For other dairy products, such as cottage cheese and pasteurized process cheese, USDA has a quality-approved shield which may appear on the carton if the products comply with established quality criteria.

The shield-shaped mark found on dairy products indicates the products have been evaluated by USDA. The term "Grade A" without the shield-shaped mark means the products meet Grade A production and processing requirements of the State, county, and municipality where they were produced. It often appears on containers of fresh fluid milk and milk products. Local requirements based on recommendations of the U.S. Public Health Service encourage a high level of milk sanitation and promote greater uniformity of product and production requirements.

Fish — Unlike other food discussed in this chapter, fishery products are the responsibility of the U.S. Department of Commerce (DOC), National Marine Fisheries Service (NMFS). The Packed Under Federal Inspection (PUFI) Mark identifies those fresh, frozen, or canned products certified by NMFS inspectors or other Federal or State cross-licensed inspectors to be safe, clean, wholesome, and properly labeled.

Grading is an added step in which the quality level of certain products is determined and certified. Grade A means top or best quality and is the only grade labeled on fish products in the supermarket. It means the products are uniform in size, practically free of blemishes and defects, in excellent condition, and possess good flavor for the species. Products of Grade B and C quality usually are marketed without any grade designations.

When buying fresh fish, make sure the fish have bright clear eyes which have not sunk into the head. The fish should be free of odor. Gills should be reddish-pink. The flesh should be firm and spring back when gently pressed with the finger. When buying frozen fishery products, read the label. Make sure the package is intact and unbroken. Avoid packages stacked above the freezing area of the store's display freezer. Take only solidly frozen packages. Avoid packages that show moisture or ice. At home, check the contents. Both breaded and unbreaded products should have a clean, uniform appearance. Individual pieces should be easily separated and not frozen together. Breading or coating should be essentially intact.

Fresh Fruits and Vegetables

Consumers will find fresh produce sold in consumer-size bags, baskets, trays or cartons or in bulk displays where they can select the quality and size desired. U.S. No. 1 is the chief trading grade for fresh produce, and the most likely to be seen on packages of fresh fruits and vegetables. It is also the most prevalent quality produced by nature. A limited amount of U.S. Fancy (the premium quality) is also available, usually in specialty stores at premium prices. Produce most likely to be grade-labeled at retail are apples, carrots, grapefruit, onions, oranges, and potatoes, in packages rather than bulk displays.

Fresh fruits and vegetables are graded primarily on a visual basis. Color, blemishes, shape, and skin texture are among external factors judged according to U.S. standards. The standards define these defects and set limits or tolerances for them. In addition there are limits for off-size fruits and vegetables and internal defects, which are not always evident on the surface but are considered in determining quality. While overall tolerances for defects may be the same in all grades, the severity of defects differs among the grades. For example, an orange may have a scar that is slightly rough, light brown, and about the size of a dime and be considered top quality. However, a rougher, darker, or larger scar could count against the percentage of defects allowed.

When shopping for fresh fruits and vegetables: *Buy in season.* Quality is usually higher, and prices more reasonable, when you buy fruits and vegetables in season. *Buy only what you need.* Home refrigeration makes it possible to keep an adequate supply of most perishable produce on hand, but never buy more than you can properly refrigerate and use without waste — even if the produce is cheaper in quantity. *Do not pinch!* Rough handling of fruits and vegetables while you are selecting them causes spoilage and waste. Such loss to the grocer usually is passed on to the consumer, so your costs go up when produce is carelessly handled. When you must handle a fruit or vegetable to judge its quality, use thoughtful care to prevent injury.

Processed Fruits and Vegetables
U.S. grade standards for canned, frozen, and dried fruits and vegetables and other related products like jams and jellies are generally based on color, uniformity of size, absence of defects, and character (tenderness, texture, and maturity). Flavor is also evaluated. You will find a number of these products grade-labeled for consumers, particularly jams and jellies, and frozen or chilled citrus products. You might find the U.S. grade name by itself or in a shield.

The U.S. grade is a good guide on how to use the fruit or vegetable product. Grade A fruits and vegetables are the best selection when appearance and texture are most important. These fruits and vegetables are carefully selected for color, tenderness, and freedom from blemishes, and they are the most tender, succulent, and flavorful. Grade B fruits and vegetables are good for most uses, and those of Grade C quality are usually a thrifty buy and just right for use in cooking.

You may find processed fruit and vegetable products labeled with a grade name, such as Grade A, without the U.S. in front. In some instances, absence of the U.S. means that quality of the product has not been certified by USDA. Some manufacturers process and grade their products using the voluntary U.S. standards without using the official USDA grading service, and some of these processors then label their products according to grade. If the grade name is used, however, the product must measure up to that quality or it could be considered not truthfully labeled.

In addition many stores, particularly chain stores, carry two or more qualities under their own name labels (private labels) that are usually packed by U.S. grade. The higher the grade, the higher the quality — and sometimes the price.

Food	Current Grade Names		What the Grades Mean
Meat Beef		*USDA PRIME	Very tender, juicy, flavorful; has abundant marbling (flecks of fat within the lean).
		*USDA CHOICE	Quite tender and juicy, good flavor; slightly less marbling than Prime.
		USDA GOOD	Fairly tender; not as juicy and flavorful as Prime and Choice; has least marbling of the three.
Lamb		*USDA PRIME	Very tender, juicy, flavorful; has generous marbling.
		*USDA CHOICE	Tender, juicy, flavorful; has less marbling than Prime.

Food	Current Grade Names	What the Grades Mean
Veal	*USDA PRIME	Juicy and flavorful; little marbling.
	*USDA CHOICE	Quite juicy and flavorful; less marbling than Prime.

Poultry

Chickens Turkeys Ducks Geese	*U.S. Grade A	Fully fleshed and meaty; uniform fat covering; well formed; good, clean appearance.
	U.S. Grade B	Not quite as meaty as A; may have occasional cut or tear in skin; not as attractive as A.
	U.S. Grade C	May have cuts, tears, or bruises; wings may be removed and moderate amounts of trimming of the breast and legs are permitted.

*Indicates grades most often seen at retail

Food	Current Grade Names		What the Grades Mean
Eggs		*U.S. Grade AA	Clean, sound shells; clear and firm whites; yolks practically free of defects; egg covers small area when broken out— yolk is firm and high and white is thick and stands high.
		*U.S. Grade A	The same as AA except egg may cover slightly larger area when broken out and white is not quite as thick.
		U.S. Grade B	Sound shells, may have some stains or shape may be abnormal; white may be weak and yolk enlarged and flattened; egg spreads when broken out.
Dairy Products			
Instant nonfat dry milk		*U.S. Extra Grade	Sweet, pleasing flavor; natural color; dissolves readily in water.

Food	Current Grade Names		What the Grades Mean
Butter		*U.S. Grade AA	Delicate sweet flavor and smooth texture; made from high quality fresh sweet cream.
		*U.S. Grade A	Pleasing flavor; fairly smooth texture; made from fresh cream.
		U.S. Grade B	May have slightly acid flavor or other flavor or body defects.
Cheddar cheese		*U.S. Grade AA	Fine, pleasing Cheddar flavor; smooth, compact texture; uniform color.
		U.S. Grade A	Pleasing flavor; more variation in flavor and texture than AA.

*Indicates grades most often seen at retail

Food	Current Grade Names		What the Grades Mean
Fish		*U.S. Grade A	Uniform in size, practically free of blemishes and defects, in excellent condition, and having good flavor for the species.
		U.S. Grade B	May not be as uniform in size or as free of blemishes or defects as Grade A products; general commercial grade.
		U.S. Grade C	Just as wholesome and nutritious as higher grades; a definite value as thrifty buy for use where appearance is not an important factor.
Fresh Fruits and Vegetables			
The grade is more likely to be found without the shield.		*U.S. Fancy	Premium quality; only a few fruits and vegetables are packed in this grade.
		*U.S. No. 1	Good quality; chief grade for most fruits and vegetables.
		U.S. No. 2	Intermediate quality between No. 1 and No. 3.
		U.S. No. 3	Lowest marketable quality.

Processed Fruits and Vegetables and Related Products

Canned and frozen fruits and vegetables.

U. S. GRADE A

*U.S. Grade A — Tender vegetables and well-ripened fruits with excellent flavor, uniform color and size, and few defects.

U.S. Grade B — Slightly mature vegetables; both fruits and vegetables have good flavor but are slightly less uniform in color and size and may have more defects than A.

U.S. Grade C — Mature vegetables; both fruits and vegetables vary more in flavor, color, and size and have more defects than B.

Dried or dehydrated fruits. Fruit and vegetable juices, canned and frozen. Jams, jellies, preserves. Peanut butter. Honey. Catsup, tomato paste.

U. S. GRADE A

*U.S. Grade A — Very good flavor and color and few defects.

U.S. Grade B — Good flavor and color but not as uniform as A.

U.S. Grade C — Less flavor than B, color not as bright, and more defects.

*Indicates grades most often seen at retail

Better Buymanship – Know Your Labels and Standards

By Elizabeth W. Murphy and Cheryl Garrett

*I*f you bought food for a restaurant chain or other large organization, you would require the food to meet precise specifications and would refuse to accept foods not meeting those specifications. As a consumer, you also need to know that foods you buy will be what you expect them to be.

Food manufacturers, food regulators, and the public all must have some agreement on what a food should be like and what it should be made from if it is to be acceptable in the marketplace. This mutual understanding is promoted by requiring foods to meet established product standards and to be clearly labeled with terms that do not mislead. Most Federal standards are for processed foods which contain more than one ingredient. Federal standards assure consumers that foods meet established specifications — whether they are sold in Salem, Massachusetts, or Salem, Oregon; in the country or in the city. (To help the food industry and consumers in buying *unprocessed* foods — fresh meat, fresh poultry, raw vegetables and fruits, and eggs — and dairy products, quality grades have been developed.)

At the Federal level, the job of setting standards and making sure that foods are accurately labeled belongs to the U.S. Department of Agriculture's Food Safety and Inspection Service (FSIS) and the U.S. Department of Health and Human Services' Food and Drug Administration (FDA). FSIS has authority over all products containing more than 3 percent fresh red meat or at least 2 percent cooked red meat or poultry meat, and FDA has responsibility over most other food products. State and local governments also issue standards for some foods.

Almost all standards enforced by FSIS are called "standards of composition." These standards state the minimum amount of meat and poultry required in a product. For example, for a product to be labeled "chicken a la king," its ingredients must include at least 20 percent cooked chicken meat. The manufacturer may, if he wishes, use more than the required amount of meat or poultry or add other ingredients to make the product unique, when preparing a food to meet a standard of composition.

"Standards of identity," on the other hand, set specific requirements for a food's makeup — that is, they are similar

Elizabeth W. Murphy is Chief of the Nutrition Branch, Food Ingredient Assessment Division, Food Safety and Inspection Service (FSIS).

Cheryl Garrett is a Food Technologist with the Standards and Labeling Division, FSIS.

to a recipe. For FSIS-regulated products, these requirements include the kind and minimum amount of meat or poultry; frequently, the maximum amount of fat or water; and any other ingredients allowed. Corned beef hash and chopped ham are two FSIS-regulated products that have standards of identity. Standards written by FDA are mostly standards of identity. FDA has issued standards of identity for more than 200 basic food items, including such familiar foods as enriched bread, margarine, mayonnaise, and ice cream.

Varying the Hash — Although standards of identity are more precise than standards of composition, it is still possible for manufacturers to produce distinctive products which meet the standard of identity. For example, corned beef hash must contain at least 35 percent beef (cooked basis), potatoes, curing agents, and seasonings, and may contain certain optional ingredients — onions, garlic, hydrolyzed plant protein, monosodium glutamate (MSG), and others. However, the potatoes may be in several forms, varying combinations of cures and seasoning are allowed, and more than the minimum amount of meat may be used. Therefore, although all products labeled "corned beef hash" would have the same basic characteristics, they could also vary considerably from brand to brand in flavor, texture, and other features influencing consumer acceptability.

For some standards of identity, the number of optional ingredients is much smaller than for corned beef hash. For instance, ingredients in brick cheese can vary only in terms of the kind of milk — cream, skim milk, concentrated skim milk, or nonfat dry milk — or clotting enzymes, and the optional use of artificial coloring, mold inhibitors (in sliced

cheese) and calcium salts (to aid in curd setting). Thus, you can expect various brands of brick cheese to be more alike than various brands of corned beef hash.

Standards for Quality and Fill

Standards of quality are issued by FDA. These standards set minimum specifications for factors such as tenderness, color, and freedom from defects in canned fruits and vegetables. FDA's quality standards limit defects like the "string" in green beans, excessive peel in tomatoes, hardness in peas, "soupiness" in cream-style corn, and pits in pitted canned cherries. These standards, which are mandatory, are different from USDA's voluntary quality grades for canned fruits and vegetables.

Fill-of-container standards set requirements as to how much material must be in a container of food. The requirements differ for different foods. Some, such as those for canned mushrooms, specify minimum weights of solid food that must be present after the drainable liquid has been poured off (referred to as minimum drained weight). Some simply require that the container, with or without added liquid, must be filled with the solid ingredients to a maximum that allows the lid to be attached and the food processed without crushing or breaking the solid ingredient. Canned cherries and peaches are foods with this kind of standard.

For some foods — canned fruit cocktail, for example — the required minimum fill is the weight of the total food, calculated as a percent of the weight of a volume of water that fills the container. Foods which fail to meet FDA's standards for quality or fill-of-container requirements may be sold, but only if they are appropriately labeled as substandard to inform the purchaser.

State or Local — For some foods which are locally processed, State or local standards are in effect. Fluid milk and milk products are frequently regulated at the State or local level. Federal standards for these products would take precedence if they entered into interstate commerce.

All States, the District of Columbia, and Puerto Rico provide standards for the composition of fluid milk and fluid milk products. For the most part, their standards are similar to Federal standards established by FDA for milk and milk products entering interstate commerce. These standards establish the amounts of milk fat and milk solids to be contained in various kinds of fluid milk and milk products. In addition, most States have established the amounts of vitamins A and D that can or must be present in fluid milk and milk products. Most States follow the FDA standards specifying that 400 International Units (IU) of vitamin D and 2,000 IU of vitamin A be present in each quart of fluid milk.

Many States also set standards for creams, yogurt, canned and dry milk products, ice cream and similar frozen desserts, and various kinds of cheeses. For example, standards for most cheeses and cheese products set minimum percentages for milk fat and maximum percentages for moisture. Information on Federal and State standards for dairy products is updated periodically and published by the U.S. Department of Agriculture (USDA). You can find out about your own State's requirements by contacting a State regulatory agency such as

your State department of agriculture or public health service.

Labeling of Processed Foods

All processed foods, whether or not they have standards of identity or composition, are required by Federal Law to be truthfully and accurately labeled. FSIS approves all labels used on federally inspected meat and poultry products before they are used on those products. This procedure — known as prior label approval — includes a review of the product's ingredients and manufacturing process. As a result, in addition to preventing inaccurate or misleading labels, the prior label approval procedure can support in-plant inspection in assuring that meat and poultry products are wholesome and unadulterated.

FSIS requires up to six labeling features on all labels for meat and poultry products: the product name, a USDA mark of inspection, the net weight or net contents, the firm's name and address, an ingredients statement for products prepared with two or more ingredients, and special handling information for perishable products. FDA also requires similar features to be shown on all labels for food products under its jurisdiction. These are the product name, the net weight or net contents, the firm's name and address, and an ingredients statement for most products.

The product name must be the name as defined by a USDA or FDA standard, the product's common or usual name, or a descriptive name. The name must accurately represent the product and must not be false or misleading to the consumer. Thus, a product accurately labeled "Beef with Gravy" contains more beef than gravy. The product name always appears on the label's principal display panel, which is that area of the label displayed to the consumer at the time the product is selected from the shelf or bin.

The net weight stated on the label must be an accurate measure of the contents, stated in pounds and/or ounces. The weight of the container is not included. Metric measures may also be listed, but may not replace the conventional measures. The net weight declaration must be located on the principal display panel.

The ingredients statement is a listing of ingredients in descending order of predominance — from most to least, according to their weight in the product recipe. USDA and FDA policies are consistent in listing ingredients this way on the label. Spices and flavorings may be grouped together and listed simply as *spices* and *flavorings*. The use of preservatives or artificial colors or flavors is always indicated in the list of ingredients. The ingredients statement appears on the principal display panel or on the information panel (the first usable surface to the right of the principal display panel).

Meat and Poultry Products

FSIS requires labels of meat and poultry products prepared from two or more ingredients to include ingredients lists. FDA operates under a different set of laws, and does not have authority to require the listing of ingredients which are mandatory under the product's standard of identity. However, many product standards allow manufacturers to add optional ingredients to foods, and these optional ingredients must be listed on the label. Many FDA standards have recently been revised to increase the number of

foods for which ingredients statements must be made.

A USDA inspection mark and establishment number must appear on all packaged meat or poultry products that have been federally inspected and approved for wholesomeness. State inspection marks are required on State-inspected meat and poultry products, which cannot be shipped from one State to another. The inspection mark on most labels is located on the principal display panel. On labels of cylindrical cans it is also allowed to appear on the information panel.

The establishment number indicates the plant where the product was produced and is often located in or near the mark of inspection. Since many companies have more than one production plant, including the establishment number in any letters you might write about a company's product will help to trace that product. The establishment number can also tell you if two products with different brand names were made in the same plant. FDA does not require an inspection mark or establishment number on labels of foods it regulates.

The firm's name and address may be that of the manufacturer, packer, or distributor of the product. It is located on the label's principal display panel or information panel. FSIS requires special handling instructions on labels of packaged products that need special handling to maintain their wholesomeness. For example, *Keep Frozen* or *Keep Refrigerated* appears on some perishable products.

Country of origin must be shown on labels of imported meat and meat products if they are sold in the same form in

In addition to the features required to appear on meat and poultry product labels, FSIS has set requirements for optional label features. Photographs or artwork used on meat and poultry product labels must accurately represent contents of the package as purchased or after preparation. For example, if five slices of meat are shown, there must be at least that number of slices inside the container. If garnishes or side dishes pictured on the label are not part of the contents, a phrase such as "suggested serving" must appear nearby. Similarly, a product's ingredients may not be misrepresented; a picture of a fresh onion may not appear if, in fact, dehydrated onions were used in the product.

USDA grade names or shields indicate the quality of many foods. The grade mark is used only on foods that have been officially graded according to Federal quality standards, which define exactly what each grade means. In the case of meat and poultry, grading is done only on products which have passed inspection for wholesomeness.

Open dating is a system of labeling food packages with calendar dates. Open dating is not mandatory under Federal law, but over 20 States require it, and a number of manufacturers and retailers provide the information voluntarily. For this reason, what the date means and where you find it often vary. Open dating may indicate: the date the food was packaged, the last date a product should be sold to allow reasonable home storage time, or the date after which the food is no longer at its most acceptable level of quality.

FSIS requires companies that use open

Universal Product Code

Product Name

Brand Name

US

Net Weight

Ingredients Statement

Firm's Name and Address

USDA Inspection Legend

which they are imported (such as canned ham). However, imported meat used as an ingredient in a meat product manufactured in the United States loses its identity. For example, if foreign beef is combined with domestic beef in producing frankfurters or other types of sausage, the country of origin of the foreign beef is not identified on the label.

In addition to the required label features, FSIS and FDA require that packaging does not give a false impression of the product's contents or quality. For example, one unacceptable practice — the use of red color on transparent bacon wrappers — could give shoppers the impression the bacon is leaner than it really is.

States	Product
Alabama	Dairy
California	Dairy
Connecticut	Milk
District of Columbia	Perishable Products
Florida	Dairy
Georgia	Milk, Eggs
Maryland	Milk
Massachusetts	Perishable & Long Shelf Life Products
Michigan	Perishable Products
Minnesota	Perishable Products
Nebraska	Eggs
Nevada	Dairy
New Hampshire	Cream
New Jersey	Dairy
New Mexico	Milk
Ohio	Perishable Products
Oklahoma	Meat, Eggs
Oregon	Perishable Products
Pennsylvania	Milk
Virginia	Dairy, Infant Formula
Washington	Dairy, others
Wisconsin	Smoked Fish

before or after you buy it, the chances are it won't measure up to your expectations, regardless of the date on the package.

Nutrition Labeling Format

Nutrition labeling is required by FDA only if a food has had nutrients added to it or a nutrition claim is made about the food. FDA regulations set forth the format, which includes the following information: the size of one serving expressed in common household measures or recognized portions such as ounces, cups, slices, pieces; the number of servings per container; the number of calories and the number of grams of protein, carbohydrate, and fat in a serving and percentages of the U.S. Recommended Daily Allowance (U.S. RDA) of protein, five vitamins, and two minerals. The vitamins and minerals are vitamin A, vitamin C, thiamine, riboflavin, niacin, calcium, and iron. (FDA also proposed in June 1982 to require that sodium be included on all nutrition labels.)

dating to explain on the label the meaning of the calendar date. For example, "For maximum freshness, use by (month and day)" may appear on a package of refrigerated luncheon meat. FDA has no requirements for how the information should be presented. Twenty-one States and the District of Columbia had guidelines for providing open date information on food labels in 1978.

While open dating is helpful — to store personnel when rotating stock, to you when you shop and when you rotate items at home — it has its limitations. If an item has not been properly stored

Nutrition Information

serving size	2 slices
servings per container	4
calories	120
protein	3
carbohydrate	18
fat	4

None of the nutrition labeling information may be omitted. However, FDA's nutrition format may be supplemented with information on other nutrients of interest to consumers, such as fatty acids and cholesterol.

For nutrition labeling on meat and poultry products, FSIS accepts the FDA format and also an abbreviated format which includes only the number of calories and the number of grams of protein, fat, and carbohydrate per serving of product. Other nutrients such as sodium may also be included. Both FDA and FSIS allow foods to be labeled for sodium alone. Some nutrient claims may appear on meat and poultry labels without requiring nutritional labeling. A comparative statement such as, "This product contains no more than ____% fat whereas the USDA standard for frankfurters allows 30% fat," has been approved. Statements like these are often accompanied by claims such as "lower fat" or "less fat."

Other labeling features sometimes seen on labels are the Universal Product Code (UPC) and Kosher symbols. The Universal Product Code is a national system of product identification used to make food marketing, wholesaling, and retailing easier. The UPC symbols consist of a small block of parallel lines and numbers unique to every product on which they appear. In supermarkets with computer systems, checkout clerks scan the symbols with a laser beam device that sends a message to the store's central computer. The name and price of the item are flashed on the terminal at the checkout counter and printed on the customer's receipt. The product code does not include price information — that comes from the store's computer.

Kosher symbols identify foods prepared according to Jewish dietary laws and certified by specified rabbis (religious leaders) or organizations. The koshering process for meat and poultry includes salting and soaking to remove the blood. Some of the commonly used trademarked symbols include: k, (K), and (U). None of the symbols are required by FDA or USDA.

State and Local Labeling

Many State and local governments have requirements for labeling food products. Often these requirements are similar to Federal labeling regulations. State and local governments do not generally have labeling requirements for all foods. Often they have regulations or guidelines for labeling only specific categories of food products such as fresh meat and poultry or dairy products. For meat and poultry products, State labeling requirements must be consistent with those of FSIS. For information on the labeling requirements for food products in your State, contact your State Department of Agriculture.

The requirement of the Pennsylvania Department of Agriculture for labeling bakery products is an example of State labeling requirements. The Pennsylvania Department of Agriculture requires that all bakery products sold in that State have on their labels the words "Registered Pennsylvania Department of Agriculture" or the abbreviation "REG. PENNA. DEPT. AGR." Among other things, the statement assures consumers that the product was produced in a bakery which is properly licensed and registered with the State of Pennsylvania. The product must also conform to other requirements set by the Pennsylvania Department of Agriculture.

At the local level, many retailers use the National Livestock and Meat Board's Uniform Retail Meat Identity Standards as a basis for labeling fresh cuts of beef, veal, pork, and lamb. The Uniform Retail Meat Identity Standards are recommended names for various meat cuts and were developed to provide consistency to the labeling of 300 fresh meat cuts for which there are over 1,000 existing names. Use of these recommended names assures you that the beef round steak in one store is the same cut of meat as the beef round steak sold in another store. FSIS accepts the names recommended in the Uniform Retail Meat Identity Standards for labeling meat cuts sold in interstate commerce.

Sodium Labels — Consumer interest in the sodium content of their diets has increased greatly in the past year. Much of this interest is the result of scientific and medical concern about the possible contribution of dietary sodium to the development of high blood pressure.

Sodium in the diet comes from several sources. It may be found naturally in food or added during processing, during cooking, or at the table. Most added sodium comes from salt (sodium chloride), but many common food ingredients such as baking soda, sodium nitrite, and monosodium glutamate (MSG) also contain sodium. Because of the use of these and other sodium-containing ingredients, processed foods are usually higher in sodium than fresh or raw foods.

For consumers who want to watch their sodium intake, the food label can help. Many manufacturers voluntarily provide sodium content information on the label.

Labels that have specific claims about the product's salt or sodium content, such as "low sodium," must also have sodium content information on the label. When sodium content is declared, it is listed as milligrams of sodium per serving, with the size of the serving also given. The sodium content includes the sodium in both raw ingredients and those added during processing. On labels where the sodium content is not given, the ingredients statement can give consumers an idea of how many sodium-containing ingredients are present.

For Further Reading

Shopper's Guide, 1974 Yearbook of Agriculture. For sale by Superintendent of Documents, U.S. Government Printing Office, Washington, DC 20402.

A Consumer's Guide to Food Labels, HHS Publication No. (FDA) 77-2083, 1979. Contact FDA, Office of Consumer Affairs (HFE-88), 5600 Fishers Lane, Rockville, MD 20857, for information on how to obtain copies.

Metric Measures and the Consumer, HHS Publication No. (FDA) 76-1018, 1977. Contact FDA, Office of Consumer Affairs (HFE-88), 5600 Fishers Lane, Rockville, MD 20857, for information on how to obtain copies.

Primer on Three Nutrients, HHS Publication No. (FDA) 81-2026, 1981. Contact FDA, Office of Consumer Affairs (HFE-88), 5600 Fishers Lane, Rockville, MD 20857, for information on how to obtain copies.

Nutrition Labels and U.S. RDA, HHS Publication No. (FDA) 81-2146, 1981. Contact FDA, Office of Consumer Affairs (HFE-88), 5600 Fishers Lane, Rockville, MD 20857, for information on how to obtain copies.

Cost Comparison Tools to Stretch Your Food Dollar

By Cynthia Cromwell Junker

Americans are increasingly concerned about food prices and good nutrition. The wise use of food dollars is a challenge to most consumers, regardless of income. For those on a limited budget, controlling food costs is a continuing concern.

One cost-comparison tool available to most food shoppers is unit pricing. Many stores show the cost per unit — ounce, pound, or pint — on the display shelf or above the display compartment. You can use the unit price to find the lowest cost per unit among different brands and size containers of a food.

If unit prices are not posted in your store, you can figure them out for yourself. On the label of the food container find the net weight or volume of the contents in ounces or fluid ounces. Divide the price by the number of ounces to find the cost per ounce of food. Example: for crackers in a 7-ounce box at 42 cents, $42 \div 7 = 6$ cents per ounce. For a 16-ounce box at 48 cents, $48 \div 16 = 3$ cents per ounce. The larger box is a better buy if you can use the crackers before they go stale.

A second way to stretch food dollars is to compare the cost of various foods you might serve, and choose the least costly

ones. The tables in this chapter have been prepared to help a highly motivated cost-cutter find the best buy.

Vegetable and fruit bargains can be found in several departments of the store, including the fresh produce, canned goods, frozen foods, and dried food sections. Some stores have a special area for generic foods — those not brand labeled — which are usually priced below store or nationally advertised brands.

To find the best buys, consider the cost of amounts of various vegetables and fruits you would buy to provide equal-size servings. This is tricky because some foods you buy have parts you don't eat; others are all edible. The tables will help you compare the costs of equal-size servings of vegetables and fruits.

Find the vegetable or fruit you plan to serve in the first column. Then find the market form and the size of the market unit you plan to buy in the second and third columns. Size of market units are shown by customary weight or volume, such as pound (lb), ounce (oz), fluid ounce (fl. oz).

Follow the line of numbers next to the name and market information to the column headed by the price most like the

Cynthia Cromwell Junker was a Home Economist with the Consumer Nutrition Center, Human Nutrition Information Service.

price of the market unit at your store. The number located there is the approximate cost of a ½-cup serving, or a serving as specified in the first column. Similarly, find the cost of a serving of other vegetables or fruits that might be served. To cut costs, use the one with the lowest cost per ½-cup serving. Big eaters, of course, may want more than ½-cup servings of vegetables and fruits.

Here are some examples: 1) When fresh carrots cost 40 cents a pound, ½ cup of cooked sliced carrots costs 8 cents. One-half cup of carrots from a frozen 20-ounce package priced at 90 cents costs 12 cents. The fresh carrots are the better buy. 2) One-half cup of applesauce from a 16-ounce can priced at 50 cents costs 14 cents; ½ cup of sliced bananas at 40 cents a pound costs 10 cents. Bananas are the better buy.

Meat, Poultry, and Fish

Meat, poultry, and fish items in meals usually cost more than other foods. But the range in prices of different types and cuts of meat is great, so careful selection can result in worthwhile savings. When you plan, consider the price per pound and how much meat the pound provides after it is cooked and after you discard the parts you do not eat, such as bones and fat.

The meat, poultry, and fish table will help you compare costs of equally sized servings of cooked lean meat from different types and cuts of meat, poultry, and fish. To use the table, locate in the first column the item you plan to buy. Follow the line on which it appears across to the column headed by the price most like the current price at your market. The figure at this point is the approximate cost of a 3-ounce serving of

cooked lean meat. As examples, the cost of a 3-ounce serving of lean from a chuck roast (bone-in) priced at $1.60 a pound is 71 cents; and from ground beef at $1.70 a pound, the cost of an equally sized serving is 44 cents.

Chicken is one of the more economical main dish foods. However, the form in which it is purchased often determines how good a bargain it is. The table for chicken can be used to estimate the added cost, if any, of using chicken parts rather than the whole chicken. Each line shows prices at which ready-to-cook whole chicken and different chicken parts are equally good buys.

For example, the table shows that breast halves with ribs at $1.02 a pound, drumsticks and thighs at 88 cents a pound, drumsticks at 86 cents a pound, thighs at 93 cents a pound, and wings at 50 cents a pound provide as much chicken meat for the money as ready-to-cook whole chicken at 73 cents a pound. Any amount above these prices for parts — when ready-to-cook whole chicken is 73 cents — pays only for the convenience of having the parts of the chicken you prefer.

The table can also be used to determine which of several chicken parts is the best to buy. For example, prices of drumsticks and thighs might be compared as follows: Locate the store price of drumsticks ($.95) in the column headed "Drumstick." Compare the price in the "Thigh" column on the same line ($1.03) to the store price of thighs. If the store price is lower than $1.03, thighs are the better buy; if the store price is higher than $1.03, drumsticks are the better buy.

Vegetables

Cost of ½-cup serving[1] of selected vegetables purchased at specified prices per market unit – canned, dried, fresh, and frozen

Vegetable, as served (cooked and drained, unless specified)	Market form	Market unit	30
Beans, green or wax	canned	15½ oz	8
	fresh	lb	5
	frozen	20 oz	4
Beans, lima	canned	16 oz	8
	fresh, in pod	lb	13
	frozen	10 oz	9
Beets, sliced	canned	16 oz	9
	fresh, no tops	lb	9
Broccoli, cuts	fresh	lb	5
	frozen	20 oz	5
Brussels sprouts	fresh	1 qt (16 oz)	5
	frozen	10 oz	8
Cabbage, wedges	fresh	lb	8
raw, shredded	fresh	lb	2
sauerkraut	canned	16 oz	5
Carrots, sliced or diced	canned	16 oz	8
sliced	fresh, no tops	lb	6
raw, sliced	fresh, no tops	lb	5
sliced	frozen	20 oz	4
Cauliflower	fresh	lb	5
	frozen	10 oz	10
Celery, diced	fresh	24-oz bunch	5
Corn, cream-style	canned	16 oz	9
whole-kernel	canned (vacuum)	12 oz	9
	canned (liquid)	16 oz	8
	frozen	10 oz	9
1 medium ear	fresh	doz	2
Cucumbers, raw, sliced	fresh	10 oz	9

[1] Except where serving size is specified in first column.
[2] Partly trimmed.

Price per market unit (cents)

40	50	60	70	80	90	100	110	120	130
				Cost of ½-cup serving (cents)					
11	14	17	20	22	25	28	31	34	36
7	9	11	13	14	16	18	20	22	23
6	8	9	11	12	14	15	16	18	20
11	14	17	20	22	25	28	31	34	36
17	21	25	29	34	38	42	46	50	55
12	14	17	20	23	26	29	32	35	38
12	14	17	20	23	26	29	32	35	38
12	15	18	21	24	27	30	33	36	39
7	9	11	13	14	16	18	20	22	23
7	9	11	13	14	16	18	20	22	23
7	9	11	13	14	16	18	20	22	23
11	14	17	20	22	25	28	31	34	36
10	13	16	18	21	23	26	29	31	34
3	4	5	6	6	7	8	9	10	10
7	8	10	12	14	15	17	19	20	22
11	14	16	19	22	24	27	30	32	35
8	10	11	13	15	17	19	21	23	25
6	8	10	11	13	14	16	18	19	21
5	6	8	9	10	12	13	14	16	17
7	9	11	13	14	16	18	20	22	23
14	17	20	24	27	31	34	37	41	44
7	8	10	12	14	15	17	19	20	22
12	14	17	20	23	26	29	32	35	38
12	16	19	22	25	28	31	34	37	40
11	14	17	20	22	25	28	31	34	36
12	14	17	20	23	26	29	32	35	38
3	4	5	6	6	7	8	9	10	10
12	15	18	21	24	27	30	33	36	39

Vegetables

Cost of ½-cup serving[1] of selected vegetables purchased at specified prices per market unit – canned, dried, fresh, and frozen

Vegetable, as served (cooked and drained, unless specified)	Market form	Market unit	30
Greens:			
Collards	fresh	lb	5
	frozen	10 oz	10
Kale	fresh	lb	5
Kale or mustard greens	frozen	10 oz	8
Spinach	fresh[2]	10 oz	11
	frozen	10 oz	18
Turnip greens	frozen	10 oz	10
Lettuce, raw, shredded	fresh	16-oz head	2
Onions:			
green, raw, sliced	fresh	lb	9
mature, raw, chopped	fresh	lb	6
Peas, green	canned	16 oz	9
	fresh, in pod	lb	15
	frozen	20 oz	5
Potatoes, whole	canned	15 oz	10
whole, 1 medium	fresh	lb	10
diced	fresh	lb	7
mashed	dehydrated flakes	16 oz	1
mashed	fresh	lb	7
French fries	frozen	9 oz	9
Squash:			
summer, yellow	fresh	lb	7
	frozen	10 oz	12
winter, mashed	fresh	lb	14
	frozen	10 oz	14
Sweetpotatoes	canned (sirup)	16 oz	11
	canned (vacuum)	17 oz	8
slices	fresh	lb	6
Tomatoes	canned	16 oz	8
raw, sliced	fresh	lb	7
Turnips, diced	fresh	lb	7

[1] Except where serving size is specified in first column.
[2] Partly trimmed.

Price per market unit (cents)

40	50	60	70	80	90	100	110	120	130
				Cost of ½-cup serving (cents)					
7	8	10	12	14	15	17	19	20	22
14	17	20	24	27	31	34	37	41	44
6	8	10	11	13	14	16	18	19	21
11	14	16	19	22	24	27	30	32	35
15	18	22	26	30	33	37	41	44	48
24	30	35	41	47	53	59	65	71	77
13	16	20	23	26	30	33	36	40	43
3	4	4	5	6	6	7	8	8	9
12	15	18	21	24	27	30	33	36	39
8	10	13	15	17	19	21	23	25	27
12	14	17	20	23	26	29	32	35	38
20	25	30	35	40	45	50	55	60	65
7	8	10	12	14	15	17	19	20	22
13	16	19	22	26	29	32	35	38	42
13	16	20	23	26	30	33	36	40	43
9	12	14	16	18	21	23	25	28	30
2	2	2	3	3	4	4	4	5	5
10	12	14	17	19	22	24	26	29	31
12	15	18	21	24	27	30	33	36	39
10	12	14	17	19	22	24	26	29	31
16	20	25	29	33	37	41	45	49	53
19	24	28	33	38	42	47	52	56	61
18	23	28	32	37	41	46	51	55	60
14	18	21	24	28	32	35	38	42	46
11	14	17	20	22	25	28	31	34	36
8	10	12	14	16	18	20	22	24	26
10	13	16	18	21	23	26	29	31	34
10	12	14	17	19	22	24	26	29	31
9	12	14	16	18	21	23	25	28	30

Fruits

**Cost of ½-cup serving[1] of selected fruits purchased at specified prices
per market unit – canned, dried, fresh, and frozen**

Fruit or juice as served (fruit without juice or sirup)	Market form	Market unit	30
Apples, sliced	canned	20 oz	7
raw	fresh	lb	5
Applesauce	canned	16 oz	8
Apricots, halves	canned	30 oz	7
cooked	dried	11 oz	7
uncooked	dried	11 oz	6
pitted	fresh	lb	5
Avocado, cubed	fresh	10 oz	11
Bananas, sliced	fresh	lb	7
Berries	fresh	pint	6
Cantaloup, diced	fresh	24-oz melon	7
wedge, ¼ melon	fresh	24-oz melon	8
Cherries, sweet, unpitted	canned	16 oz	11
sour, pitted	canned	16 oz	9
all varieties, pitted	fresh	lb	6
sour, pitted, sweetened	frozen	12 oz	13
Grapefruit, sections	canned	16 oz	14
sections	fresh	lb	14
½ fruit	fresh	lb	14
Grapes	fresh	lb	6
Juice:			
Any fruit or vegetable	canned or bottled	46 fl oz	3
	canned or bottled	32 fl oz	4
	frozen concentrate	6 fl oz	5
Grapefruit	fresh	lb	17
Orange	fresh	lb	16
Mixed fruit	canned	16 oz	11
Oranges, whole, 1 medium	fresh	doz	2
sections	fresh	doz	3
Orange sections, mandarin	canned	11 oz	15

[1]Except where serving size is specified in first column.

Price per market unit (cents)

40	50	60	70	80	90	100	110	120	130
				Cost of ½-cup serving (cents)					
9	11	13	15	18	20	22	24	26	29
6	8	10	11	13	14	16	18	19	21
11	14	17	20	22	25	28	31	34	36
10	12	14	17	19	22	24	26	29	31
9	11	13	15	18	20	22	24	26	29
8	10	12	14	16	18	20	22	24	26
7	9	11	13	14	16	18	20	22	23
15	18	22	26	30	33	37	41	44	48
10	12	14	17	19	22	24	26	29	31
8	10	13	15	17	19	21	23	25	27
9	12	14	16	18	21	23	25	28	30
10	12	15	18	20	22	25	28	30	32
14	18	22	25	29	32	36	40	43	47
12	14	17	20	23	26	29	32	35	38
8	10	11	13	15	17	19	21	23	25
18	22	26	31	35	40	44	48	53	57
18	23	28	32	37	41	46	51	55	60
19	24	29	34	38	43	48	53	58	62
18	23	28	32	37	41	46	51	55	60
8	10	12	14	16	18	20	22	24	26
4	4	5	6	7	8	9	10	11	12
5	6	7	8	10	11	12	13	14	16
7	8	10	12	14	15	17	19	20	22
23	28	34	40	46	51	57	63	68	74
22	27	32	38	43	49	54	59	65	70
14	18	21	24	28	32	35	38	42	46
3	4	5	6	6	7	8	9	10	10
4	5	7	8	9	10	11	12	13	14
20	24	29	34	39	44	49	54	59	64

Fruits

Cost of ½-cup serving[1] of selected fruits purchased at specified prices per market unit – canned, dried, fresh, and frozen

Fruit or juice as served (fruit without juice or sirup)	Market form	Market unit	30
Peaches, halves or slices	canned	29 oz	7
halves, cooked	dried	8 oz	9
uncooked	dried	8 oz	12
slices	fresh	lb	8
	frozen	10 oz	18
Pears, halves	canned	16 oz	13
slices	fresh	lb	7
Pineapple, chunks or slices	canned	20 oz	8
diced	fresh	2½-lb fruit	4
Plums, whole	canned	30 oz	8
halves or slices	fresh	lb	6
Prunes, whole	canned	16 oz	10
pitted, cooked	dried	12 oz	7
uncooked	dried	12 oz	8
unpitted, cooked	dried	16 oz	5
uncooked	dried	16 oz	6
Raisins, cooked	dried	15 oz	4
uncooked	dried	15 oz	5
Rhubarb, cooked, sweetened	fresh	lb	8
	frozen	16 oz	6
Strawberries, whole, hulled	fresh	pint	7
sliced	frozen	10 oz	21
whole	frozen	12 oz	15
Tangerine, sections or whole, 1 medium	fresh	doz	2
Watermelon, diced	fresh	lb	10

[1] Except where serving size is specified in first column.

Price per market unit (cents)

40	50	60	70	80	90	100	110	120	130
				Cost of ½-cup serving (cents)					
9	12	14	16	18	21	23	25	28	30
12	15	18	21	24	27	30	33	36	39
16	20	23	27	31	35	39	43	47	51
10	12	15	18	20	22	25	28	30	32
24	30	36	42	48	54	60	66	72	78
17	21	25	29	34	38	42	46	50	55
10	12	14	17	19	22	24	26	29	31
11	14	16	19	22	24	27	30	32	35
5	6	7	8	10	11	12	13	14	16
10	13	16	18	21	23	26	29	31	34
8	10	12	14	16	18	20	22	24	26
13	16	20	23	26	30	33	36	40	43
10	12	14	17	19	22	24	26	29	31
10	12	15	18	20	22	25	28	30	32
7	8	10	12	14	15	17	19	20	22
8	10	11	13	15	17	19	21	23	25
5	6	7	8	10	11	12	13	14	16
7	8	10	12	14	15	17	19	20	22
10	13	16	18	21	23	26	29	31	34
8	10	11	13	15	17	19	21	23	25
10	12	14	17	19	22	24	26	29	31
28	35	42	49	56	63	70	77	84	91
20	26	31	36	41	46	51	56	61	66
3	4	5	6	6	7	8	9	10	10
14	17	20	24	27	31	34	37	41	44

Cost of 3 ounces of cooked lean from selected kinds and cuts of meat, poultry, and fish at specified retail prices

Kind and cut	.50	.60	.70	.80	.90	1.00	1.10	1.20	1.30	1.40	1.50	1.60	1.70
						Price per pound[1] (dollars)							
						Cost of 3 ounces (dollars)							
Beef: Brisket, bone out	.20	.24	.28	.33	.37	.41	.45	.49	.53	.57	.61	.65	.69
Chuck, bone in	.22	.27	.31	.36	.40	.45	.49	.54	.58	.62	.67	.71	.76
Chuck, bone out	.17	.21	.24	.28	.31	.35	.38	.42	.45	.48	.52	.56	.59
Ground lean	.13	.16	.18	.21	.23	.26	.29	.31	.34	.36	.39	.42	.44
Porterhouse steak, bone in	.26	.31	.36	.42	.47	.52	.57	.62	.68	.73	.78	.83	.88
Rib roast, bone in	.22	.27	.31	.36	.40	.45	.49	.54	.58	.62	.67	.71	.76
Round, bone in	.17	.20	.23	.27	.30	.34	.37	.40	.44	.47	.50	.54	.57
Round, bone out	.16	.19	.22	.25	.28	.31	.34	.37	.40	.44	.47	.50	.53
Rump roast, bone out	.17	.20	.24	.27	.31	.34	.38	.41	.44	.48	.51	.54	.58
Short ribs	.29	.35	.41	.47	.53	.59	.64	.70	.76	.82	.88	.94	1.00
Sirloin steak, bone in	.21	.26	.30	.34	.38	.43	.47	.51	.55	.60	.64	.68	.72
Sirloin steak, bone out	.20	.23	.27	.31	.35	.39	.43	.47	.51	.55	.59	.62	.66
T-bone steak, bone in	.28	.33	.38	.44	.50	.55	.61	.66	.72	.77	.83	.88	.94
Fish: Filets, fresh or frozen	.13	.16	.19	.21	.24	.27	.29	.32	.35	.38	.40	.43	.46
Steaks, fresh or frozen, backbone in	.14	.17	.20	.23	.26	.28	.31	.34	.37	.40	.43	.45	.48
Tuna, canned[1]	.23	.28	.32	.37	.41	.46	.51	.55	.60	.64	.69	.74	.78
Lamb: Leg roast, bone in	.21	.25	.29	.33	.38	.42	.46	.50	.54	.58	.62	.67	.71
Loin chop, bone in	.23	.27	.32	.36	.41	.46	.50	.55	.59	.64	.68	.73	.78
Rib chop, bone in	.28	.33	.38	.44	.50	.55	.61	.66	.72	.77	.83	.88	.94
Shoulder roast, bone in	.23	.27	.32	.36	.41	.46	.50	.55	.59	.64	.68	.73	.78
Liver: Beef	.14	.16	.19	.22	.24	.27	.30	.33	.35	.38	.41	.44	.46
Chicken	.14	.17	.20	.23	.26	.29	.32	.34	.37	.40	.43	.46	.49
Pork: Butt, cured, bone in	.18	.22	.25	.29	.32	.36	.40	.43	.47	.50	.54	.58	.61
Ham, cured: whole, bone in	.17	.21	.24	.28	.31	.35	.38	.42	.45	.48	.52	.56	.59
whole, bone out	.13	.16	.18	.21	.23	.26	.29	.31	.34	.36	.39	.42	.44
slices	.16	.19	.22	.25	.28	.31	.34	.37	.40	.44	.47	.50	.53
canned	.12	.15	.18	.20	.22	.25	.28	.30	.32	.35	.38	.40	.42
Loin, fresh: chops, bone in	.22	.27	.31	.36	.40	.45	.49	.54	.58	.62	.67	.71	.76
roast, bone in	.25	.30	.35	.40	.46	.51	.56	.61	.66	.71	.76	.81	.86
roast, bone out	.17	.21	.24	.28	.31	.35	.38	.42	.45	.48	.52	.56	.59
Picnics: cured, bone in	.23	.27	.32	.36	.41	.46	.50	.55	.59	.64	.68	.73	.78
cured, bone out	.18	.21	.25	.28	.32	.35	.39	.42	.46	.50	.53	.57	.60
fresh, bone in	.27	.32	.38	.43	.48	.54	.59	.64	.70	.75	.80	.86	.91
Rib chops, fresh, bone in	.25	.30	.35	.40	.46	.51	.56	.61	.66	.71	.76	.81	.86

[1] For tuna fish, use price for 6.5-ounce can.

						Price per pound[1] (dollars)										
1.80	1.90	2.00	2.10	2.20	2.30	2.40	2.50	2.60	2.70	2.80	2.90	3.00	3.10	3.20	3.30	3.40
						Cost of 3 ounces (dollars)										
.73	.78	.82	.86	.90	.94	.98	1.02	1.06	1.10	1.14	1.18	1.22	1.26	1.31	1.35	1.39
.80	.85	.89	.94	.98	1.02	1.07	1.12	1.16	1.20	1.25	1.29	1.34	1.38	1.43	1.47	1.52
.62	.66	.69	.73	.76	.80	.83	.87	.90	.94	.97	1.01	1.04	1.08	1.11	1.15	1.18
.47	.49	.52	.55	.57	.60	.62	.65	.68	.70	.73	.75	.78	.81	.83	.86	.88
.94	.99	1.04	1.09	1.15	1.20	1.25	1.30	1.35	1.41	1.46	1.51	1.56	1.62	1.67	1.72	1.77
.80	.85	.89	.94	.98	1.02	1.07	1.12	1.16	1.20	1.25	1.29	1.34	1.38	1.43	1.47	1.52
.60	.64	.67	.70	.74	.77	.80	.84	.87	.90	.94	.97	1.00	1.04	1.07	1.11	1.14
.56	.59	.62	.66	.69	.72	.75	.78	.81	.84	.87	.90	.94	.97	1.00	1.03	1.06
.61	.65	.68	.72	.75	.78	.82	.85	.89	.92	.95	.99	1.02	1.06	1.09	1.13	1.16
1.05	1.11	1.17	1.23	1.29	1.35	1.41	1.46	1.52	1.58	1.64	1.70	1.76	1.82	1.88	1.93	1.99
.77	.81	.85	.89	.94	.98	1.02	1.06	1.11	1.15	1.19	1.24	1.28	1.32	1.36	1.41	1.45
.70	.74	.78	.82	.86	.90	.94	.98	1.02	1.06	1.09	1.13	1.17	1.21	1.25	1.29	1.33
.99	1.05	1.10	1.16	1.21	1.27	1.32	1.38	1.43	1.49	1.54	1.60	1.65	1.71	1.76	1.82	1.87
.48	.51	.54	.56	.59	.62	.64	.67	.70	.72	.75	.78	.80	.83	.86	.88	.91
.51	.54	.57	.60	.62	.65	.68	.71	.74	.77	.80	.82	.85	.88	.91	.94	.97
.83	.87	.92	.97	1.01	1.06	1.10	1.15	1.20	1.24	1.29	1.33	1.38	1.43	1.47	1.52	1.56
.75	.79	.83	.88	.92	.96	1.00	1.04	1.08	1.12	1.17	1.21	1.25	1.29	1.33	1.38	1.42
.82	.87	.91	.96	1.00	1.05	1.10	1.14	1.19	1.23	1.28	1.32	1.37	1.42	1.46	1.51	1.55
.99	1.05	1.10	1.16	1.21	1.27	1.32	1.38	1.43	1.49	1.54	1.60	1.65	1.71	1.76	1.82	1.87
.82	.87	.91	.96	1.00	1.05	1.10	1.14	1.19	1.23	1.28	1.32	1.37	1.42	1.46	1.51	1.55
.49	.52	.54	.57	.60	.62	.65	.68	.71	.73	.76	.79	.82	.84	.87	.90	.92
.52	.55	.58	.60	.63	.66	.69	.72	.75	.78	.81	.84	.86	.89	.92	.95	.98
.65	.68	.72	.76	.79	.83	.87	.90	.94	.97	1.01	1.05	1.08	1.12	1.16	1.19	1.23
.62	.66	.69	.73	.76	.80	.83	.87	.90	.94	.97	1.01	1.04	1.08	1.11	1.15	1.18
.47	.49	.52	.55	.57	.60	.62	.65	.68	.70	.73	.75	.78	.81	.83	.86	.88
.56	.59	.62	.66	.69	.72	.75	.78	.81	.84	.87	.90	.94	.97	1.00	1.03	1.06
.45	.48	.50	.52	.55	.58	.60	.62	.65	.68	.70	.72	.75	.78	.80	.83	.85
.80	.85	.89	.94	.98	1.02	1.07	1.12	1.16	1.20	1.25	1.29	1.34	1.38	1.43	1.47	1.52
.91	.96	1.01	1.06	1.12	1.17	1.22	1.27	1.32	1.37	1.42	1.47	1.52	1.57	1.62	1.67	1.72
.62	.66	.69	.73	.76	.80	.83	.87	.90	.94	.97	1.01	1.04	1.08	1.11	1.15	1.18
.82	.87	.91	.96	1.00	1.05	1.10	1.14	1.19	1.23	1.28	1.32	1.37	1.42	1.46	1.51	1.55
.64	.67	.71	.74	.78	.81	.85	.88	.92	.96	.99	1.03	1.06	1.10	1.13	1.17	1.20
.96	1.02	1.07	1.12	1.18	1.23	1.29	1.34	1.39	1.45	1.50	1.55	1.61	1.66	1.72	1.77	1.82
.91	.96	1.01	1.06	1.12	1.17	1.22	1.27	1.32	1.37	1.42	1.47	1.52	1.57	1.62	1.67	1.72

Cost of 3 ounces of cooked lean from selected kinds and cuts of meat, poultry, and fish at specified retail prices

Kind and cut	.50	.60	.70	.80	.90	1.00	1.10	1.20	1.30	1.40	1.50	1.60	1.70
					Cost of 3 ounces (dollars)								
Poultry: Chicken,													
whole, ready-to-cook	.28	.33	.38	.44	.50	.55	.60	.66	.72	.77	.82	.88	.94
Turkey, whole,													
ready-to-cook	.20	.24	.29	.33	.37	.41	.45	.49	.53	.57	.61	.65	.69
Veal: Chuck roast,													
bone in	.23	.28	.33	.38	.42	.47	.52	.56	.61	.66	.70	.75	.80
Leg roast, bone in	.26	.31	.36	.42	.47	.52	.57	.62	.68	.73	.78	.83	.88
Loin chop, bone in	.20	.24	.28	.32	.36	.40	.44	.48	.52	.56	.60	.64	.68
Rib chop, bone in	.25	.30	.34	.39	.44	.49	.54	.59	.64	.69	.74	.79	.84

Price per pound[1] (dollars)

Eggs in a processing plant on their way to retail outlets.

Price per pound[1] (dollars)																
1.80	1.90	2.00	2.10	2.20	2.30	2.40	2.50	2.60	2.70	2.80	2.90	3.00	3.10	3.20	3.30	3.40
						Cost of 3 ounces (dollars)										
.99	1.04	1.10	1.16	1.21	1.26	1.32	1.38	1.43	1.48	1.54	1.60	1.65	1.70	1.76	1.82	1.87
.73	.78	.82	.86	.90	.94	.98	1.02	1.06	1.10	1.14	1.18	1.22	1.26	1.31	1.35	1.39
.84	.89	.94	.98	1.03	1.08	1.12	1.17	1.22	1.27	1.31	1.36	1.41	1.45	1.50	1.55	1.59
.94	.99	1.04	1.09	1.15	1.20	1.25	1.30	1.35	1.41	1.46	1.51	1.56	1.62	1.67	1.72	1.77
.72	.76	.80	.84	.88	.92	.96	1.00	1.04	1.08	1.12	1.16	1.20	1.24	1.28	1.32	1.36
.89	.94	.99	1.04	1.08	1.13	1.18	1.23	1.28	1.33	1.38	1.43	1.48	1.53	1.58	1.63	1.68

Chicken

If the price[2] per pound of whole fryers, ready to cook, is —	Chicken parts are an equally good buy if the price per pound is —						
	Breast half (with rib)	Drumstick and thigh	Drumstick	Thigh	Wing	Breast quarter	Leg quarter
Dollars	Dollars	Dollars	Dollars	Dollars	Dollars	Dollars	Dollars
.45	.63	.54	.53	.57	.31	.54	.52
.47	.65	.57	.55	.60	.32	.56	.54
.49	.68	.59	.57	.62	.33	.59	.57
.51	.71	.61	.60	.65	.35	.61	.59
.53	.74	.64	.62	.67	.36	.64	.61
.55	.77	.66	.65	.70	.38	.66	.64
.57	.79	.69	.67	.72	.39	.68	.66
.59	.82	.71	.69	.75	.40	.71	.68
.61	.85	.74	.72	.77	.42	.73	.71
.63	.88	.76	.74	.80	.43	.76	.73
.65	.91	.78	.76	.83	.44	.78	.75
.67	.93	.81	.79	.85	.46	.80	.78
.69	.96	.83	.81	.88	.47	.83	.80
.71	.99	.86	.83	.90	.49	.85	.82
.73	1.02	.88	.86	.93	.50	.88	.85
.75	1.04	.90	.88	.95	.51	.90	.87
.77	1.07	.93	.90	.98	.53	.92	.89
.79	1.10	.95	.93	1.00	.54	.95	.92
.81	1.13	.98	.95	1.03	.55	.97	.94
.83	1.16	1.00	.97	1.05	.57	1.00	.95
.85	1.18	1.02	1.00	1.08	.58	1.02	.98
.87	1.21	1.05	1.02	1.10	.59	1.04	1.01
.89	1.24	1.07	1.04	1.13	.61	1.07	1.03
.91	1.27	1.10	1.07	1.16	.62	1.09	1.05
.93	1.30	1.12	1.09	1.18	.64	1.12	1.08
.95	1.32	1.15	1.11	1.21	.65	1.14	1.10
.97	1.35	1.17	1.14	1.23	.66	1.16	1.12
.99	1.38	1.19	1.16	1.26	.68	1.19	1.15

[1]Based on yields of cooked chicken meat without skin, from frying chickens that weighed about 3 pounds.
[2]Price based on weight of chicken with neck and giblets.

Meats and Meat Alternates

Cost of 20 grams of protein from specified meats and meat alternates

Food	Amount, ready-to-eat, to give 20 grams of protein[1]	Market unit	Part of market unit to give 20 grams of protein	Price per market unit[2]	Cost of 20 grams of protein
					(Dollars)
Dry beans	1½ cups	pound	.24	.57	.14
Bread, white enriched[3]	8 slices	22 oz	.37	.44	.16
Eggs, large	3⅓	dozen	.28	.80	.22
Beef liver	2⅔ oz	pound	.24	.96	.23
Turkey, ready-to-cook	2⅓ oz	pound	.33	.72	.24
Chicken, ready-to-cook	2⅓ oz	pound	.42	.62	.26
Peanut butter	4½ tbsp	12 oz	.23	1.19	.27
Milk, whole, fluid[4]	2½ cups	½ gal	.31	.98	.30
Bean soup, canned	2½ cups	11¼ oz	.82	.40	.33
Tuna, canned	2½ oz, drained	6½ oz	.44	.87	.38
Cured ham, bone in	3⅓ oz	pound	.30	1.25	.38
Chicken breast halves	2½ oz	pound	.27	1.45	.39
Ground beef, lean	3 oz	pound	.25	1.89	.47
Process American cheese ...	3¼ oz	8 oz	.40	1.23	.49
Frankfurters	4	pound	.39	1.39	.54
Chuck roast of beef, bone in .	3¼ oz	pound	.35	1.63	.57
Ocean perch filet, frozen	3½ oz	pound	.31	1.94	.60
Rump roast of beef, boned ..	3 oz	pound	.26	2.40	.62
Round beefsteak, bone in ...	2½ oz	pound	.23	2.99	.69
Bacon, sliced	10½ slices	pound	.52	1.45	.75
Bologna	6 oz	8 oz	.75	1.04	.78
Pork chops, center	2¾ oz	pound	.35	2.66	.93
Porterhouse beefsteak	3⅔ oz	pound	.34	4.39	1.49

[1]About one-third of the daily amount recommended for a man.

[2]Average prices from several Washington, D.C. area supermarkets. Prices for processed items are for the least costly brand in the market unit specified.

[3]Bread and other grain products, such as pasta and rice, are frequently used with a small amount of meat, poultry, fish, or cheese as main dishes in economy meals. In this way the high quality protein in meat and cheese enhances the lower quality of protein in cereal products.

[4]Although milk is not used to replace meat in meals, it is an economical source of good quality protein.

Eggs

When the price of large eggs, per dozen, is (in cents) —		Buy the larger size if the price difference between it and the next smaller size is less than —
65 to 72	. . . .	9
73 to 80	. . . .	10
81 to 88	. . . .	11
89 to 96	. . . .	12
97 to 104	. . . .	13
105 to 112	. . . .	14
113 to 120	. . . .	15

Meat and Alternates — Another way to cut food costs and add variety to meals is to replace some of the meat with alternates such as dry beans, peanut butter, and eggs. These foods provide the protein and many other nutrients for which meat, poultry, and fish are valued.

The table on protein from meats and meat alternates allows you to compare the costs of amounts of selected foods that each provide about 20 grams of protein. To figure costs of these foods using local prices, determine the price per market unit in your store. To obtain the cost of 20 grams of protein, multiply the price by the decimal part of the market unit needed to furnish 20 grams of protein. For example, the price of tuna in a 6½-ounce can is 87 cents. That means 20 grams of protein costs 87 cents × .44, or 38 cents.

Eggs — Prices of eggs vary by size and grade. Sizes most often found in stores are small, medium, large, and extra large. Although larger sizes usually cost more by the dozen than smaller sizes of the same grade, they are sometimes cheaper by weight.

The small table gives general guidelines for finding the best buy between one size and the next larger or smaller size if you want the most egg, by weight, for your money. For example, when the price of large eggs is 90 cents, extra large ones are a better buy if priced at less than 12 cents more, or $1.02 a dozen. If medium eggs cost less than 78 cents, they are a better buy than the large ones priced at 90 cents.

Convenience Foods – What They Cost You

By Dianne Odland and Julein Axelson

onvenience foods have earned themselves a regular place on the shopping lists of many consumers. In fact, convenience foods of one type or another are probably used by nearly all households in the United States.

Convenience foods include a wide range of products that have been fully or partially prepared by food manufacturers rather than in the home. In effect, convenience foods include all products except fresh items such as meat, produce, and eggs and basic processed food items that are used as ingredients, such as flour, sugar, fluid milk, butter, and spices.

A recent U.S. Department of Agriculture (USDA) survey including over 14,000 households showed that about 45 cents of every dollar spent for food at home was for convenience items. Some households relied more heavily on use of convenience foods than others. For example, the survey showed that convenience foods accounted for more of the food dollar in households with higher rather than lower levels of income and education.

Younger people and adult males who prepared household meals spent a greater percentage of the food dollar on convenience products than older people and female adults. On the average, a larger share of the food dollar was used for purchase of convenience foods in white households than in black households and by people in the Northeast than by people in other regions of the country.

Understanding the differences in types of convenience foods on the market can be helpful in making food buying decisions. Convenience foods can be classified as either basic, complex, or manufactured. *Basic* convenience foods are products in which basic processing techniques such as canning, freezing, or drying have been applied to single-ingredient items or products with a limited number of ingredients. Although these foods may save some preparation time, they do not have built-in "culinary expertise." Examples include instant dry potatoes, canned green beans, and frozen orange juice concentrate. Many of the basic-type convenience foods are vegetable and fruit products.

Dianne Odland is a Home Economist, Consumer Nutrition Center, Human Nutrition Information Service.

Julein Axelson is an Assistant Professor, Human Nutrition and Foods, Virginia Polytechnic Institute and State University, Blacksburg.

Complex convenience foods include multi-ingredient "prepared" mixtures that usually have a high level of timesaving features and culinary expertise. Some examples include frozen ready-to-heat plate dinners and entrees, frozen vegetables with a sauce or in a casserole, and ready-to-eat baked products. *Manufactured* convenience foods have no home-prepared counterparts. Products in this category include foods such as ready-to-eat cereals, crackers, some candies, carbonated beverages, and most alcoholic beverages.

Households in the survey spent about 42 percent of their convenience food dollar on basic items, about 42 percent on complex items, and about 16 percent on manufactured items. Basic convenience food products that were used by a large percentage of households included peanut butter, frozen orange juice concentrate, pasteurized process cheese, instant coffee, and several canned and frozen vegetables. Commonly used complex convenience foods included white bread, luncheon meats, canned baked beans, dry mix for macaroni and cheese, canned soups, jellies and jams, and ready-to-eat cookies. Cola-type carbonated beverages and alcoholic beverages represented a large portion of the money spent for manufactured convenience foods.

What Makes Foods Convenient?
Changing lifestyles in the United States and an increased variety of convenience foods available have led to increased use

of many kinds of convenience foods. In the modern household, everyone's busy — homemakers often work outside the home, and meals are not always eaten at set times or as a family. Time is at a premium. Frequently, eating becomes a rushed affair and there is little time to prepare elaborate meals. Preparing, eating, and cleaning up after meals must fit into busy schedules. Many convenience

Which to buy . . . a readymade cake or a cake mix? The dry mix in this homemaker's left hand contains all the dry ingredients to make a cake. However, it must be mixed and cooked to achieve a ready-to-serve form. The cake in her right hand is already made and ready to eat.

foods offer ways to save time and effort by eliminating preparation activities such as cleaning, peeling, mixing, and cooking. Also, their use substantially reduces pre-preparation chores (such as planning, buying, and storing ingredients) and clean-up chores (such as dishwashing).

Convenience foods have varying degrees of built-in services. The built-in culinary expertise offered by some products is convenient for people who lack food preparation skills or who have little equipment available for preparing foods. Convenience foods may expand the variety of foods served in such families.

The ultimate in convenience is offered by products that are ready to eat or use as purchased. Some products need only to

William E. Carnahan

be thawed before serving; some are prepared items which need only heating or rehydrating with hot water. Others, such as dry mixes that have most of the required ingredients assembled in one package, must be mixed and cooked to achieve ready-to-serve form. Several convenience forms, offering varying degrees of "readiness," are available for some foods. In fact, often the decision is not so much whether to buy the convenience product or to prepare the food from scratch, but which convenience food form to buy.

Besides laborsaving and timesaving advantages associated with food preparation, other desirable features of convenience foods include ease of storage, change in storage space requirements, ease in transporting the food from the grocery to the home because of lighter weight or reduced bulk, and extended storage life compared to fresh foods.

Small Households — Single-portion packages of entrees and snack items and small containers of fruits and vegetables are tailor-made for one- or two-member households and thus offer convenience to this group, particularly since many fresh foods and many recipes for home-prepared foods provide too many servings to be practical. Their use, especially in small households, may reduce leftovers and decrease the chance of waste.

Making Cost Comparisons
Rising food prices and the seemingly unlimited choice of convenience foods available at the supermarket complicate food buying decisions. Some convenience foods are far more expensive, some cost about the same or even less than similar foods prepared at home. In selecting food forms, be sure the cost of the item

is appropriate for your food budget and that you're not paying more for convenience than you intend. In making cost comparisons, remember that many factors influence the cost relationship between home-prepared and convenience food forms. These include price in the store where purchased; "special" prices of items; brands selected; quality and packaging of items selected; and type and quantity of ingredients in convenience products compared to those used in home recipes.

The following general guidelines illustrate basic cost relationships for equal amounts of convenience foods and their fresh or home-prepared counterparts. They are based on prices for items in three Washington, D.C., area supermarkets in June 1982. Relative percentage costs are based on equal weight servings of each food form.

- Basic-type convenience foods, particularly vegetables, often cost less than their fresh or home-prepared counterparts. An important point to remember, however, is that cost comparisons between fresh and processed produce items depend upon seasonal price fluctuations. Fresh fruits and vegetables in season are sometimes available at bargain prices and may cost less than processed food forms.

- Complex-type convenience products that offer a high level of culinary expertise often cost more than similar foods made from home recipes. Main dishes and baked goods made from a mix often cost about the same as or less than their homemade versions. In figuring comparative costs, remember to include ingredients that must be added to mixes.

Cost Comparisons — Basic-Type Convenience Foods

	Relative cost
	Percent
Fresh green beans	100
Canned green beans	62
Frozen green beans	90
Home-prepared french-fried potatoes	100
Frozen french-fried potatoes	83
Juice squeezed from fresh oranges	100
Ready-to-drink orange juice reconstituted from frozen concentrate	65
Pasteurized orange juice	86
Canned orange juice	63
Frozen orange juice concentrate	46
Fluid skim milk	100
Instant nonfat dry milk	65

- Manufactured-type convenience foods such as carbonated and alcoholic beverages offer calories but little in the way of nutrients. They are expensive "extras." If you need to trim your food budget, this might be a good place to start.

- Some items have more than one convenience food form (pizza is an example). Those with more built-in convenience usually cost more.

- Buying the large rather than the small container size of a convenience food sometimes results in worthwhile savings. Unit prices posted on the shelves of many supermarkets can help you find the most economical size to buy. Buy only what you can store properly and use without waste, though. Buying large containers doesn't save money if the food spoils before you use it.

Prices differ from store to store and from brand to brand. Some price differences may be associated with food quality differences; others may not. Store brands and generic foods (no brand name shown) often cost less than widely known products. For example, generic green beans priced in Washington, D.C. area supermarkets cost about three-fifths as much as a nationally advertised brand.

Fuel You Use, and Your Time
Usually the largest cost in preparing a food at home is for ingredients, but it is not necessarily the only cost to consider in making food purchase decisions. You may also want to consider the cost of fuel for preparation and the value of the

Cost Comparisons — Complex-Type Convenience Foods

		Relative cost Percent
Main dishes	Homemade fried chicken with mashed potatoes and carrots	100
	Frozen, ready-to-heat fried chicken plate dinner	144
	Homemade lasagna	100
	Frozen lasagna	144
Vegetables	Fresh broccoli with butter sauce	100
	Frozen broccoli with butter sauce (boil-in-the-bag)	180
Baked products	Homemade white bread	100
	Ready-to-eat white bread (firm-crumb type)	227
	Ready-to-eat white bread (soft-crumb type)	82
	Homemade waffles	100
	Frozen waffles	268
	Homemade apple pie	100
	Ready-to-eat apple pie	185

Cost Comparisons — Convenience Items Made From a Mix

	Relative cost Percent
Homemade chili-macaroni	100
Chili macaroni from a mix	116
Homemade macaroni and cheese	100
Macaroni and cheese from a mix	33
Homemade pancakes	100
Pancakes from a mix (just add water)	102
Homemade chocolate cake	100
Chocolate cake from a mix	53

Pizza Cost Comparisons

	Relative cost Percent
Homemade pizza	100
Pizza from a mix	144
Frozen pizza	179

Pizza Cost Comparisons (includes cost for food and active preparation time)

	Relative cost Percent
Homemade pizza	100
Pizza from a mix	82
Frozen pizza	88

time you spend preparing the food. Even though the cost of fuel is a delayed cost and is usually insignificant compared to the cost of food ingredients, you may want to consider it if cost is the primary basis for food purchase decisions.

Foods cooked on the stovetop usually require less fuel for preparation than those cooked in a conventional oven and, of course, longer cooking periods at higher temperatures require more fuel than shorter periods at lower temperatures. Thus, comparing the amount of fuel required for preparing home recipes versus convenience products depends on cooking methods as well as times and temperatures used for cooking. Many convenience foods require about the same or less fuel than similar foods made from a home recipe. Ready-to-eat convenience foods, of course, require no fuel for home preparation.

The Time Factor — Because most convenience foods require less preparation

time than their fresh or home counterparts, the cost of labor for preparing convenience products at home is sometimes appreciably lower than for preparing similar foods from a recipe. Recent studies by both USDA and the Virginia Polytechnic Institute and State University show that if the cost of preparation time is added to food costs, many convenience foods become less expensive than their homemade counterparts.

The cost of time is a theoretical rather than a real, out-of-pocket cost. However, assigning a monetary value to the worth of your time may be helpful in weighing alternatives. The 1982 Federal minimum wage was used in calculating cost for the second pizza example. Calculations were based on the time for all preparation steps that require full or partial attention (active preparation time). Time for steps such as baking were not included since "the cook" is free for other activities.

Family food preferences need to be con-

Container Size Cost Comparisons

	Relative cost Percent
Peaches — 29-ounce can	100
Peaches — 16-ounce can	131
Peaches — 8-ounce can	211
Peaches — individual serving containers	210

sidered in determining the acceptability of convenience foods. The best way to determine whether a product suits you is to try it. Some items may not live up to your standards. For example, you may prefer more of an ingredient such as meat, poultry, fish, or cheese than is provided by a convenience entree. Or you may prefer the appearance, texture, and/or flavor of fresh or homemade foods. If your cooking skills are limited, however, some convenience products may be superior to homemade versions. Although some convenience products may be less acceptable than foods you prepare yourself from home recipes, they may be satisfactory on occasions when limited time is available for food preparation or if their cost is low enough.

Nutrition, Additives
Many consumers are concerned about the nutritional quality and healthfulness of processed foods. Some are particularly uneasy about the use of food additives. Many convenience foods are similar in nutrient content to fresh or home-prepared foods; others may differ. Fresh fruits and vegetables are usually at the peak of their nutritional value immediately after harvest. Food processors make every effort to preserve them while they are fresh to assure the best quality. As served, there is not a great deal of difference in the nutritional content of fresh, canned, and frozen vegetables. Fresh fruits at their peak, however, may be higher in some vitamins than frozen and canned fruits.

The overall nutritional content of *complex* convenience products compared to similar home-prepared foods depends primarily on the ingredients used. The composition of convenience foods sometimes differs from products prepared from typical home recipes. For example, some convenience entrees contain a higher proportion of components such as pasta or sauce and a lower proportion of meat, poultry, fish, or cheese than their home-prepared counterparts. Therefore, they may provide less protein, vitamins, and minerals.

Some convenience foods may contain more fat, sugar, and salt than foods made from scratch. However, in response to consumer concerns regarding excessive consumption of these substances, many food processing companies are beginning to reduce the amount of fat and salt in complex convenience foods such as soups, beef stew, and boil-in-a-bag foods and the amount of sugar in canned fruits and dessert items.

Food additives are frequently used in convenience foods to maintain nutritional content; improve keeping quality; enhance appearance, texture, and flavor; and aid in processing. For example, mold growth on bread and other baked products is controlled by use of mold inhibitors, and the quality of gravy in dishes such as frozen meat pies or the filling in frozen fruit pie is improved by using specially developed starches that can withstand freezing and thawing. The safety aspects of food additives, such as these, are under continuous review by the Food and Drug Administration (FDA).

You have more control over composition if you prepare food yourself. Therefore, if you and your family have dietary restrictions or are concerned about the amounts of substances such as fat, sugar, sodium, and additives in food, you may prefer to prepare foods yourself.

Keep in mind that the total nutritional quality of your diet depends more on the combination of foods you select over a period of time, rather than on whether you use convenience foods or not. The best way to ensure a nutritionally adequate diet is to include a variety of food items in your meals. Build your meals around a varied selection of vegetables and fruits; whole-grain and enriched breads and cereals; milk and milk products; and lean meat, poultry, fish, and dry beans and peas.

Making the Final Decision

Which food form to buy is a personal decision. You must weigh the benefits and disadvantages of buying alternative food forms. Every family has different priorities and different expectations from the food products purchased.

Although cost may be a major consideration in making food choices, it is not always the only one. For example, even at a higher cost than similar foods prepared at home, some convenience products may be a good buy if they suit your individual needs. By the same token, convenience products that are much less expensive than home-prepared foods may *not* be a good buy if you are not satisfied with their quality, if they don't contribute significantly toward your planned nutritional intake, or for other reasons.

Answering the following questions will help you determine whether a convenience food is suitable for you and your family's use: Will the convenience food form save a significant amount of preparation time over preparing the product from scratch or from alternative convenience food forms? Will the product provide the desired number of servings? Are facilities available for proper storage of the product? Will eating quality of the product be acceptable to your family? How will the food contribute to the nutritional quality of your meals? Does cost of the food fit into your family food budget?

If you like the convenience features of products but think they cost too much, or if you prefer homemade quality, you can always make your own convenience foods. When you have time, prepare extra food and freeze in the desired portion sizes for use on occasions when you're in a hurry. Pancakes, waffles, dinner rolls, plate dinners, spaghetti sauce, and lasagna are examples of convenience items you can make yourself.

How We Waste $31 Billion in Food a Year

By EE Fung and W.L. Rathje

ossing $31 billion into garbage cans sounds incredible, but Americans do it every year. At the very end of an energy-intensive food chain, families waste about 10 percent of their food at home, and maybe more outside. An average household spends at least $140 a year for food which is hauled to landfills or washed down sewers.

Only 40 percent of the food discarded in garbage cans is hard-to-save plate scrapings; the other 60 percent is identifiable single items, from beef chunks and bread slices to heads of lettuce and half-eaten apples. While no one intends to waste, our actions often lead to food losses. With study, this unintended behavior can be understood and perhaps changed.

As our era of cheap energy and resources is ending, consumers, industry, and policymakers are increasingly interested in food conservation. Avoidable food waste is the largest and most economical source of additional food available in our society. In mining this potential resource, we need to evaluate food losses at all levels. Wastage during production, processing, and marketing has often been researched by professionals.

Food discarded at the retail level has been studied from time to time, and groups like the Community for Creative Non-Violence in Washington, DC, are feeding people at soup kitchens with food salvaged from supermarket dumpsters.

Most food decisions, however, are made by consumers as family units. Our discussion will focus on this family level, where household food managers can use any and all information available on efficient food strategies. Small changes in domestic food utilization could result in substantial savings in both an economic and ecological sense.

How much food waste takes place in the home? Why does it differ among households? What is the potential for reducing such losses? The U.S. Department of Agriculture has long recognized the need for reliable data on food waste. Some early surveys have suggested the extent and nature of the problem. We will discuss the estimates of food loss calculated by comparing records of the foods that go into households with records of individual consumption, and the household characteristics related to patterns of food waste, based on the National

EE Fung is a Nutrition Specialist with the Garbage Project, Department of Anthropology, University of Arizona, Tucson.

W.L. Rathje is Director of the Garbage Project and Professor of Anthropology at the university's Department of Anthropology.

Household Food Consumption Survey (1977).

An inherent problem in these self-reported surveys is the moral implications of waste. Few Americans like to admit wasting food, even to themselves. Therefore, some researchers have turned directly to garbage cans where food debris can be carefully recorded.

For 9 years, the Garbage Project of the University of Arizona has been analyzing scientifically selected samples of household refuse. The basic procedure involves sorting refuse to calculate 1) the quantity of foods purchased by summing the net weights and fluid volumes on package labels and 2) the quantity of foods wasted by summing the actual weights of discarded foods. This method does have its limitations, such as lack of coverage of food not purchased in labeled packages, and food sent down garbage disposals. Nevertheless, the absolute weight of once-edible foods found in residential refuse represents the minimum level of household food waste. Garbage studies in several urban centers, supplemented by interviews and panel discussions, have provided many clues to patterns of food waste.

We can begin to build a model of household food waste behavior by looking at food discard as the material leftover of a series of purchasing, storage, preparation, and consumption behaviors. Attitudes toward the environment, waste, and health are constantly shaping food management patterns, and food waste is often the result of complex behaviors which are directed toward goals, such as convenience, other than simple efficiency. Within this intricate web of attitudes and actions, some patterns in food waste behavior have been identified.

General Environmental Factors

Consumers today do their hunting and gathering in a quickly changing environment. All along, we let common sense be our guide through storms of inflation, new product innovations, and commodity shortages. How correct are our intuitions? Logically, we might assume that when inflation increases, food losses decrease. In fact, as the rate of inflation rises, waste as a percentage of purchased food declines only slightly, and this results mainly from fewer plate scrapings. It is likely that serving sizes have been cut while other shopping, storage, and preparation behaviors remain largely unchanged. Logically, we might assume that when the price goes up on a particular food commodity, it is wasted less. Sometimes this expectation is fulfilled. As cost increases gradually, poultry, fresh fruit, and grain products are thrown away less.

Sometimes there are surprises. During the beef shortage of 1973 and sugar shortage of 1975, when newspaper headlines were shouting about soaring prices and scarce supplies, larger quantities of these foods were found wasted in garbage cans. This was probably the result of buying cheaper cuts of beef, more sugar substitutes, and larger quantities than normal. Most likely, these drastic experiments ("crisis buying") led to unexpected waste, either because of taste preferences or unforeseen problems in meal-planning or storage. Innovative moneysaving food experiments by homemakers may not be appreciated by the family and the shortrun response to a shortage can be decreased efficiency.

Logically, we might assume that busy

city life leads to overflowing trash cans. In fact, estimated food losses show little difference among central cities, suburbs, and nonmetropolitan areas. There may be regional differences, but city lights probably do not deserve too much of the blame.

Income Level — Social class stereotypes are poor predictors of food waste; in fact, food efficiency is predicted more strongly by attitudes, knowledge, and food management behaviors than by more fixed, unchanging characteristics of households. Nevertheless, such characteristics do have an influence on food waste. Low-income populations tend to discard less edible food overall as well as a lower proportion of single identifiable items. Middle-income populations do not typically respond to inflation by economizing on food. Although "guilt" over food waste is as popular as ever, middle-income consumers have not made the same shift downward in food losses as lower income households. In general, it is the allocated food budget rather than the gross income that determines waste behavior — the greater the budget the greater the waste and the greater the potential for savings.

Large families and those with children usually do not have much problem with leftovers or food waste. Nevertheless, many parents think their children waste food at alarming rates and that lessons of conservation have not been communicated successfully. How much of this feeling is attributable to the "good old days syndrome" remains an interesting question. Homemakers often claim that shrinking family size is just as difficult to adjust to in their cooking habits as it is emotionally. Because of larger appetites, adult men in small households can more easily accommodate standard package sizes than women.

Ethnicity — At present, information relating ethnicity to food waste is scarce, except for studies in Tucson, Ariz. There, Mexican-American households are more efficient food users than Anglos, independent of income. This may be due to cultural patterns which influence when, and the extent to which, leftovers are re-used. Mexican-American homemakers tend to keep leftovers for less than 3 days. However, the more common utilization of leftovers as snacks, the practice of cooking from scratch, and incorporation of the same food ingredients — tomato puree, green chili, tortillas, cheese and others — into many different meals throughout the week all lead to less food waste.

Food discard is predicted by food safety knowledge — the more known about food safety, the less waste — but not by formal education or nutrition knowledge. In fact, the highly educated throw away more food as large single items. "When in doubt, throw it out" is still a good slogan, but consumer education programs should be designed to decrease doubt. Available kitchen facilities have an effect on purchase and utilization patterns. Lack of freezer space may prevent adequate storage of perishable foods. An automatic defrosting refrigerator may dry out foods before use. Heating leftovers in a microwave oven brings out fresher flavor than conventional reheating and may change patterns of food waste. Nevertheless, it is not clear to what extent these material factors influence efficient food management.

Working Mothers — A working mother is often considered an important factor contributing to food waste, but a recent national survey reaches no such conclusion. When a homemaker starts an outside job, orderly consumption of purchased food may be disrupted, and the family may take some time to rearrange priorities. In the long run, however, this arrangement seems compatible with normal efficiency.

How the Pitch Rate Varies

How much food waste is caused by unexamined family habits? What are the priorities that we trade food efficiency for? Can Americans afford the luxury of deploring leftovers? Different loss patterns are found with different types of foods, packages, and processing techniques. Not surprisingly, the majority of foods lost are unprocessed, with fresh fruits and vegetables being the leading items.

There are other differences in wastage rates which are related to food type: white bread is discarded at a higher rate than dark bread, chicken higher than beef, and pastries are the highest of all sweet snacks. Frozen fruits and vegetables are pitched at a higher rate than canned products. Different kinds of processed meat are thrown out at significantly different rates, with lunchmeat leading, ham next, and bologna the last.

Two other patterns should be noted here. First, households that consume larger amounts of convenience foods waste a greater percentage of their fresh produce. This may relate to attitude differences — where less thought and effort are put into meal-planning and preparation, more waste is likely to occur overall. Second, the more frequently an item is purchased and consumed, the less it is wasted. Specialty items, used only infrequently, are wasted at much higher rates. For example, just about every household regularly consumes bread in standard 16 oz or 24 oz wrappers. Waste with these wrappers is only the last one or two slices. Specialty breads — hotdog buns, muffins, and others — are used much less frequently, and their wrappers are usually associated with 40 percent or more waste. Obviously, efficient use of specialty items takes considerable foresight and planning.

Single items discarded in large quantities are mostly foods purchased but never used. Such waste is often the result of compulsive buying or buying foods of inferior quality. Nutritionists recommend consuming a wide variety of foods. Whether this compensates for food losses awaits further investigation.

The Ham and the Pan — Food preparation habits, some traced back to childhood lessons, can lead to differences in waste behavior. For example, during a panel discussion one woman remembered that her mother always cut the end off a ham before cooking it. Following her mother's example, the woman always cut the end off a ham and threw the end away. She did this for years until she found out that her mother had cut the ham so that it would fit into a particular pan.

A more typical example is the habit of peeling potatoes rather than preparing them with the skin still on. Even in peeling, the skillful use of a paring knife produces much less waste than the use of a vegetable peeler. Habits in food storage also affect food waste. For example, cleaning habits determine how likely it is that foods will be "hidden" in refrigerators or cabinets until spoiled.

A strong predictor of the amount of food loss is knowledge concerning the safety of perishable foods. People who throw food away based on an expiration date or an arbitrary time limit without using sensory means as a check are apt to have more waste. Changes in dining plans lead to waste. Family lifestyles that involve irregular or separate meal schedules for members, frequent house guests or parties, or different persons doing the grocery shopping and cooking, may require extra planning efforts to avoid food losses. Each family member has specific nutritional needs and food preferences. Sometimes the changing nutritional needs of an individual may not be recognized by the food manager and result in rejection of prepared foods. Family members demanding different diets again leave additional room for food waste.

Leftover Rankings — In some households, foods perceived safe but unpalatable or too little for one serving are thrown away routinely. Some types of leftovers are generally desirable and often planned for, such as stews or chili, while others, such as fish, carry negative connotations. Leftovers get recycled in many different ways in households — some families save leftover pizza for another dinner, some throw it out, and some even present it for breakfast.

When families accept the sweet agony of raising their own foods, they may be producing food for thought at the same time. We do not yet know how much is saved in the home food budget, but people who feel responsible for the environment tend to throw out less food. Lessons such as "remember the starving children in . . ." and "clean your plate or else . . ." may affect the attitudes and behaviors of children. Will enforcement of guilt feelings turn into positive habits of food conservation? We do not know.

Doing Battle Against Waste

Is it reasonable to think that household food losses can be salvaged? Home food

Student volunteers working on the garbage project at the University of Arizona.

Lori Stiles

waste ranges from approximately 6 to 25 percent or more. Some kinds of household food loss may be inevitable, but the waste of large quantities of single items — probably the most susceptible to change — runs as high as 80 percent of food waste. Setting a moderate goal for reducing waste is realistic and achievable.

When we look at the ways environmental, sociocultural, and food management factors shape food waste behavior, the prospect for change is encouraging. Food safety knowledge, attitude toward the environment, food managing skills, types of food, packaging and processing, all affect food efficiency behavior in systematic ways. Fortunately, factors difficult to change — such as household size, education, working mothers, and available kitchen facilities — are not always good predictors of waste behavior.

Income seems to be a motivational factor in food efficiency rather than a determining factor. In addition, rising food prices do not necessarily lead to common sense corrections of efficiency on the part of consumers themselves. Programs through education, technology, and policy have a good potential for success, particularly if they do not conflict with other priorities which are related to food choices and handling behaviors.

Changes in consumer behavior may prove to be an effective solution to food availability without an increased expenditure of energy. Consumer education programs will be most successful if directed at population groups with more variable behaviors and thus more capacity to change. Middle-income families so far retain more options for adjustment in food utilization than low-income families that are closer to the lower limit of efficiency.

Programs to decrease food waste at the household level could profitably include information on food safety, values of personal responsibility for the environment, and food management methods emphasizing ways to save money and cope with economic stress.

For years, a major thrust of the food industry has been to modify food processing and delivery systems to meet customers' needs. With increasing consumer concern over food efficiency, industry might be expected to study the magnitude of household food losses related to specific packaging and processing systems and the cost-benefit relationship of alternative food products.

Obviously, we still have more questions than answers. Food resource utilization is not a single, tightly knit set of behaviors. The apparently efficient food patterns of some subcultures (like the Mexican-Americans) need to be examined further. It is important to apply what we already know to practical program planning. It is equally important to monitor consumer behavior in a changing environment on a long-term basis for program evaluation. Since each research method in this area — interview, questionnaire, and garbage analysis — has its own advantages and biases, a combination of methods should be used to build a comprehensive model of the factors which affect food discard behaviors.

Further Reading

Rathje, W.L. "Food Utilization and Discard at the Household Level — A View from the Garbage Can." In: *Key Issues in Population and Food Policy*. University Press of America, 4720 Boston Way, Lanham, MD 20706. For sale $15.75.

How Consumers Can Affect the Marketplace

By Georgia Stevens Neruda, Mildred Brooks, and Karen Brown

When you purchase a product, voice a concern, or write a letter of complaint, you are engaging in the simplest form of public policy, citizen participation. As a consumer/citizen, you are communicating your preferences to decisionmakers and applying pressure to bring these preferences into existence.

When all of us address our problems constructively, we are also exercising our rights as citizens to be involved in the decisions made by government and business. A real gap exists between how much people expect to be involved in decisions that affect them and how much they really are. People want to participate and influence decisions. One person and one vote also means a dollar in the marketplace. Individuals *can* make a difference in the decisionmaking process.

There are several ways you can get involved. Consumer advisory boards have been organized by several government agencies, supermarket chains, and food cooperatives. These groups encourage increased consumer participation in decisionmaking. Groups usually meet with an agenda for discussion, then send suggestions to the decisionmakers. Watch your local newspaper for announcements on meetings. Attend a meeting to become better acquainted with the process. Contact the local county Cooperative Extension Service office to learn about advisory groups in your area.

Groups representing various perspectives, such as the Society for Nutrition Education, the National Nutrition Consortium, the Center for Science in the Public Interest, and the Community Nutrition Institute play an active role in creating an awareness of problems and in mobilizing to work together on food issues. Most publish a newsletter to inform the membership of upcoming problems with recommendations for group action.

Such organizations as the General Federated Women's Clubs, American Association of University Women, League of Women Voters, Extension Homemakers, and the Rotary Club have often included food issues in their plans of action for local clubs. Church groups often work on food issues.

Georgia Stevens Neruda is Industry and Consumer Affairs Advisor, Office of the Administrator, Agricultural Marketing Service.

Mildred Brooks is Director, Food, Nutrition and Health, Office of the Mayor, Washington, DC.

Karen Brown is Vice President, Consumer Affairs, Food Marketing Institute, Washington, DC.

Forming Your Own Group

It may be necessary to form your own group to respond to local problems, such as encouraging local agriculture to promote food production. Bringing a group together to focus on a local issue is a logical way to get involved because citizens can get a "hands-on" experience by participating in issues that are right around the corner. Organizing involves skills in communicating with the group about plans for action, alerting media to the group activities, and keeping the group involved so members work together effectively.

Starting at the grassroots level can help citizens develop their own methods to deal with problems. Group action includes a set of resources that can have more impact than if they were scattered among individuals.

Public hearings often are held on food issues of interest to the general public. Watch your local newspaper for announcements. Those announcements will often tell you to consult the *Federal Register* for more information. The Register provides information about what the Federal agencies are doing and when comments are solicited. It is published Monday through Friday and can be found in many local libraries, or at the county courthouse or Federal building. Before any Federal agency can establish, amend, or revoke most of their rules and regulations, the proposed regulation must be published, comments must be solicited and analyzed, and the final regulation published.

Consumer/citizens should remember that most regulations are proposed to correct problems. So it is especially important to

It may be necessary to form your own group to respond to local problems. Bringing a group together to focus on a local issue is a good way to get involved.

describe how the proposal will affect you — both good and bad effects. Write also when you agree with a proposal, not just when you disagree. Consumer groups will sometimes call their own public hearing to expose a perceived problem to public scrutiny. Key decisionmakers, the media, and interested citizens are invited to participate in airing a matter of concern.

Action at the Checkout Counter

Preferences you register through your purchases have a great deal of impact on business decisions to market an item. Since word-of-mouth is so important to the success of a business, most stores are especially sensitive to their efforts to please customers and maintain customer

loyalty. Research from the Food Marketing Institute indicates that 85 percent of shoppers are willing to refuse to buy products that cost too much. A majority (53 percent) of shoppers returned products for a refund or exchange when dissatisfied with a product, and about one-third made an in-person complaint to a food store or supermarket manager when dissatisfied.

Making a creditable complaint involves a few steps in organizing to determine exactly what the problem is, what you believe would be a fair settlement of the complaint (money back, exchanges, or repair), and deciding what to say to the person who must be confronted. Locate any documentation available to present

the complaint (for instance, sales receipt, canceled check, can or box label, or codes from product). Double check that you personally are not to blame.

Start the complaint process with the local establishment that sold the product or rendered the service. If possible, speak with the same person who aided you with the original purchase. If this person cannot help, ask to speak with the manager. Many complaints are resolved at the retail level, so it may not be necessary to pursue the complaint any further.

Beyond the Retail Level

If there is no satisfaction at the retail level, contact the president or consumer office of the manufacturer. Telephone

calls may be quicker and easier, but are usually ineffective unless followed by a letter. Check to see if there is a local office of the company. If not, the public library should have *Standard and Poor's Register of Corporations, Directors and Executives,* or *Thomas Registry* for manufacturers and products by name.

The letter of complaint should be written or typed as any business letter. It is especially helpful to keep standard business forms from an office supply store with carbon paper already inserted for a quick and easy response. Set out the facts carefully and accurately. Include all details: name, code number, style, date and location of purchase, what is wrong, and the steps you have taken to correct the problem. If the complaint has a history — for instance, if your letters have not been answered, or persons have failed to act — state the problem.

Send copies and *keep originals* of all documents. If there is no response in 3 weeks, send a registered letter inquiring what is being done on the matter. Ask for a signed receipt, which can be used as proof later if nothing is done to resolve your complaint.

Getting Help — It may be necessary to contact other sources for information and help. These could include the Better Business Bureau, the local or State consumer protection office; a media action reporter, small claims court, or a government agency such as the U.S. Department of Agriculture (USDA) or the Food

William E. Carnahan

Word-of-mouth is important to the success of business, so most stores are sensitive to their customers' concerns—and like this store will usually make adjustments on unsatisfactory purchases.

and Drug Administration (FDA) of the U.S. Department of Health and Human Services.

Within USDA, several agencies can be of assistance on food problems. The Food Safety and Inspection Service (FSIS) conducts regulatory programs to assure the wholesomeness of meat and poultry products for human consumption. Specifically, FSIS inspects meat and poultry, both fresh and processed, for safety and wholesomeness. It approves recipes and labels for meat and poultry and establishes standards of identity defining specific ingredients in these products.

FSIS operates a consumer response system to help consumers find answers to their questions about meat and poultry products. Questions or complaints should be directed to Food Safety Consumer Inquiries, Room 1165-S, USDA, Washington, DC 20250; telephone 202-472-4485.

FDA enforces laws and regulations to prevent distribution of adulterated or misbranded foods other than meat, poultry, and egg products. Regional FDA offices monitor the safety, labeling, and ingredients of these food products. The Federal Trade Commission (FTC) handles problems involving suspected false advertising. The National Marine Fisheries Service (NMFS) administers a consumer education program on the voluntary fishery inspection service and issues information on the nutritional value, preparation, and availability of fishery products. The White House Office of Consumer Affairs (OCA) fosters consumer education with the public, business, and local, State, and Federal Government agencies.

Consumers should contact their local health department if they suspect cases of food poisoning. Local health departments often have authority to monitor the sanitation of restaurants and food stores and also will direct questions to any of the previously mentioned agencies.

The Cooperative Extension Service of USDA is listed in local phone books under county government. It may be able to provide pamphlets and classes on meal preparation, food purchasing, storage, and handling. Local health departments, Young Women's Christian Association (YWCA), and community colleges often offer classes or health fairs on topics of interest to consumers. Professional organizations such as the American Dietetic Association, American Heart Association, American Red Cross, American Home Economics Association, and the American Association of Retired Persons have local chapters that may sponsor workshops on food-related topics.

Many supermarkets feature a consumer information center offering educational brochures and bulletin board space for flyers about meetings. Cable television in a number of areas provides the latest tips on food shopping, including prices at local stores.

Consumer/citizens can participate more actively in the decisionmaking process by keeping informed on food issues, joining consumer advisory groups, and by attending public hearings and commenting on proposals. They can register preferences through buying decisions, by contacting retailers and manufacturers, or by contacting government regulatory agencies. Consumer/citizens should take stands on issues and help to direct the decisionmaking that shapes public policy.

For Additional information

What	Where	Phone Number
Inside USDA:		
Food Grades	Agricultural Marketing Service, USDA Information Division Washington, DC 20250	202-447-6766
Food Supplies and Prices	Agricultural Marketing Service, USDA Information Division Washington, DC 20250	202-447-6766
Meat and Poultry Inspection	Food Safety and Inspection Service, USDA Food Safety Consumer Inquiries Room 1163-S Washington, DC 20250	202-472-4485
Economics-Related Research	Economic Research Service, USDA Information Division Washington, DC 20250	202-447-4230
Food Stamps and Feeding Programs	Food and Nutrition Service, USDA Information Division 3101 Park Center Drive Alexandria, VA 22302	703-756-3276
Nutrition-Related Questions	Consumer Nutrition Center Human Nutrition Information Service, USDA 522 Presidential Building Hyattsville, MD 20782	301-436-7725
Food-Related Scientific Research	Agricultural Research Service, USDA Information Division Washington, DC 20250	202-447-3987
Home Economics	Extension Service, USDA Office of Administrator Washington, DC 20250	202-447-3377

For Additional Information

What	Where	Phone Number
Outside USDA:		
Suspected False Advertising	Federal Trade Commission Office of Public Information Pennsylvania Avenue at 6th St NW Washington, DC 20580	202-523-3830
Inspected or Graded Fish Products	National Oceanic and Atmospheric Administration National Marine Fisheries Service U.S. Department of Commerce Seafood Research Inspection, and Consumer Services Division Washington, DC 20235	202-634-7458
Grade A Fresh Fluid Milk and Milk Products	Food and Drug Administration Milk Safety Branch (HFF-305) Health and Human Services 200 C Street SW Washington, DC 20204	202-472-7852
All Other Food Products	Food and Drug Administration Office of Consumer Affairs Health and Human Services HFE-88 5600 Fishers Lane Rockville, MD 20857	301-443-3170

Credits

Photography

Nearly all the photographs in this Year-book were taken by USDA photographers or freelance photographers working under contract to USDA. A few photos came from industries that were most cooperative in providing them. The editors are especially indebted to Robert Hailstock, visual information specialist in USDA's Photography Center, who researched the photos for the color section.

The editors also appreciate the excellent cooperation of Barry Scher, director of public affairs for Giant Foods, Inc., Washington, D.C., who made it possible to take photos at their dry grocery warehouse in Jessup, Md., and at a newly opened Giant supermarket in Laurel, Md.

Credit, when the source was known, is either given with its respective photograph or listed below. Prints or duplicate slides of the photos taken for or by USDA are available at a nominal charge from the Photography Center, U.S. Department of Agriculture, Washington, D.C. 20250.

William E. Carnahan: xxv, xxx; Danny Gardner: Cover; Jim Knight, *Florida Grower and Rancher Magazine:* 368; Tim McCabe: xxxiii; Warren Uzzle: xxii; David F. Warren: xiii, xviii, xx.

William E. Carnahan
Photography Editor
Extension Service

Design, Printing, Editing:

Design Coordinator: George Baka, Design Center, Office of Governmental and Public Affairs (GPA)
Printing Coordinator: Warren Bell, Printing Center, GPA
Design: Deborah Shelton, Design Center, GPA
Editor: Jack Hayes, Publishing Center, GPA. Assistant, Mocile C. Trotter
GPA Proofreaders: Ray Barrett, Printing Center. Charles Hobbs, Congressional Section

Index

N.B. Italicized page numbers are references to tables.

Advertising, 125, 136, 164-67
Agricultural Adjustment Act: of
1933, 21; of 1938, 22
Agricultural marketing. *See*
Food marketing system;
Marketing
Agricultural policy: history of,
20-27; development of
modern, 20-25; shift in, 24-
26; future of, 26-27; pro
export, 228. *See also* Farm
policy
Agricultural productivity,
defined, 2
Agricultural programs,
government: 67-70; effect
on input industries, 50-51
Agricultural Stabilization and
Conservation Service
(USDA), 69
Agriculture, U.S. Department
of. *See* USDA
Agriculture: U.S. history of, 2,
10-11; critical role of, 2-9;
employment data for *4*;
as employer, 5-9;
internationalization of, 7;
trend toward dual, 12, 16-
19; and productivity, *56*;
employment in, *56*, 57;
financial condition of, 61-66;
and exports, 97-101, *100*;
and world economy, 105-11;
and trade policies, 112-18
Andrilenas, Paul, 41-51
Appliances. *See* Consumer
appliances
Assemblers, 147
Assembly, in marketing chain,
137-39
Away-from-home market, 123-
24
Axelson, Julein, 343-51

Banks, 66-68; commercial, 67-
68
Behavioral characteristics: of
farmers, 84-86; of
consumers, 258-59
Benson, James N., 28-40
Boehlye, Michael, 82-91
Brake, John R., 59-71
Breimyer, Harold F., 10-19

Brooks, Mildred, 358-62
Brown, Karen, 358-62

Capper-Volstead Cooperating
Marketing Act of 1922, 21,
149
Carter, Carolyn G., 253-56
Chicago Board of Trade, 149
Chicago Merchant Exchange,
149
Clayton, Kenneth C., 20-27
Cleveland, Linda E., 285-89
Commodity Credit Corp., 66,
69-70, 115
Competition, in pricing system,
152-54
Computers. *See* Technology,
new
Connor, John M., 119-26
Consumer advisory boards,
358-60
Consumer assistance agencies,
362, *363-64*
Consumer appliances:
refrigerators, 271-72;
ovens, 272-74; canning
equipment, 299-301
Consumer behavior, 250-52
Consumer buying: 237-49, 253-
56, 259-62, 270-75, 285-89,
302-42; of food, 58; habits,
58; effect on farmers, 119-
26; and spending patterns,
124-26; of vegetables, *328-
31*; of fruits, *332-35*; of
meat, poultry, and fish,
336-41; of eggs, *342*; and
complaints, 360-61
Consumer demographics, 253-
56, 260-62, 263-66
Consumer Expenditure Studies,
Annual, 230
Consumer guidelines, food
safety, 295-301
Consumer help, 361-62
Consumerism: 276-83, 318-25,
346-51, 358-62; and
grading, 159-63; and food
dollars, *231*, *233*; in Annual
Consumer Expenditure
Studies, 230; in Nationwide
Food Consumption Surveys,
230; in National Household
Menu Census, 230; and
processed food, 232-33; and
at-home food, 234, 237; and
away-from-home food, 234,
237-40

Consumer preferences, 257-62
Consumer price index, 52
Consumer research, 250-52,
253-56
Consumers: productivity of, 58;
eating habits of, 123-24; and
food marketing system,
151; effect on prices, 238-
240; away-from-home, 253-
54
Contracts, marketing, 124-25,
156-57, 178, 182-84, 188,
191-93
Contracts, production, 45, 124-
25
Conservation tillage, 28-29
Convenience stores, 245-46.
See also "Fast food" chains
Capper-Volstead Act, 149
Cooperative Farm Credit
System, 66, 67
Cooperative farming, 180-82
Corporate farming, 14-16
"Cost-price squeeze," 47-48
Cotton Research and Promotion
Act of 1966, 167
Credit, 59-60. *See also* Credit
suppliers
Credit suppliers: 66-70, 87-89;
Cooperative Farm Credit
System, 66, 67; operating
banks, 66, 67-68;
individuals, 66, 68; life
insurance companies,
66; Farmers Home
Administration (FmHA), 66,
68-69; Commodity Credit
Corp., 66, 69-70; Small
Business Administration
(SBA), 66, 69-70
Crop Insurance Program,
Federal All-Risk (FmHA),
69
Cropland acreage, U.S., 29
Crop output, *42*,
Currency exchange rate: effect
on farmers, 110-111; and
world economy, 107-109

Daily Food Guide (USDA), 230-31, 265 *passim*, 278
Davis, Carole A., 295-301
Davis, Merry Jo, 257-62
Department of Commerce, U.S., 116
Department of Agriculture, U.S. *See* USDA
Depository Institutions Deregulation and Monetary Control Act of 1980, 68
Depression, effect on world trade, 12, 112
Deregulation, 222
Disaster Loan Program (SBA), 69-70
Distribution, in marketing chain, 137, 141-43
Diversifying, 187
Dual agriculture: 12; defined, 16-19
Durst, Ron, 82-91

Economic emergency programs (FmHA), 69
Economic growth rates, 105
Economic policy: supply-side, 106-07; centrally planned, 108-09; effect on farmers, 109-11
Economic Recovery Tax Act of 1981, 90
Economy, U.S.: agriculture's effect on, 7-9; effect on farm size, 19; stagflation, 105; growth rates, 105; inflation rate, 105; and prices, 105
Economy, world: and agriculture, 105-11; inflation rate, 105; money supply, 105; currency exchange rate, 107-09
Egg Products Inspection Program, Federal, 293
Egg Research and Consumer Act of 1974, 167
Eichers, Ted, 41-51
Electronic Commodity Markets, 186
Electronic marketing, 134, 200-02
Embargoes: export, by U.S., 116-18; effect of, 228
Emergency Disaster Program, (FmHA), 69
Employment, in agriculture, *4, 56*, 57, 121, *122*
Energy use: agricultural fuel, 45-47; *47*; effect of Organization of Petroleum Exporting Countries (OPEC) on, 49; in transportation, 217; and conservation, 222

Environmental Protection Agency, 291
Erosion, soil, 28, 29
Export Administration Act of 1977, 118
Export Incentive Programs, 226
Exports: 92-104, *102*, 223-30; effect on U.S. trade deficit, 5; Public Law 480, 92-93; growth of, 93-95; importance to U.S. agriculture, 96-97; of commodities, 97-101, *100*; to developing countries, 98; of primary products, 98; of processed products, 98-101; to industrial countries, 99-101; future of, 104; subsidies of, 115-16; taxes, 115, 116; U.S., embargoes, 116-18; policy, 228; incentives to, 225-26. *See also* Agricultural policy

Family farm: 12-15; "how-to" start, 89-91
Family structure, and consumer buying, 254-55
Farm Credit Administration, 21
Farm Credit System Banks, 57
Farm debt, 59-60, 65-66
Farmer-Owned Reserve, 118
Farmers: credit for, 18-19; tax provisions for, 71; behavioral characteristics of, 84-86; lifestyle of, 86; and inheritance, 90-91; and inflation, 109; and interest rates, 109-11; and currency exchange rate, 111; role in food marketing, 121; employment data on, 122; and contracts with processors, 124-25; effect on food prices, 136; role in pricing system, 155-56; and grading, 164; marketing alternatives for, 179; marketing risk management for, 187-90; and production, 223-24
Farm financing, options, 66-71

Farmers Home Administration (FmHA): 19, 66; programs of, 68-69
Farmers' income, 64-65
Farm income, 64-65
Farming: new technology for, 3; corporate, 14-16; "how-to" start, 82-91; policy of, 82; capital for, 82-83; and management, 84; risks of, 84-86
Farm input industries: 41-51, *42, 43*; research and development in, 50; pesticides, 51; fertilizer, 51; feed, 51
Farmland, leasing of, 70
Farm machinery: 44-45; manufacture of, 49
Farm Ownership Program (FmHA), 69
Farm policy; history of, 20-26; future of, 26-27; and beginning farmers, 82. *See also* Agricultural policy
Farms: types of, 11-16; as proprietary units, 11-12; family, 12-14; corporate, 14-16; size of, 12-19; ownership of, 11-19; credit for, 59-60; risk of, 65-66; incorporation of, 70-71; as business, 72-81; and marketing, 129; and food safety, 290-91
Farm size: 12-19, 82; effect of U.S. economy on, 19
"Fast food" chains, 123, 246. *See also* Convenience stores
Federal Farm Board, 21
Federal Reserve Board and System, 65, 67
Federal Trade Commission, 149
Fertilizers: 41, 48-49, 51; nitrogen, 41, 48; phosphate, 41, 48; potash, 41, 48-49
Financing. *See* Credit. *See also* Credit suppliers; Farm financing
Financial planning and management, "how-to" for farmers, 72-81
Flooding, 38
Flood plains, 29
Foods: consumer buying of, 58; prices of, 121; synthetic, 125-26; buying patterns for, *231, 233*; shopping for, 242-49; generics, 256; and shelf-life, 275; and quality control, 291-94; handling and storage, 295-98; convenience of, 343-51. *See also* Consumer buying

Food and Drug Administration (FDA), 149, 290, 294, 318, *passim*
Food and Drug Act and the Meat Inspection Act of 1906, 20
Food buying. *See* Consumer buying
Food Consumption Surveys, Nationwide, 230
Food Control Act of 1917, 195
Food cooperatives, 248
Food Goal Inventory, 276
Food groups, 230-32, 285-89
Food habits, 251-62
Food marketing system: 119-26, 211; postwar changes in, 119; employment data on, *122*; diversification of, 150; and form utility, 151; and place and time utility, 151; and consumers, 151; grading in, 159-63. *See also* Consumers; Farmers; Marketing; Marketing chain; Processors; Retailers; Wholesalers
Food prices, trends in, 52-58, *53, 54*
Food preparation: 283-84, 296-99; canning, 299-301
Food, processed, 232-33
Food safety: 20-21, 290-94; consumer guidelines for, 295-301. *See also* Foods
Food Safety and Inspection Service (USDA), 291, 318, *passim*
Foodstores, types, 242-49
Food substitutes, 207-08
Food waste: 352-57; socioeconomic factors in, 354-55
Forest lands, 30-32
Forestry, 40
Forest Service (USDA), 30, 31
Formula pricing, 133-34
Forward trading, 134, 135-36
Frey, Thomas L., 72-81
Friend, Reed, 92-104
Fung, E. E., 352-57

Futrell, Gene A., 170-78
Futures trading, 134, 135-36

Gabriel, Stephen C., 59-71
Gallimore, William W., 216-22
Garbage Project, University of Arizona, 353, *passim*
Gardner, Bruce, 209-15
Garrett, Cheryl, 318-25
Garrick, Joyce R., 257-62
Generic foods, 256
Grading: 159-63, 302-17; USDA, *312-17*; and pricing, 152-54; of pork, 162-63; of meat, 304-05; of poultry, 305-06; of eggs, 306-09; *309*; of dairy products, 309-10; of fish, 310; of fruits and vegetables, 310-11. *See also* Labeling; Standards
Gross National Product, 31, 105, 223
Ground water, 29

Hacklander, Effie, 250-52
Harp, Harry, 119-26
Health and nutrition, 267-69
Herbicides, 44
Homestead Act of 1862, 20
Household Menu Census, National, 230
Hunt, Fern E., 270-75

Imports: *102*; complementary, 101-03; supplementary, 101, 103-04; and variable levy tariff, 114-15; restrictions on by U.S., 115; quality control of, 292-93
Income, disposable, *238*
Incorporation, of farm, 70-71
Inflation, effect on farmers, 109
Inflation rate, 105
Insurance, 187
Interest rates, 48, 105, 109-10
Interstate Commerce Commission, 222
Investor-owned firms, 180, 181-82
Irrigation, 29

Jesse, Edward V., 137-44
Johnson, Neal Sox, 72-81
Junker, Cynthia Cromwell, 326-42

Kenney, Mary C., 159-63
Kerr, Richard L., 230-36

Labeling: 320-22; of meat and poultry, 321-22; open date, 322-23, *323*; nutrition, 323-35. *See also* Grading; Standards

Lamm, R. McFall, 2-9
Land, price of, 15
Land-Grant College Act of 1862, 149
Land use: factors affecting, 29; conversion, 33-34
Lawrence, Frances Cogle, 253-56
Leasing, of farmland, 70
Lee, Chung Ja, 263-69
Legislation: McNary-Haugen, 21; Capper-Volstead Cooperating Marketing Act of 1922, 21, 149; food safety, 20-21; Food and Drug Act and Meat Inspection Act of 1906, 20; Agricultural Adjustment Act of 1933, 21; Agricultural Adjustment Act of 1938, 22; Plant Variety Protection Act of 1970, 50; Depository Institution Deregulation and Monetary Control Act of 1980, 68; Economic Recovery Tax Act of 1981, 90; Tax Reform Act of 1976, 91; Public Law 480, 92-93; Export Administration Act of 1977, 118; Land-Grant College Act of 1862, 149; Smith-Lever Act of 1914, 149; Research and Marketing Act of 1946, 149; Cotton Research and Promotion Act of 1966, 167; Egg Research and Consumer Act of 1974, 167; Wheat and Wheat Foods Research and Nutrition Act of 1977, 168; National Wool Act of 1954, 168; Packers and Stockyards Act, 193-95; Food Control Act of 1917, 195; Perishable Agricultural Commodities Act (PACA), 196; U.S. Warehouse Act, 196-97. *See also* Regulations

Licensing, 197
Lifestyle: of farmers, 86; of consumers, 344-46
Limited partnership, 71
Liquidity, 61, 187
Longmire, Jim, 105-11

McNary-Haugen legislation, 21
Manchester, Alden C., 128-36
Market coordination, 206
Marketing: specialization of, 128; and prices, 130; and transportation, 131; institutional structure of, 145-50; changes in organization of, 146, 149-50; middle men in, 146-49; efficiency of, 157-58; by production cycles, 170-76; of crops, 172-74; of livestock and poultry, 174-76; information on, 176-78, *363-64*; alternatives, 179-86; minimizing risks of, 187-90; fairness in, 191-97; new technology in, 198-208; outcomes of, 213-14; incentives for, 225-26; consumer research on, 250-52. *See also* Food marketing system; Marketing chain
Marketing alternatives: 179-81, 184-86; for farmers, 179; investor-owned firms, 180-181; farm cooperatives, 180
Marketing chain; 137-44; assembly, 137-39; processing, 137, 139-41; distribution, 137, 141-43
Marketing, foreign. *See* Exports; Trade
Marketing policy, 149-50, 212
Marketing risks, management of, 187-90
Market plan, 189-90
Market service firms, 190
Market stability: 209-215; and government regulation, 212-13
Market, terminal, 131
Marshall Plan, 98
Meat Inspection Act, 149
Meat and Poultry Inspection Program, Federal 292, 293
Mennes, Mary E., 272-83
Menu planning, 276-82
Mickle, Sharon J., 237-41
Milk Marketing Order Program, Federal, 166
Money supply, 105
Morey, Arthur, 105-11

Morrill Land Grant College Act, 20
Multilateral Trade Negotiations, 113
Murphy, Elizabeth W., 318-25

Neighborhood stores, 246-48
Neruda, Georgia Stevens, 358-62
Nichols, T. Everett, Jr., 187-90
Nuttall, John, 105-11
Nutrition: 240-41, *241*, 263-69, 285-89, 350-51; and health, 267-69; and physical fitness, 269; labeling, 323-25

Odland, Dianne, 343-51
Oil prices, effect on developing countries, 108
Operating Loan Program (FmHA), 69
Organization of Petroleum Exporting Countries, 49

Paarlberg, Philip L., 112-18
Packers and Stockyards Act, 149, 193-95
Packers and Stockyards Administration (USDA), 193
Pastureland, 33
Pearson, James L., 198-208
Perishable Agricultural Commodities Act (PACA), 149, 196
Pesticides: 41, 44, 51; research and development, 49; and food safety, 291
Peterkin, Betty B., 230-36
Physical fitness, and nutrition, 269
Plant Variety Protection Act of 1970, 50
Pooling, 184-86
Price index, commodity and prodution items, *47*
Price support, origin of, 24
Price support programs, 19
Prices: 170-78; received by farmers, 7; paid by farmers, 7; of land, 15; of food, 58, 121; effect of currency exchange rate, 110-11;

effect of variable import levy, 114; information systems for, 121; effect of supply and demand, 121; and marketing, 130; fixing of, 215; stabilization of, 215; of transportation, 219-20; to consumers, 238-40; at food stores, 242-49. *See also* Pricing systems
Pricing systems: 132-36, 151-57; formula, 133-34; efficiency of, 132-33; forward trading, 134, 135; futures trading, 134, 135-36; electronic marketing, 134; price premium, 151-52; price discounts, 152. *See also* Prices
Processed products, export of, 98-101
Processing: *141*; in marketing chain, 137, 139-41; and food safety, 291
Processors: 121, 147; contracts with farmers, 124-25; branding, 131
Production: surplus in 1950's and 1960's, 22-25; by contractual agreement, 45; of cotton, 203; of cattle, 203-04; of vegetables, 204-06; of broilers, 206; and shelf life, 207; and transportation, 216-22; of exports, 223-24. *See also* Production cycles
Production cycles: 170-76; and storage, 171-73. *See also* Production
Productivity: of agricultural system, *56*; of consumers, 58. *See also* Resource management
Profitability, of agriculture, 63-64
Promotion. *See* Advertising
Public Law 480, 92-93
Purcell, Wayne D., 151-58

Quality control programs, 291-94

Rahe, Dewain, 92-104
Rangeland, 32
Rathje, W. L., 352-57
Research and development: of pesticides, 49; in farm input industries, 50; of products, 131
Research and Marketing Act of 1946, 149

Recommended Daily Allowance (U.S. RDA), 323
Reese, Robert B., 237-41
Regulations: government, 50; Meat Inspection Act, 149; Packers and Stockyards Act, 149; U.S. Warehouse Act, 149; Perishable Agricultural Commodities Act, 149; Agricultural Marketing Agreement Act, 166. *See also* Legislation
Regulatory bodies, 212-13
Resource management: 28-40; of forests, 31-32; of croplands, 28-30; of rangelands, 32; of pasturelands, 33; of wildlife habitats, 34; of water, 34-40; and new technology, 38-40. *See also* Land use
Retailers: 122-23, 141-43, 148, 154; and supermarkets, 123; and product date indicators, 296
Rhodes, V. James, 179-86
Ricker, Harold S., 198-208
Risbrudt, Chris, 28-40
Risks: of farming, 84-86; of marketing, 187-190

Sale-leaseback, 71
Sale-leaseback-buyback, 71
Schertz, Lyle P., 10-19
Schuh, G. Edward, 112-18
Sheep Producers Council, American, 168
Shellfish Sanitation Program, National, 294
Shelf life: of foods, 275; and labeling, 322-23, *323*
Shopping: 276-83, 285-89, 295; comparison, 280-81, 326-42, 347-50. *See also* Consumer buying
Slipsheets, 202-03
Small Business Administration (SBA), 69-70
Smith-Lever Act of 1914, 149
Solvency, of agriculture, 61-62
Spending patterns. *See* Consumer buying
Stabilization board, 213-14
Stagflation, 105
Standards, 318-20. *See also* Grading, Labeling

Stockpiling, by government, 214-15
Stoddard, Everett O., 191-97
Stolfa, Patricia F., 290-94
Subsidies, exports, 115-16
Supermarkets: 242-44; warehousing, 244-45
Supply-side policies, 106-07

Tariffs: 112-14; variable levy on imports, 114-15. *See also* Exports, Imports, Trade
Tariffs and Trade, General Agreement on, 112-14
Taxes: estate, 90-91; export, 115, 116
Tax Reform Act of 1976, 91
Tax provisions, for farmers' income, 71
Technology, new: and farming, 3; for resource management, 38-40; information systems, 121; synthetics and food substitutes, 125-26; electronic commodity markets, 186; and marketing, 198-208; in transportation, 221-22; computer-assisted shopping, 249; and food availability, 260
Teigen, Lloyd D., 52-58
TELCOT, 201-02
Television, 200
Tillage techniques, for conservation, 29-30
Timber, commercial, 30-31
Topsoils, 28
Total Residue Avoidance Program (USDA), 290
Trade: foreign, 50; policies, 112-18; non-tariff barriers to, 115; and import restrictions, 115; and export barriers, 115-18; and export embargoes, 116-18; ethics of, 209-11; monopoly of, 209-11; international, 223-230. *See also* Exports; Imports; Marketing; Tariffs
Trade barriers, 224-25
Trade deficit, U.S., and agricultural exports, 5
Trade offices, USDA, 226-27
Trade policies, grain embargo, 117-18
Transportation: 180; and production, 216-22; trucks, 216-17, 219-20; railroads, 217-18; rail-truck combinations, 218-19; barges, 221

Uhl, Joseph N., 145-50
Uniform Commerical Code, 191
Uniform Communication System, 199
Universal Product Code, 198, 324
USDA: 116, 117, 118; established, 20; marketing service, 149; grading, 160; new marketing techniques, 198; market development, 225

Walsh, Thomas M., 191-97
War credits, 21
Warehouse Act, U.S., 149, 196-97
Water management, 34-40
Water pollution, 35-38
Water quality, 29
Watkins, Edgar P., 242-49
Wheat and Wheat Foods Research and Nutrition Act of 1977, 168
Wheat Industry Council, 168
Wholesalers, 121-22, 124, 147, 154-55
Wicks, Robert J., 223-30
Wildlife habitat quality, 34
Wisner, Robert N., 170-78
Wool Act of 1954, National, 168
World War I, war credits, 21
World War II, 22, 97, 112, 119, 121

Zellner, James A., 2-9